COMPLETE CATALOGUE
OF THE
SAMUEL H·KRESS COLLECTION

RENAISSANCE MEDALS

BY

G·F·HILL AND G·POLLARD

RENAISSANCE MEDALS

FROM THE SAMUEL H·KRESS COLLECTION AT THE NATIONAL GALLERY OF ART

BASED ON THE CATALOGUE OF RENAISSANCE MEDALS
IN THE GUSTAVE DREYFUS COLLECTION
BY G·F·HILL
REVISED AND ENLARGED
BY GRAHAM POLLARD

PUBLISHED BY THE PHAIDON PRESS
FOR THE SAMUEL H·KRESS FOUNDATION

THE REPRODUCTIONS IN THIS VOLUME ARE FROM NEW PHOTOGRAPHS
TAKEN BY BULLATY-LOMEO PHOTOGRAPHERS · NEW YORK CITY

PRINTED IN GREAT BRITAIN 1967 BY ROBERT MACLEHOSE & CO. LTD · GLASGOW

CONTENTS

PREFACE
page vii

INTRODUCTORY NOTE
page ix

CATALOGUE
page 3

ILLUSTRATIONS
page 133

CONCORDANCES
page 273

INDEX OF INSCRIPTIONS
page 278

GENERAL INDEX
page 293

INDEX OF PERSONS
page 300

INDEX OF ARTISTS
page 306

PREFACE

THE first and only catalogue of the collection of medals formed by Gustave Dreyfus appeared in 1931. Its author was Sir George Hill, who had studied the collection in depth when it was still in Dreyfus' hands in the Boulevard Malesherbes in Paris. In a prefatory note, Hill observed that 'keenly as Gustave Dreyfus appreciated all his beautiful things, he had a particularly soft place in his heart for the Italian medals, and . . . he would have agreed with the German critic who declared that the medallic art was *par excellence* the art of the Renaissance, the expression of the quintessence of the spirit of that age.' The preface continues with the tribute: 'His was perhaps the finest collection that has ever been in the hands of a private collector — the "perhaps" might be omitted, but that it is difficult to range the great collections in a true perspective.' Thanks to the Kress Foundation, the Dreyfus collection of medals was not dispersed, like so many other medallic collections, but is preserved intact in the National Gallery of Art in Washington, where it bears out Hill's claim to be regarded as the finest private collection of medals ever to have been formed. Its claim to superiority rests first on the range it covers, second on the emphasis that is accorded to medals which are of aesthetic and not simply of historical or archaeological significance, and third on the altogether exceptional quality of the single medals it contains. In the case of the companion collection of plaquettes, we know that Dreyfus spared no pains to substitute better for less good impressions, and of the medals that is also true. Owing to the casual manner in which they were built up, public collections of medals are almost invariably of inconsistent or unequal quality. The collection in Washington, on the other hand, is stamped through its whole length by the fastidiousness of individual choice.

When the matter of preparing catalogues of the Kress collection of medals, small bronzes and plaquettes was first considered, it was apparent that the status of the three existing catalogues of the then Dreyfus collection was far from uniform. Whereas the catalogues of the small bronzes and plaquettes were in large part out of date and required to be replaced, Hill's volume on the medals had successfully stood the test of time. There were experts on Renaissance medals before Hill, but none of them could approach his mastery of the whole field. His earliest contribution to the study of Renaissance medals appeared in 1902, and the summation of his researches, his two-volume *Corpus of Italian Medals of the Renaissance before Cellini*, was issued in 1930, a year before the Dreyfus catalogue. The *Corpus* is not simply an unrivalled compendium of information about medals; it is a definitive statement on the Italian medal, which owes much of its value to the sureness of Hill's eye and to the accuracy of his qualitative judgements. For all these reasons it was concluded that the substance of Hill's volume on the Dreyfus medals should not be tampered with. The editor of the present volume, Mr. Graham Pollard of the Fitzwilliam Museum, Cambridge, himself a notable specialist on medals, shared this view. But however great the scholar and however deterrent the effect his work may have upon the students who come after him, knowledge does not stand still, and Mr. Pollard, as he indicates in his note on the present edition, has made a number of significant emendations and additions to Hill's catalogue.

The new book therefore has a triple purpose, it makes available for the first time one of the masterpieces of the art-historical literature of the years between the two world wars — Hill's catalogue, it should be noted in parenthesis, was privately printed and was never placed on public sale —, it constitutes a companion to historical studies, and it provides a comprehensive survey of a now neglected aspect of Renaissance art.

JOHN POPE-HENNESSY

INTRODUCTORY NOTE

THE Gustave Dreyfus collection of Renaissance medals was, during the owner's lifetime, the most celebrated private collection of such materials in existence. In 1945 Rush H. Kress (1877–1963) purchased for the Samuel H. Kress Foundation the whole of the Gustave Dreyfus collection of Renaissance bronzes, which with the medals numbered just over 1300 items. Through the personal interest of Rush Kress and of Guy Emerson, Art Director of the Foundation, the collection was given to the National Gallery of Art, Washington, D.C., in 1957. This fortunate act of generosity gave to America a national collection of medals worthy of comparison with the few great national collections of Europe.

During the lifetime of Gustave Dreyfus (1837–1914) the only publication of the collection was that included in a series of articles on the bronzes, plaquettes and medals, which were published by Gaston Migeon in *Les Arts*, 1908. The whole collection was acquired from the executors of Gustave Dreyfus by Sir Joseph Duveen, and fully published in 1931 by a three-volume catalogue, *Renaissance Medals* by G. F. Hill, *Renaissance Bronzes* and *Reliefs and Plaquettes* by Seymour de Ricci. In 1951, when the collection was first exhibited in the National Gallery of Art, a catalogue *Renaissance Bronzes from the Kress Collection* was published, edited by Perry B. Cott from the Hill and de Ricci catalogues.

The first edition of this catalogue had remained a work of such continued usefulness for the study of medals that it was decided for this edition to preserve the numbering of the collection as established by Hill. The Note on p. 1 gives guidance to the changes and additions which have taken place. Indexes have been made in the manner of Hill's *Corpus of Italian Medals*.

The bibliographical abbreviations given for this catalogue do not form a full guide to the literature of the subject. A convenient bibliography for medals is to be found in P. Grierson, *Bibliographie Numismatique* (Cercle d'Etudes Numismatique) Brussels, 1966. The second edition of M. Bernhart, *Medaillen und Plaketten*, Berlin, 1920, contains a large bibliography, and a list of the principal sales by auction. The third edition of the work (edited by T. Kroha), *Medaillen und Plaketten*, Brunswick, 1966, omits this bibliography, and substitutes a few recent references. The many writings by G. F. Hill on medals are included in his complete bibliography, *A tribute to Sir George Hill on his eightieth birthday*, Oxford (privately printed) 1948. The quarterly periodical *Numismatic Literature*, published since 1947 by the American Numismatic Society, contains a section in each issue in which are discussed current publications concerning medals. The only general accounts of Renaissance medals remain G. F. Hill, *Medals of the Renaissance*, Oxford, 1920; G. F. Hill, *A Guide to the Exhibition of medals of the Renaissance in the British Museum*, London, 1923; and J. Babelon, *La médaille et les médailleurs*, Paris, 1927.

I wish to thank Mr John Pope-Hennessy for being instrumental in my undertaking this edition, for his kindness in discussing problems, and for arranging access to the comparative materials in his care. I wish to record my gratitude to the late Carl Winter, formerly Director of the Fitzwilliam Museum, for his interest in the project.

My principal expression of gratitude for help with the preparation of this edition must go to Professor Ulrich Middeldorf, whose extraordinary generosity extended to the freedom of his annotated books and private papers concerning medals, the hospitality of his home, and a continuous exchange of letters. Professor Middeldorf has read a draft of the text, and has made many improvements, especially in directing me to materials in the literature of the fine arts. I have not indicated where this kindness has given me a published source, but Professor Middledorf's private opinion has always been clearly indicated by the form 'Middeldorf (private communication) . . .' I trust that he will accept this acknowledgment as sufficient recompense for his kindness.

Mr A. E. Popham provided the materials for one of the catalogue entries, and amongst other scholars and collectors who were patient of enquiries I would mention Mr Philip Grierson, Mr Michael Jaffé, Dr J. R. Jones, Mr Mark Salton, and Professor Roberto Weiss. Dr and Mrs Clain-Stefanelli were kind enough to inspect the coins in the collection for me, and to confirm my views on them. M. Albert Chatelet and Dr Paul Grotemeyer kindly provided comparative materials, and my wife pursued Italian sources and helped with the trials of indexing and proof-reading.

In Washington, the Chief Curator of the National Gallery of Art, Mr Perry B. Cott, and his colleague Mr David E. Rust, made the handling of the collection a great pleasure. In New York the staff of the American Numismatic Society enabled me to accomplish much work in a short time and in London, my colleagues in the British Museum, and the staff of the Warburg Institute and the Victoria and Albert Museum Library bore patiently with my demands.

GRAHAM POLLARD

A NOTE ON THE PRESENT EDITION

THE numbering for this edition of the catalogue is that established by Hill. There are three principal changes from this scheme to be noted. An Appendix of twenty-nine medals has been made, for those pieces of which the quality did not warrant a place in the main body of the catalogue. They are mostly after-casts or reproductions. Several medals have been re-attributed, and have been re-numbered accordingly. Sixteen medals overlooked by Hill have been added to the catalogue, twelve of them to the German series. The corrections and additions are indicated by letters added to the catalogue numbers, and Tables at p. 277 list these alterations. Only one of the medals in the catalogue, no. 575a, does not come from the Gustave Dreyfus collection, but was acquired independently by the Samuel H. Kress Foundation for the National Gallery of Art. One addition has been made to the provenances as published by Hill, and will be found at no. 33. As in the previous publication of the collection, the fabric of the medals may be understood to be cast bronze, patinated, unless there is some other indication.

Publications concerning the lives of the medallists have been added where they date after 1930. In Section I, Hill's *Corpus* may be understood as the source for biographies. Additions have been made for only thirteen of the artists in this section. The only important correction to the *Corpus* appears to be the re-attribution noted at Giancristoforo Romano, p. 19.

The following list indicates the medals at which the more interesting additions will be found, excluding the re-attributed pieces: 1, 3, 4, 6, 8, 15, 19, 22, 31, 43, 55, 56, 57, 69, 83, 102, 129 (Appendix), 141, 142, 143, 150, 188, 194, 198, 205, 215, 220, 230, 233, 280, 282, 286, 288, 290, 296, 303, 304, 314, 315, 338 (Appendix), 355, 362, 370, 381, 382, 385a (Appendix), 412, 420, 423, 426, 429, 430, 437, 443, 445, 446, 448, 453, 460, 480, 483, 492, 508, 514, 521, 524, 525, 527, 531, 554, 556, 561, 623, 629, 657, 659.

G.P.

CATALOGUE

BIBLIOGRAPHY AND ABBREVIATIONS

ITALIAN MEDALS

I. ITALIAN MEDALS TO THE BEGINNING OF THE SIXTEENTH CENTURY

NOS. 1–312

II. ITALIAN MEDALS OF THE SIXTEENTH CENTURY AND LATER

NOS. 314–523

III. FRENCH MEDALS

NOS. 524–582

IV. GERMAN MEDALS

NOS. 583–628

V. MEDALS OF THE LOW COUNTRIES

NOS. 629–640

VI. COINS

NOS. 641–667

VII. APPENDIX

BIBLIOGRAPHY AND ABBREVIATIONS

ALVAREZ-OSSORIO	Francisco Alvarez-Ossorio, *Catálogo de las medallas de los siglos xv y xvi conservadas en el Museo Arqueológico Nacional*, Madrid, 1950.
ARM.	Alfred Armand, *Les Médailleurs italiens*, Paris, 1883–1887, three vols.
	Archiv für Medaillen- und Plakettenkunde, Halle a. S., 1913–1926.
	J. Babelon, *La médaille en France*, Paris 1948.
BANGE	Staatliche Museen zu Berlin: *Die Bildwerke des Deutschen Museums, ii: Die Bildwerke in Bronze und in anderen Metallen*, bearbeitet von E. F. Bange. Berlin and Leipzig, 1923.
BERLIN, *Simon collection*	Berlin, Königliche Museen, Kaiser Friedrich-Museum, *Sammlung von Renaissance-Kunstwerken gestiftet von Herrn James Simon zum 18 Oktober 1904*, Berlin, 1904.
BERNAREGGI	Ernesto Bernareggi, *Monete d'oro con ritratto del Rinascimento Italiano 1450–1515*, Milan, 1954.
BERNHART, *Nachträge*	M. Bernhart, 'Nachträge zu Armand', in: *Archiv für Medaillen- und Plakettenkunde*, 5 (1925–6) pp. 69–90, pls. xii–xvi.
B.F.A.C., 1905	Burlington Fine Arts Club: *Exhibition of pictures of the school of Siena and examples of the minor arts of that city*. By R. L. Douglas. London, 1904.
B.F.A.C., 1912	Burlington Fine Arts Club: *Catalogue of a collection of Italian sculpture and other plastic arts of the Renaissance*. By E. R. D. Maclagan, G. F. Hill, and C. F. Bell, London, 1913.
BOTTARI-TICOZZI	G. Bottari, *Raccolta di lettere sulla Pittura, Scultura ed Architectura*, continued by S. Ticozzi, 8 vols., Rome, 1822–1825.
Burl. Mag.	*The Burlington Magazine*.
CAMBRIDGE	The Fitzwilliam Museum, Cambridge, England.
C.N.I.	*Corpus Nummorum Italicorum*, vols. I–XIX, Rome, 1910–1940.
Corpus	Sir G. F. Hill, *A Corpus of the Italian Medals of the Renaissance before Cellini*, 2 vols., London, 1930.
COTT	National Gallery of Art, Washington (D.C.): *Renaissance Bronzes: Statuettes, Reliefs and Plaquettes, Medals and Coins from the Kress Collection*, Washington, 1951. (Edited by Perry B. Cott).
DOMANIG, *Deutsche Medaille*	K. Domanig, *Die deutsche Medaille in kunst- und kulturhistorischer Hinsicht nach dem Bestande der Medaillensammlung des A. H. Kaiserhauses*. Vienna, 1907.
ERMAN	A. Erman, 'Deutsche Medailleure des sechzehnten und siebzehnten Jahrhunderts', in *Zeitschrift für Numismatik*, 12 (1885) pp. 14–102.
FABRICZY	Cornelius von Fabriczy, *Italian Medals* (translated by Mrs G. W. Hamilton), London, 1904.
FORRER	L. Forrer, *A Biographical Dictionary of Medallists*, 8 vols., London, 1904–1930.
FOSSI TODOROW	Maria Fossi Todorow, *I disegni del Pisanello e della sua cerchia*, Florence, 1966.
	A. W. Franks and H. A. Grueber, *Medallic Illustrations of the History of Great Britain and Ireland*, London, (British Museum), 2 vols., 1885. (The plates illustrating the work, 19 folio parts, London, British Museum, 1904–1911).
FRIEDLÄNDER, *Ital. Schaumünzen*	Julius Friedländer, *Die italienischen Schaumünzen des fünfzehnten Jahrhunderts*, Berlin, 1882.
GREENE, T. WHITCOMBE	T. Whitcombe Greene collection, sale catalogue, Sotheby, London, 30 October 1933.

HABICH — G. Habich, *Die Medaillen der italienischen Renaissance*, Stuttgart-Berlin, 1924.

HABICH, *Deutsche Schaumünzen* — G. Habich, *Die deutschen Schaumünzen des XVI. Jahrhunderts*, 5 vols., Munich, 1929–1935.

HABICH FESTSCHRIFT — *Georg Habich zum 60. Geburtstag*, Munich, 1928.

HAINAUER COLLECTION — W. von Bode, *Die Sammlung Oscar Hainauer*, Berlin, 1897 (medals from this collection to which reference is made formed part of the Widener gift to the National Gallery of Art, Washington, D.C.).

HEISS — Aloiss Heiss, *Les Médailleurs de la Renaissance*, 9 vols., Paris, 1881–1892. (The volumes are denoted by the principal word in the volume title).

HILL, B.M.G. — G. F. Hill, *A Guide to the exhibition of medals of the Renaissance in the British Museum*, London, 1923.

HILL MSS. — G. F. Hill, *Manuscript list of Italian Renaissance Medals supplementary to the Corpus of Italian Medals.* (Manuscript preserved in the Department of Coins and Medals, British Museum, London.)

HILL, *Med. Ren.* — G. F. Hill, *Medals of the Renaissance*, Oxford, 1920.

HILL, N.I.A. — G. F. Hill, 'Not in Armand', in: *Archiv für Medaillen- und Plakettenkunde*, 2 (1920–21), pp. 10–28; 45–54.

HILL, P.M.I.A. — G. F. Hill, *Portrait medals of Italian Artists of the Renaissance*, London, 1912.

G. F. Hill, *A Corpus of the Italian Medals of the Renaissance before Cellini*, 2 vols., London, 1930. (Cited as *Corpus*.)

KEARY, B.M.G. — C. F. Keary, *A Guide to the Exhibition of Italian Medals*, (British Museum) London, 2nd. edition, 1893.

KRIS — E. Kris, *Meister und Meisterwerke der Steinschneidekunst in der italienischen Renaissance*, 2 vols., Vienna, 1929.

LANNA — Adalbert von Lanna collection, sale catalogue: *Sammlung des + Freiherrn Adalbert von Lanna Prag, dritter Teil, Medaillen und Münzen* (by K. Regling). Lepke, Berlin, 16–19 May 1911.

Les Arts — Gaston Migeon, *La Collection de M. Gustave Dreyfus* (Les Médailles), in *Les Arts,* August 1908. (The pagination quoted is that of the number of *Les Arts*, not of the separate issue).

LITTA — Pompeo Litta, *Famiglie Celebri Italiane,* Milan-Turin, 1819–1885.

LÖBBECKE — Arthur Löbbecke collection, sale catalogue: *Sammlung Arthur Löbbecke Braunschweig. Kunstmedaillen und Plaketten des XV. bis XVII. Jahrhunderts*, Hirsch, Munich (catalogue no. xxiii) 26 November, ff. 1908.

MAGNAGUTI — Conte Alessandro Magnaguti, *Ex Nummis Historia IX, Le medaglie dei Gonzaga*, Rome, 1965.

MARTINORI, *Annali* — E. Martinori, *Annali della zecca di Roma. Serie papale*, 24 fasc., Rome (Istituto italiano di numismatica) 1917–1922.

MAZEROLLE — F. Mazerolle, *Les Médailleurs francais du XVe au milieu du XVIIe siècle*, 2 vols., Paris, 1902–4.

MIDDELDORF, *Morgenroth* — Ulrich Middeldorf and Oswald Goetz, *Medals and Plaquettes from the Sigmund Morgenroth Collection*, Chicago, 1944.

MOLINIER — E. Molinier, *Les Plaquettes: catalogue raisonné*, 2 vols., Paris, 1886.

MÜLLER, NACHTRAG — R. Müller, 'Nachtrag zu Armand', in: *Archiv für Medaillen- und Plakettenkunde*, 3 (1921–22), pp. 41–44.

Museum Mazzuchellianum — P. A. Gaetani, *Museum Mazzuchellianum, seu numismata virorum doctrina praestantium*, 2 vols., Venice, 1761–3.

Num. Chron. — *The Numismatic Chronicle.*

OPPENHEIMER — The Henry Oppenheimer collection, sale catalogue, Christie, Manson and Woods, London, 27–29 July, 1936.

OXFORD	The Ashmolean Museum, Oxford.
PANOFSKY	E. Panofsky, *Studies in Iconology*, New York and Evanston, 1962.
PLANISCIG	Vienna, Kunsthistorisches Museum: *Die Bronzeplastiken*, bearbeitet von L. Planiscig, Vienna, 1924.
POPE-HENNESSY, *Kress Bronzes*	J. Pope-Hennessy, *Renaissance Bronzes from the Samuel H. Kress collection. Reliefs, plaquettes, statuettes, utensils and mortars*, London, 1965.
	J. Pope-Hennessy, *Italian High Renaissance and Baroque Sculpture*, Text vol., Catalogue vol., Plates vol., London, 1963.
PROBSZT	G. Probszt, *Ludwig Neufahrer*, Vienna, 1960.
	G. Probszt, 'Unbekannte Renaissance-Medaillen', in *Numismatische Zeitschrift*, 74 (1951) pp. 86–95.
Rev. belge de Num.	*Revue belge de Numismatique.*
Rev. Num.	*Revue Numismatique.*
RIZZINI	P. Rizzini, *Illustrazione dei civici musei di Brescia: parte ii, Medaglie*, Brescia, 1892–3.
RODOCANACHI	E. Rodocanachi, *La femme italienne à l'époque de la Renaissance; sa vie privée et mondaine, son influence social*, Paris, 1907.
ROSENHEIM	Max and Maurice Rosenheim collection, sale catalogue, Sotheby, London, 30 April–4 May, 1923.
SALTON COLLECTION	M. and L. Salton, *The Salton collection. Renaissance & Baroque medals and plaquettes*, Brunswick, Maine, (Bowdoin College Museum of Art) 1965.
SEYMOUR, *Masterpieces*	C. Seymour, *Masterpieces of Sculpture from the National Gallery of Art, Washington, D.C.*, New York, 1949.
SIMON COLLECTION *see*	BERLIN, *Simon collection.*
SIMONIS	J. Simonis, *L'Art du Médailleur en Belgique*, vol. 1, Brussels, 1900; vol. 2, Jemeppe, 1904.
SUHLE	A. Suhle, *Die deutsche Renaissance Medaille*, Leipzig, 1950.
SUPINO	I. B. Supino, *Il Medagliere Mediceo nel R. Museo Nazionale di Firenze*, Florence, 1899.
TERVARENT	Guy de Tervarent, *Attributs et symboles dans l'art profane, 1450–1600*, Geneva, 1959. *Supplément et index*, Geneva, 1964.
THIEME-BECKER	U. Thieme, F. Becker, F. C. Willis, H. Vollmer (editors) *Allgemeines Lexikon der bildenden Künstler*, 37 vols., Leipzig, 1907–1950.
Trésor	*Trésor de numismatique et de glyptique*, ed. P. Delaroche, H. Dupont, and C. Lenormant. *Médailles françaises*, 3 parts, Paris, 1834–7. *Choix historique des médailles des papes*, Paris, 1839.
TRICOU	Jean Tricou, *Médailles lyonnaises du XVe au XVIIIe siècle*. Paris, 1958.
WARBURG *Journal*	*Journal of the Warburg Institute* (vols. 1–2); *Journal of the Warburg and Courtauld Institutes* (vols. 3 ff.).
WELLENS-DE DONDER	L. Wellens-De Donder, *Medailleurs en Numismaten van de Renaissance in de Nederlanden*. Brussels (Koninklijke Bibliotheek) 1959.
WIDENER COLLECTION *see*	HAINAUER COLLECTION.
WIND	E. Wind, *Pagan Mysteries of the Renaissance*. London, 1958.

I

ITALIAN MEDALS TO THE BEGINNING OF THE SIXTEENTH CENTURY

The medals are arranged according to G. F. Hill, *Corpus of Italian Medals of the Renaissance before Cellini,* London, 1930.

PISANELLO

(b. *ca.* 1395; d. 1455)

Antonio di Puccio Pisano, called Pisanello was born about 1395 or earlier, probably at Pisa. He worked especially at Verona, Ferrara, Mantua, Milan, Rimini, and Naples, and died at Rome in 1455. He was the founder of the modern medal, and the greatest exponent of that branch of art. Before he made his first medal in 1438, he was already famous as a painter of portraits and of animals. A remarkable series of his drawings have survived (chiefly in the Louvre), many of them connected with his pictures and his medals, and including animal studies which show amazing fidelity and power of observation. The Kress collection is remarkably rich in fine examples of his medals, cast both in bronze and lead.

To the bibliographies in the *Corpus*, may be added Hill, in Thieme-Becker, 27 (1933) pp. 92–3; Hill, 'A lost medal by Pisanello', in *Pantheon,* 8 (1931) pp. 487–8; M. Salmi, 'Appunti su Pisanello medaglista', in *Annali dell'Istituto Italiano di Numismatica,* 4 (1957) pp. 13–23. Monographs on Pisanello are Hill, *Pisanello,* London, 1905; B. Degenhart, *Pisanello,* Vienna, 1940, Turin 1945; E. Sindona, *Pisanello,* Milan, 1961 (with bibliography and hitherto un-illustrated specimens of medals). The catalogue of the Verona exhibition of 1958 by L. Magagnato, *da Altichiero a Pisanello,* Venice, 1958 contains a bibliography, pp. 111–115, and also reproduces medals from Italian museums which had not previously been illustrated. The latest commentary on the drawings by Pisanello concerning medals is to be found in Maria Fossi Todorow, *I disegni del Pisanello e della sua cerchia,* Florence, 1966, with full bibliography.

1. JOHN VIII PALAEOLOGUS, Emperor of Constantinople, 1425–48.

Obv. Bust to right, wearing hat with tall crown and upturned brim. Around, ΙΩΑΝΝΗϹ ΒΑϹΙΛΕΥϹ ΚΑΙ ΑΥΤΟΚΡΑΤΩΡ ΡΩΜΑΙΩΝ Ο ΠΑΛΑΙΟΛΟΓΟϹ, 'John, King and Emperor of the Romans, Palaeologus.'

Rev. OPVS PISANI PICTORIS and ЄΡΓΟΝ ΤΟΥ ΠΙϹΑΝΟΥ ΖΩΓΡΑΦΟΥ The Emperor riding to right, raising his hands folded as he passes a wayside cross; behind him, a mounted page, seen from behind; rocky landscape.

Lead, 103 mm. A737–1A

Made at Ferrara, between 29 Feb. 1438 and 10 Jan. 1439, at the Council of the two Churches. The emperor is depicted on the reverse riding towards Ferrara.

Other specimens in lead are *Corpus,* nos. 19, *i* and *k.*; de Jonghe collection, auction catalogue, Schulman, Amsterdam, 24 Nov. 1936, lot 1; Morgenroth collection, nos. 1, 2; Paris, Cabinet des Médailles.

Literature: Les Arts, Aug. 1908, pp. 4–5, no. i; cp. Arm. 1, 7, 20; *Corpus,* no. 19; Middeldorf, *Morgenroth,* nos. 1, 2; R. Weiss, *Pisanello's medallion of the Emperor John VIII Palaeologus,* London (British Museum), 1966 (including bibliography, an examination of the titulature on the medal, and the derivations from the portrait type in painting, engraving, sculpture, and manuscript illumination); Cott p. 160. J. A. Fasanelli, 'Some notes on Pisanello and the Council of Florence', in *Master Drawings,* 3 (1965) pp. 36–47 (suggesting that the medal was made at Florence between 6 July and 26 August 1439, and that the reverse represents the emperor on a journey to a shrine at Prato). Fossi Todorow, nos. 57r, 58r, 33 (drawings by Pisanello relating to this medal). J. Babelon, 'Un thème iconographique dans la peinture de la Renaissance. L'empereur Jean Paléologue et Ponce Pilate', in *Actes du XIIe congrès international d'historie de l'art,* Brussels, 20–29 September, 1930, pp. 544–552.

2. GIANFRANCESCO I GONZAGA, first Marquess of Mantua, 1433–44.

Obv. Bust of the Marquess to left, wearing tall fluted hat. Inscriptions: IOHANES FRANCISCVS DE GONZAGA CAPIT(aneus) MAXI(mus) ARMIGERORVM PRIMVS MARCHIO MANTVE

Rev. OPVS PISANI PICTORIS The Marquess in armour riding to left; on the right, a mounted page seen from behind; in the field, a ring-shaped door-knocker.

Lead, 100 mm. A738–2A

Probably made at Mantua sometime between 1439 and 1444, and nearer the former date. The figure of the Marquess on the reverse was copied by Rembrandt in his etching *The Three Crosses*. The *Corpus* records two other lead specimens.

Literature: Les Arts, Aug. 1908, pp. 4–5, no. ii; cp. Arm. I, 4, 11; *Corpus*, no. 20; Cott p. 161.

3. FILIPPO MARIA VISCONTI, Duke of Milan, 1412–47.

Obv. Bust of the Duke to right, in tall soft cap. Around, PHILIPPVS MARIA ANGLVS DVX MEDIOLANI ETCETERA PAPIE ANGLERIE QVE COMES AC GENVE DOMINVS

Rev. OPVS PISANI PICTORIS The Duke riding to left; on the right a small mounted page seen from behind; between them, armed horseman to front. Mountainous landscape with tops of buildings in background.

104 mm. A739–3A

About 1441. The Duke is called *Anglus* after a mythical ancestor of the Visconti, eponym of Angera on Lago Maggiore. He keeps the title of Lord of Genoa, although he lost the place in 1435. The Widener collection contains a bronze specimen (ex. Hainauer collection).

Collection: His de la Salle (sale London, Sotheby, 22 Nov. 1880, lot 25).

Literature: Les Arts, Aug. 1908, p. 3, nos. iv, v; cp. Arm. I, 8, 23; *Corpus*, no. 21; Cott p. 161; Middeldorf, *Morgenroth*, no. 3 (lead); Hess/Leu auction, Lucerne, 11 Oct. 1961, lot 970 (lead). Fossi Todorow, no. 305 (for a drawing which copies the medal portrait).

4. NICCOLÒ PICCININO, condottiere, about 1380–1444.

Obv. Bust to left in plate-armour, in tall cap; on the shoulder-piece, Milanese armourer's mark AA crowned. Around, NICOLAVS PICININVS VICECOMES MARCHIO CAPITANEVS MAX(imus) AC MARS ALTER

Rev. PISANI P(ictoris) OPVS The she-griffin of Perusia (PERVSIA on collar) suckling two infants, the condottiere Braccio da Montone (BRACCIVS) and Piccinino (N. PICININVS)

90 mm. A740–4A

About 1441. The design of the reverse was suggested by the Roman wolf and twins. Piccinino bore the name of Visconti from his adoption by the Duke of Milan in 1439 to his adoption by the King of Naples in 1441 or 1442. Three lead specimens are recorded in the *Corpus* of which 22 *c* is Verona exhibition no. 119, pl. cxxiv *a*.

Collection: Signol (sale Paris, 1 April 1878, lot 155).

Literature: Les Arts, Aug. 1908, p. 3, no. iii; cp. Arm. I, 7, 21; *Corpus*, no. 22; Cott p. 161; Middeldorf, *Morgenroth*, no. 4 (excavated from the foundations of a house in Verona). Fossi Todorow, nos. 297, 303 (for drawings which copy the medal).

5. FRANCESCO SFORZA (1401–66), afterwards fourth Duke of Milan.

Obv. Bust of Sforza to left in armour, wearing tall cap. Around, FRANCISCVS SFORTIA VICECOMES MARCHIO ET COMES AC CREMONE D(ominus).

Rev. OPVS PISANI PICTORIS Bust of charger to left; three closed books and a sword.

88 mm. A741–5A

About 1441. Sforza's titles of Visconti and Lord of Cremona were acquired by his marriage with Bianca Maria Visconti in Oct. 1441. Lead specimens are *Corpus* 23 *j*, and at Cambridge.

Literature: Les Arts, Aug. 1908, p. 7, nos. i, ii; cp. Arm. I, 8, 22; *Corpus*, no. 23; Cott p. 161.

6. LEONELLO D'ESTE, Marquess of Ferrara, succeeded 1441, died 1450.

Obv. Bust of Leonello to right, wearing surcoat with scale-decoration over mail. Around, LEONELLVS MARCHIO ESTENSIS (olive-branches separating words).

Rev. OPVS PISANI PICTORIS A head with three infantile faces; on either side a knee-piece suspended from an olive-branch.

68 mm. A742–6A

The threefaced head means Prudence as the defender of peace and prosperity (Hill) or defender of peace and property (Middeldorf). The branches between the words are interpreted by Tervarent as being of laurel.
About 1440–4, to which period all the medals of Leonello with Pisanello's signature seem to belong. Some doubt has been expressed as to whether the smaller medals (i.e. all but the marriage-medal no. 10) are actually from his hand; but there is no uncertainty in the signature and they are surely of the time.

Literature: Les Arts, Aug. 1908, p. 7, no. vii; cp. Arm. I, 3, 4; *Corpus*, no. 24; (and no. 31 note, for Hill's cautious view of Kress medals nos. 6–9); Cott p. 161; Middeldorf, *Morgenroth*, no. 5 (ca. 1441–1444). Tervarent, col. 409. Fossi Todorow, no. 192v (for a drawing possibly related to the medal reverse).

7. *Obv*. Bust to left, wearing surcoat over mail. Around, LEONELLVS MARCHIO ESTENSIS (olive-branches separating words).

Rev. OPVS PISANI PICTORIS Two nude men (old and young) each carrying a basket filled with olive-branches; in the background, two vessels on which rain drops from clouds.

68 mm. A743–7A

Probably before the end of 1443. The reverse type has been interpreted as an allegory of the blessings of peace (Hill) or as an *impresa* expressing the idea *Festina Lente* (Wind).

Literature: Les Arts, Aug. 1908, p. 7, no. ix; cp. *Corpus*, no. 27; Cott p. 161; Wind, p. 90, n.

8. *Obv.* Bust of Leonello d'Este to left; the inscription removed.

Rev. PISANVS PICTOR FECIT (sprays between the words). A blindfolded lynx seated to left on a cushion.

69 mm. A744–8A

Probably of *ca.* 1441–1444. The blindfolded lynx is a symbol of statecraft; on another medal of Leonello, by Nicholaus, it is accompanied by the motto 'what you see do not see'. The reverse type is also interpreted as an *impresa* expressing the idea *Festina Lente* (Wind).

Literature: Les Arts, Aug. 1908, p. 7, no. viii; cp. *Corpus*, no. 28; Cott p. 161; Middeldorf, *Morgenroth*, cp. no. 7 (*Corpus* no. 75, medal by Nicholaus, before 1441). Wind, p. 90 n, 91, n. 3. Fossi Todorow, no. 44 (studies of a lynx by Pisanello, perhaps related to the medal reverse).

9. *Obv.* Bust to left, wearing embroidered surcoat over mail; around, between two plain circles, LEONELLVS MARCHIO ESTENSIS D(ominus) FERRARIE REGII 7 (et) MVTINE

Rev. PISANI PICTORIS OPVS in a sunk band. A nude youth lying to right before a rock on which is a vase containing olive-branches, the ends of which pierce its sides; attached to each handle an anchor, one of which is broken; below, in the sunk band, olive-branches.

70 mm. A745–9A

The meaning of the device, which is found on other works connected with the Estensi (e.g. on the sleeve of the dress of Pisanello's *Principessa di Casa d'Este* in the Louvre), is unknown.

Literature: Cp. Arm. I, 4, 10; *Corpus*, no. 30; Cott p. 161; Hill, *Pisanello*, pp. 73–4, pl. 14 (portrait of the princess, as Ginevra d'Este); Verona exhibition, no. 106, pl. cxi (portrait, as princess of the house of Este, with discussion of the sitter).

10, 11. *Obv.* Bust of Leonello to left; inscriptions: LEONELLVS MARCHIO ESTENSIS D(ominus) FERRARIE REGII ET MVTINE GE(ner) R(egis) AR(agonum).

Rev. OPVS PISANI PICTORIS A lion (Leonello) being taught by Cupid to sing; on a pillar in background, the mast and sail *impresa* of the Este and the date MCCCCXLIIII; on rocks on the left, the Este eagle.

103 mm. A746–10A

Commemorates the marriage of Leonello in April 1444 to Maria, daughter of the King of Aragon-Naples. The portrait of Leonello by Pisanello in Bergamo may relate to the medal, or may date from 1441. The collection also contains a poor lead specimen of the medal, 103 mm. (A747–11A). The *Corpus* records four specimens in lead.

Literature: Les Arts, Aug. 1908, p. 3, nos. viii, ix; cp. Arm. I, 3, 8; *Corpus*, no. 32; Cott p. 161; Verona exhibition, no. 107, pl. cx (portrait painting, date uncertain). E. Sindona, *Pisanello,* Milan, 1961, p. 121, pl. 137 (portrait painting, dated 1442–5, with literature).

12. SIGISMONDO PANDOLFO MALATESTA, Lord of Rimini and Fano, born 1417, inherited Rimini 1432, died 1468.

Obv. Bust of Sigismondo to right in surcoat, embroidered with Malatesta roses. Around, SIGISMVNDVS PANDVLFVS DE MALATESTIS ARIMINI FANI D(ominus).

Rev. OPVS PISANI PICTORIS Sigismondo standing, fully armed, holding sword; on left, on a heraldic rose-tree, his helmet and elephant's head crest; on right his shield.

90 mm. A748–12A

Probably about 1445, when Sigismondo recovered Fano. The *Corpus* illustrates from a lead specimen, and records two other specimens in lead.

Literature: Les Arts, Aug. 1908, p. 7, nos. iii, iv; cp. Arm. I, 5, 15; *Corpus*, no. 33; Cott p. 161.

13, 14. The same as Captain General of the Roman Church, 1445.

Obv. Bust to right in armour. Around, SIGISMVNDVS DE MALATESTIS ARIMINI 7C(etc.) ET ROMANE ECLLESIE CAPITANEVS GENERALIS

Rev. OPVS PISANI PICTORIS Sigismondo on charger to left before a fortress, on the walls of which are the date M CCCC XLV and his shield of arms.

Lead, 104 mm. A749–13A

The fortress may be Rocca Contrada, captured by Sigismondo in 1445, the date of the medal. The collection contains another specimen, also in lead, 102 mm. (A750–14A). The *Corpus* records one specimen in lead, 101.5 mm.

Literature: Les Arts, Aug. 1908, pp. 4–5, no. v (no. 14 illustrated); cp. Arm. I, 5, 14; *Corpus,* no. 34; Cott p. 161.

15. DOMENICO NOVELLO MALATESTA, born 1418, Lord of Cesena, 1429, died 1465.

Obv. Bust of the younger Malatesta to left. Inscription: DVX EQVITVM PRAESTANS MALATESTA NOVELLVS CESENAE DOMINVS

Rev. OPVS PISANI PICTORIS Malatesta in full armour, kneeling before a Crucifix; behind him, his horse seen from behind.

85 mm. A751–15A

Probably about 1445. May refer to a vow to found the Hospital of the Holy Crucifix, made by Malatesta when in straits at the battle of Montolmo, 1444.

Literature: Les Arts, Aug. 1908, p. 7, nos. v, vi; cp. Arm. I, 6, 16; *Corpus*, no. 35; Cott p. 161; Middeldorf, *Morgen-*

roth, nos. 8, 9; Seymour, *Masterpieces*, p. 37, note 6; Hill, *Pisanello*, pp. 165–6, n. The *Corpus* records three lead specimens, Morgenroth collection no. 9 is also lead. Fossi Todorow, no. 298 (for a sixteenth century drawing which copies the bust); no. 300 (for a drawing, perhaps sixteenth century German, which copies the medal reverse).

16. LODOVICO III GONZAGA, second Marquess of Mantua, born 1414, succeeded 1444, died 1478.

Obv. Bust of Lodovico to left in armour, with armourer's mark AA crowned. Inscription: LVDOVICVS DE GONZAGA CAPITANEVS ARMIGERORVM MARCHIO MANTVE ET CET(era).

Rev. OPVS PISANI PICTORIS The Marquess in full armour, with globular crest to his helmet, riding to right; in the field above, sun and sunflower.

102 mm. A752–16A

Probably 1447 or 1448, when Lodovico was Captain General of the Florentines. The armourer's mark is more easily seen on the specimen illustrated in the *Corpus*.

Literature: Les Arts, Aug. 1908, p. 3, nos. vi, vii; cp. Arm. I, 5, 13; *Corpus*, no. 36 (illustrating a lead specimen); Cott p. 161. Tervarent, col. 385 (for the sunflower symbol).

17. CECILIA GONZAGA, daughter of Gianfrancesco I, Marquess of Mantua, born 1424?, took the veil 1444 or later, died 1451 ?

Obv. Bust of Cecilia to left. Around, CICILIA VIRGO FILIA IOHANNIS FRANCISCI PRIMI MARCHIONIS MANTVE.

Rev. OPVS PISANI PICTORIS M CCCC XLVII In a rocky moonlit landscape, the figure of Innocence seated, her hand on the head of a unicorn. The inscription is on a pillar in the middle distance.

Lead, 86 mm. A753–17A

The unicorn, according to legend, could only be tamed by Innocence. This monster is modelled on a he-goat, which symbolizes knowledge. No lead specimens are recorded by the *Corpus*.

Literature: Les Arts, Aug. 1908, pp. 4–5, no. iii; cp. Arm. I, 5, 12; *Corpus*, no. 37; Cott p. 162; G. Fiocco, 'Disegni di Stefano da Verona', in *Proporzioni*, 3, 1950, pl. xlv. fig. 19 (for a drawing in the Uffizi illustrating the reverse type). Tervarent, col. 236 (ii. Unicorn).

18. VITTORINO RAMBALDONI DA FELTRE, humanist, 1379–1446.

Obv. Bust of Vittorino to left, in tall cap. Around, VICTORINVS FELTRENSIS SVMMVS

Rev. MATHEMATICVS ET OMNIS HVMANITATIS PATER and, in inner circle, PISANI PICTORIS OPVS Pelican in her piety.

57 mm. A754–18A

Probably made soon before or after the death of Vittorino, 2 Feb. 1446. One lead specimen is recorded in the *Corpus*. Another specimen in bronze is in the Widener collection, (ex. Hainauer).

Collection: His de la Salle (sale London, Sotheby, 22 Nov. 1880, lot 24).

Literature: Les Arts, Aug. 1908, p. 7, no. xi; cp. Arm. I, 8, 24; *Corpus*, no. 38; Cott p. 162; Middeldorf, *Morgenroth*, no. 10.

19. ALFONSO V of Aragon, King of Naples and Sicily, born 1394, established in Naples 1442, died 1458.

Obv. Bust of Alfonso to right, in armour; on left, helmet, with device of open book on its side, and above it a sun; on right, open crown and date MCCCCXLIIII Around, DIVVS ALPHONSVS REX TRIUMPHATOR ET PACIFICVS

Rev. In a rocky landscape, eagle on tree-stump above a dead fawn, surrounded by lesser birds of prey; inscription: LIBERALITAS AVGVSTA and PISANI PICTORIS OPVS

Lead, 110 mm. A755–19A

Made at Naples, 1449. The eagle, which allows lesser birds to feast on its leavings, was the medieval symbol of royal liberality. The *Corpus* illustrates a lead specimen, and cites one other.

Literature: Les Arts, Aug. 1908, p. 7, no. x; cp. Arm. I, 6, 17; *Corpus*, no. 41; Cott p. 162; Tervarent, col. 4. Middeldorf, *Morgenroth*, nos. 11, 12. Fossi Todorow, no. 160 (for the drawing of the obverse which Hill believed to be by Pisanello, now classed as a workshop copy of the original); no. 44 (for studies of an eagle, by Pisanello, perhaps related to the medal reverse).

20. *Obv.* Bust of Alfonso V to right, in robe. Below, crown.

Without reverse.

Octagonal, 88 × 59 mm. A756–20A

Made from the obverse of a medal (with the King hunting a boar on the reverse) by cutting out all but the bust and crown.

Literature: Les Arts, Aug. 1908, p. 3, no. i; cp. Arm, II, 29, I; III, 2, *a*; *Corpus*, no. 42 note; Cott p. 162. E. Sindona, *Pisanello*, Milan, 1961, p. 126, pl, 157 (comparable specimen in New York, 90 × 50 mm., across field, ALFO[S] REX).

21. See Appendix.

22. DON IÑIGO D'AVALOS, in service of Alfonso, King of Naples, as Grand Chamberlain from 1442.

Obv. Bust of Don Iñigo to right in broad-brimmed hat. Around, DON INIGO DE DAVALOS

Rev. OPVS PISANI PICTORIS A sphere representing earth, sky, and sea; below, PER VVI SE FA; above, shield of arms of Avalos.

79 mm. A758–22A

About 1448–9, at Naples.

The portrait, in lower relief than usual, is perhaps the most delicate and beautifully designed of all that he executed. The reverse is inspired by the Homeric description of the shield of Achilles. A drawing of a fantastic landscape, once attributed to Pisanello, has been associated with the medal reverse. Degenhart accepted the attribution, but was the first to doubt the connection with the medal. Fossi Todorow believes the drawing to be of uncertain attribution, and more probably connected with the circle of Pisanello in Ferrara.

Literature: Les Arts, Aug. 1908, p. 3, no ii; cp Arm. I, 2, 1; *Corpus*, no. 44; Cott p. 162; Tervarent, col. 362 (on reverse). Verona exhibition no. 112, pl. cv; B. Degenhart, *Pisanello*, Turin, 1945, pp. 55, 79; Fossi Todorow, no. 87 (for the drawing).

PAOLO DA RAGUSA

(Active *ca.* 1450)

The medallist is believed to be identical with the Paolo d'Antonio da Ragusa who was an assistant to Donatello in Padua in 1447. The three medals signed by the artist are all dated to 1450, and were made in Naples. To the bibliography in the *Corpus*, p. 13 may be added Ivo Uzorinac, 'Paulus de Ragusio', in *Numismatika*, Zagreb, nos. 2–4 (1934–6), pp. 106–121 (claiming as the work of Paolo some coins issued at Ragusa in 1464 and 1469).

23. ALFONSO V OF ARAGON, King of Naples (see no. 19).

Obv. Bust to right, wearing surcoat over mail. Around, ALFONSVS REX ARAGONVM

Rev. Female figure standing, holding purse and serpent-entwined sceptre. Around, OPVS PAVLI DE RAGVSIO

45 mm. A759–23A

Literature: Cp. Arm. I, 26, 2; *Corpus*, no. 45; Cott p. 162.

FRANCESCO LAURANA

(b. *ca.* 1420–5; d. *ca.* 1502)

Born in Dalmatia; worked in Naples about 1458–60 and 1474; in France about 1477–1500; died before 12 March 1502. To the bibliography in the *Corpus*, p. 16, may be added Ivo Uzorinac, 'Francesco Laurana (Frano Vranjanin)', in *Numizmatičke Vijesti*, 12, no, 23 (1965), pp. 21–43.

24, 25. RENÉ D'ANJOU (King of Naples 1435, dispossessed 1442, died 1480) and JEANNE DE LAVAL (his second wife 1454, died 1498).

Obv. Jugate busts of René and Jeanne to right. Around, DIVI HEROES FRANCIS LILIIS CRVCEQ(ue) (I)LLVSTRIS INCEDVNT IVGITER PARANTES AD SVPEROS ITER

Rev. Peace (PAX AVGVSTI) standing holding olive-branch and helmet; on right, an olive-tree, on left a cuirass; in field, M CCCC LXIII; below, FRANCISCVS LAVRANA FECIT

Lead, 90 mm. A760–24A

The left hand of Peace does not, as described in the *Corpus*, rest on a cippus. The collection contains a second specimen in lead, much decayed (A761–25A).

Literature: Les Arts, Aug. 1908, p. 14, no. vi; *Corpus*, no. 59 *c*; cp. Arm. I, 41, 4; Cott p. 162.

26. JEAN D'ANJOU, Duke of Calabria and Lorraine (born 1427, died 1470).

Obv. Bust to right in tall cap. Around, IOHANES DVX CALABER ET LOTHORINGVS SICVLI REGIS PRIMOGENITVS

Rev. Circular temple surmounted by figure of St Michael. Around, MARTE FEROX RECTI CVLTOR GALLVSQ(ue) REGALIS Across field, M CCCC LXIIII

85 mm. A late cast. A762–26A

Lacks the signature, which it should have below the reverse design.

Literature: Cp. Arm. I, 42, 6; III, 7, *a*; *Corpus*, no. 61; Cott p. 162.

27. LOUIS XI, King of France (1461–83).

Obv. Bust to right, wearing high woolly hat, and dress with collar at back. Around, DIVVS LODOVICVS REX FRANCORVM

Rev. Concordia, wearing shirt of mail, tunic and mantle, seated to right, holding lily-sceptre and olive-branch, crested helmet at her feet. Around, CONCORDIA AVGVSTA

Lead, 86 mm. A good deal decayed. A763–27A

Köhler has published a specimen (now lost) having the signature FRANCISCVS LAVRANA FECIT on the reverse. Other specimens like the present are in the British Museum, at Paris, and Vienna.

Literature: Cp. Arm. I, 41, 3; *Corpus*, no. 65; Cott p. 162. J. D. Köhler, *Historische Münzbelustigung*, 6 (Nuremberg, 1734), p. 161 (for the lost variant of the medal).

AMADIO DA MILANO

(d. 1483 or later)

Amadio was a Milanese goldsmith, seal-engraver, and medallist, who was active at the court of Ferrara from

1437 to 1482. His will was dated 1483. The technique of his medals is unusual. The inscriptions were cut on a separate moveable ring of metal, placed round the model, and the whole pressed into the mould. See Hill, *Med. Ren.*, pp. 21–2 on the technique, and *Corpus*, p. vii, note 1, on the bibliography of technique in general.

28. BORSO, Marquess of Este (1413–71), succeeded Leonello 1450, Duke of Modena and Reggio 1452, first Duke of Ferrara 1471.

Obv. Bust to left. Around, DOMINVS BORSIVS MARCHIO ESTENSIS

Rev. Marigold with two long leaves; above and in front of the flower and hanging from a rosette, a door-knocker with bar ending in dragon's head. Around, incised, AMADE MEDIOLAN(i) AR(ti)FEX FEC(i)T.

51 mm. A764–28A

The device of the door-knocker is found in Este MSS. of the time of Borso. This medal probably dates from before the death of Borso's father Niccolò, 26 Dec. 1441.

Literature: Cp. Arm. I, 16, 2; *Les Arts*, Aug. 1908, p. 13, no. xxiii; Heiss, *Niccolò*, etc., p. 19, no. 2, pl. i, 4; *Corpus*, no. 69; Cott p. 162. Fossi Todorow, no. 89 (for profile drawing, perhaps by the medallist).

29. NICCOLÒ III D'ESTE, Marquess of Ferrara, 1393–1441.

Obv. Bust to right. Around, incised, NICOLAI MARCHIO ESTENSIS FER(rariae).

Rev. On florally diapered field, Este shield between n m

54 mm. Later cast. A765–29A

Ferrarese, resembling the work of Amadio da Milano.

Literature: Cp. Arm. I, 10, 30; *Corpus*, no. 73; Middeldorf *Morgenroth*, no. 13 (specimen in lead); Cott p. 162.

NICHOLAUS

(Active *ca.* 1440–1454)

Medallist working at Ferrara about 1440, possibly to be identified with Niccolò d'Alemagna who painted a member of the d'Este household in 1454.

30. ANTONIO PISANO, called PISANELLO, the medallist (*ca.* 1395–1455).

Obv. Bust of Pisanello to left, elderly, in brocaded dress. Around, PISANVS PICTOR. Fine dotted border.

Without reverse.

34 mm. A766–30A

Probably about 1445–50. Often without reason attributed to Pisanello, of whom the design seems unworthy; the treatment of the border on the obverse suggests Nicholaus. The reverse of this medal is similar to the reverse of no. 32, the initials of the seven virtues.

Literature: Les Arts, Aug. 1908, p. 7, no. 12; cp. Arm. I, 9, 26; *Corpus*, no. 77; Cott p. 162.

ANTONIO MARESCOTTI

(Active 1444–1462)

Nothing appears to be known, biographically, of the artist except that he worked in Ferrara from 1444 to 1462.

31. SAINT BERNARDINO OF SIENA, famous preacher, Minorite of the Observance (1380–1444), canonized 1450.

Obv. Bust to left in habit, hood drawn over head, eyes closed, book clasped in arm; indication of halo. Around, COEPIT FACERE ET POSTEA DOCERE

Rev. The trigram yhs in a flaming halo, the top of the h forming a cross with INRI on label. Around, in two circles, MANIFESTAVI NOMEM (sic) TVVM HOMINIBVS and ANTONIO MARESCOTO DA FERARA F

77 mm. After-cast. A767–31A

The portrait of the celebrated Franciscan preacher, which has the appearance of being based on a death-mask, was made just after his death in 1444, or after his being canonised in 1450. Bernardino founded the devotion to the name of Jesus which the reverse illustrates.

Literature: Cp. Arm. I, 28, 1; *Corpus*, no. 84; Cott p. 162. Fossi Todorow, no. 383 (drawing after the medal).

32. ANTONIO PISANO, called PISANELLO, the medallist (*ca.* 1395–1455).

Obv. Bust to left, wearing high crumpled cap, and brocaded dress. Around, PISANVS PICTOR

Rev. F. S. K. I. P. F. T. in wreath.

58 mm. A768–32A

The old attribution to Pisanello is not borne out by any marks of style. The handling of the relief is not unlike that of Marescotti. The portrait is copied in a fresco in S. Maria della Scala at Verona, said to have been painted by Giovanni Badile in 1443. The letters are the initials of the seven virtues, Faith, Hope, Charity, Justice, Prudence, Fortitude, Temperance.

Collection: Signol (sale Paris, 1 April 1879, lot 150).

Literature: Cp. Arm. I, 9, 25; *Corpus*, no. 87; Cott p. 162.

33. GIULIO CESARE VARANO, Lord of Camerino (about 1430–1502).

Obv. Bust left, in flat cap and embroidered coat; in field, engraved, A F

Without reverse.

Rectangular, 54 × 44 mm. The only specimen known.

A769–33A

The portrait is identified by its resemblances to an inscribed medal (*Corpus*, no. 88) which is sometimes attributed to Marescotti; A F has been explained as A(ntonius) F(ecit), which is unlikely. (The dimensions are incorrect in the *Corpus* and the illustration is oversize).

Collection: Charles Sackville Bale (sale London, Christie, 25 May 1881, lot 2163).

Literature: Arm. II, 67, 32; *Les Arts*, Aug. 1908, p. 9, no. X (as Sperandio); J. de Foville, 'La medaille de Jules-César Varano seigneur de Camerino', in *Rev. Num.* 16(1912), pp. 268–275; *Corpus*, no. 89; Cott p. 163.

34. GINEVRA SFORZA, wife of Giovanni II Bentivoglio, 1464, died 1507.

Obv. Bust to left, in jewelled head-dress, with short veil. Around, +DIVAE GENEVRAE SFORTIAE BENTIVOLLAE

Without reverse.

Lead, 86 mm. Twice pierced. A770–34A

This is close in style to Marescotti. It may have been made by him or some one in his neighbourhood about 1464, at the time of the marriage to Bentivoglio, when Ginevra was about 30 years old.

Literature: Cp. Arm. II, 66, 23; *Corpus*, no. 91; Cott p. 163 (as Marescotti ?).

JACOPO LIXIGNOLO

(Active *ca.* 1460)

Nothing is known of this artist except that he made, in 1460, the following medal of Borso, and another of an unknown Beata Maria Anna of Siena.

35. BORSO D'ESTE, Duke of Modena and Reggio, 1460 (see no. 28).

Obv. Bust to right, wearing cap with fluted crown and jewel at side, and rich dress. Around, BORSIVS DVX MVTINE ET REGII MARCHIO ESTENSIS RODIGIIQ(ue) COMES ETC.

Rev. In mountainous landscape, unicorn dipping its horn into a stream; above, sun shining. Around, OPVS IACOBVS LIXIGNOLO MCCCCLX

Lead, 82 mm. A771–35A

The unicorn according to legend purified streams of vermin by dipping its horn into the water.

Literature: Cp. Arm. I, p. 33; *Corpus*, no. 94; Cott p. 163. Tervarent, cols. 235–6 (Unicorn as purifyer), col. 240, ix (Unicorn as a device of Borso).

PETRECINO OF FLORENCE

A medallist of whom nothing certain is known except that he made three medals at Ferrara in 1460.

36. BORSO D'ESTE, Duke of Modena and Reggio, 1460 (see no. 28).

Obv. Bust to left, with long hair, wearing cap and rich robe, all as on the preceding medal. Around, BORSIVS DVX MVTINE Z(et) REGII MARCHIO ESTENSIS RODIGIIQ(ue) COMES

Rev. In a rocky landscape, a hexagonal font with open lid, showing a ring within; crosses incised on sides of font; above, the sun's face shining. Around, OPVS PETRECINI DE FLORETIA MCCCCLX

Lead, 96 mm. A772–36A

The font is mentioned in documents as an Este device (*el batesmo*).

Literature: Cp. Arm. I, 33, 1; *Corpus*, no. 96; Cott p. 163.

BALDASSARE D'ESTE

A natural son of Niccolò III, worked as a painter and medallist 1461–74, died about 1504.

37. ERCOLE I D'ESTE, Duke of Ferrara, Modena, and Reggio (1471–1505).

Obv. Bust to left, wearing dress with jewel on breast; below, 1472; at sides and above, incised, HER(cules) FER(ari)E DVX

Without reverse.

Octagonal, 82 × 55 mm., with loop. Brass. A773–37A

Made from Baldassare's signed medal (*Corpus*, no. 99), with slight retouching; the Duke appears in the medal to be wearing a cuirass, but here coat with pleated front. Both the specimens in the Victoria and Albert (1177–1864) and Morgenroth collections are in bronze, patinated.

Literature: Heiss, *Niccolò*, etc., pl. V, 2; *Corpus*, no. 99 note; Cott p. 163; Middeldorf, *Morgenroth*, no. 16.

LODOVICO CORADINO

Medallist of Modena, in the service of Ercole d'Este in 1472.

38. ERCOLE I D'ESTE, Duke of Ferrara, Modena, and Reggio (1471–1505).

Obv. Bust of Ercole to left in cap with fluted crown and jewel. Around, HERCVLES DVX FERARIE MVTINE ET REGII Incised on truncation, MCCCCLXXII

Rev. Hercules standing, resting on spear, holding shield charged with Este device of a ring and flower; on left, three columns in the sea; above, GADES HERCVLIS; below, OPVS CORADINI M(utinensis).

57 mm. Twice pierced, with loop for suspension. A774–38A

Literature: Heiss, *Niccolò*, etc., p. 42, pl. v, 6; *Les Arts*, Aug. 1908, p. 13, no. x; cp. Arm. I, 53, I; *Corpus*, no. 102; Cott p. 163.

SCHOOL OF FERRARA *ca.* 1475–1505
ESTE MEDALS

39. ACARINO D'ESTE, legendary ancestor of the Estensi.

Obv. Bust to right, with long hair, in cap. Inscription: D(omi)N(u)S ACHARIVS ATEST(inus) FERRARIOLAE P(rinceps) I (primus).

Without reverse.

Rectangular. Lead, 83 × 66 mm. A775–39A

A fictitious portrait, made in the last quarter of the fifteenth century.

Literature: Arm. II, 9, 9; Heiss, *Niccolò*, etc., p. 43, no. I, pl. vi, I; *Les Arts*, Aug. 1908, p. 14, no. xii; *Corpus*, no. 106 *d*; Cott p. 163.

40. BORSO D'ESTE, Marquess of Este (1413–71), Duke of Modena and Reggio, 1452, first Duke of Ferrara, 1471.

Obv. Bust to left in fluted cap. Around, BORSIVS DVX MVTINE ET REGI(i).

Rev. Shield of Este between B(orsius) D(ux) on floriated ground, all in enclosure of six lobes and six points.

30 mm. A776–40A

Other specimens at Ferrara (silver, after-cast), in the British Museum, and at Milan. Goldsmith's work, not far from Amadio da Milano.

Literature: Arm. II, 21, 2; *Corpus*, no. 114 *d*; Cott p. 163.

41. See Appendix.

42. ERCOLE I D'ESTE, 1505. Duke of Ferrara, Modena, and Reggio (1471–1505).

Obv. Bust to left, in cap. Around, HERCVLES DVX FERRARIE MVTINE ET REGII RODIGII Q(ue) COMES 1505

Rev. Four putti receiving from the sky a shower of Este diamond rings intertwined with flowers. Around, IVPPITER EX ALTO NOBIS ADAMANTA REMISIT

93 mm. A weakish cast. A778–42A

The reverse has been made by recasting from Sperandio's medal of Ercole, omitting his signature. The portrait dimensions of this and the following piece are the same.

Literature: Heiss *Niccolò*, etc., p. 49, no. 10, pl. vii, 4; cp Arm. II, 43, 2; III, 169 *a*; *Corpus*, no. 120 *f* (diameter wrongly recorded, 89 mm.); Cott p. 163.

43. *Obv.* Same bust as preceding, without inscription.

Without reverse.

69 mm. Gilt. A779–43A

Literature: Heiss, *loc. cit.*, no. 11, pl. viii, I; *Corpus*, no. 120 note (diameter wrongly recorded, 63 mm.); Cott p. 163. P. Grotemeyer, 'Seltene italienische Medaillen in der münchner Münzsammlung', in *Mitteilungen der Bayerischen Numismatischen Gesellschaft*, 53 (1935), pp. 138–144 (portrait plaque of Ercole I d'Este; a portrait of an unknown man).

FERRARESE AND OTHER NORTH ITALIAN SCHOOLS
About 1470–1500

44. UNKNOWN MAN.

Obv. Bust to left, aged about 50 to 60, in truncated conical cap.

Without reverse.

Rectangular, 69 × 48 mm. A780–44A

Usually, but wrongly, identified as Politian, whose name is scratched on the back in a modern hand. The second specimen recorded by the *Corpus* has disappeared. A third specimen is in the Salton collection.

Literature: Les Arts, Aug. 1908, p. 8, no. ii; Arm. II, 51, 19; *Corpus*, no. 126 *a*; Cott p. 163; Salton, no. 7 (79·5 × 57·5 mm).

45. UNKNOWN MAN.

Obv. Bust to left of young man, wearing tall cap and surcoat over armour.

Without reverse.

Rectangular, 44 × 34 mm. A781–45A

Sometimes thought to be Borso d'Este. There is another specimen in the Victoria and Albert Museum, differing slightly in details.

Literature: Cp. *Corpus*, no. 127; Cott p. 163.

46. UNKNOWN MAN.

Obv. Bust to left, middle-aged, with short hair, wearing cap with soft top.

Without reverse.

50 mm. The only specimen known. A782–46A

Literature: Corpus, no. 134 *a*; Cott p. 163.

47. UNKNOWN BOY.

Obv. Bust to left, in round cap. Moulded border.

Without reverse.

Rectangular, 43 × 37 mm. A783–47A

The only specimen known. A rectangular plaque in the Salton collection depicts the same sitter, but is from a larger model.

Literature: Les Arts, Aug. 1908, p. 14, no. xiii; *Corpus*, no. 140 *a* (dimensions wrongly given); Salton, no. 8 (illustrated; 66·5 × 53·5 mm).

48. UNKNOWN MAN.

Obv. Bust to left, with thick wavy hair, sash over right shoulder.

Without reverse.

65 mm. A784–48A

The only specimen known. A thick runnel on the reverse.
Literature: Les Arts, Aug. 1908, p. 13, no. xx. *Corpus*, no. 135 *a*; Cott p. 164.

49. UNKNOWN MAN.

Obv. Bust to left, wearing round cap and robe.

Without reverse.

Rectangular, 55 × 38 mm. A785–49A

Late cast, but the only specimen known.

Literature: Cott p. 164.

50. UNKNOWN MAN.

Obv. Bust, young, to left, wearing cap.

Without reverse.

Rectangular, 60 × 37 mm. A786–50A

Very doubtfully identified as Giangaleazzo Sforza, whose name is stamped on the back in much later lettering. The only specimen known.

Literature: Les Arts, Aug. 1908, p. 13, no. vii; F. Malaguzzi Valeri, *La Corte di Lodovico il Moro*, vol. I (Milan, 1913), p. 37; *Corpus*, no. 139 *a* (the dimensions wrongly given); Cott p. 164.

51. UNKNOWN MAN.

Obv. Bust to right, wearing mortier and surcoat over mail. Around, VNA TI DIRO ALTRA TI FERO

Rev. Outline of object resembling a double axe-head.

74 mm. A787–51A

The only known specimen.

Literature: Arm. II, 130, 16; *Les Arts*, Aug. 1908, p. 14, no. ix; *Corpus*, no. 137 *a*; Cott p. 164.

52. UNKNOWN WOMAN.

Obv. Bust to left, back hair in coif and band, incised ornament on dress.

Without reverse.

Octagonal, 63 × 42 mm. A788–52A

Another specimen is in the Victoria and Albert Museum.

Literature: Les Arts, Aug. 1908, p. 14, no. x; Rodocanachi, *La femme italienne*, p. 220; *Corpus*, no. 145 *b*; Cott p. 164.

53. UNKNOWN WOMAN.

Obv. Bust to right, hair dressed on foundation with figured net and jewel, rich dress with mantle over left shoulder.

Without reverse.

Rectangular to oval, 52 × 38 mm. A789–53A

Other specimens in the Victoria and Albert Museum and at Modena.

Literature: Les Arts, Aug. 1908, p. 13, no. viii = 14, no. xiv; *Corpus*, no. 152 *c*; Cott p. 164.

54. UNKNOWN WOMAN.

Obv. Bust to right, with long formal curls, small coif on forehead.

Without reverse.

Rectangular, 48 × 37 mm. The only specimen known. A790–54A

Literature: Les Arts, Aug. 1908, p. 14, no. viii; Rodocanachi, *La femme italienne*, p. 220; *Corpus*, no. 153 *a*; Cott p. 164.

MATTEO DE' PASTI
(Active from 1441; d. 1467/8)

Matteo is first recorded in Venice in 1441. He was in Verona in 1446, and then settled at Rimini in the same year. He worked on the Tempio Malatestiano under Alberti and for Sigismondo Malatesta, most of his medals being concerned with Malatesta and Isotta degli Atti. Besides his reputation as a medallist he practised as illuminator, sculptor, and architect.

See *Corpus*, p. 38; Thieme-Becker, 26 (1932) pp. 287–8. It may be noted that the listing of specimens of the various medals by Matteo de' Pasti given in Hill's article 'The medals of Matteo de' Pasti', in *Num. Chron.* 17 (1917), pp. 298–312 is fuller that his final listings in the *Corpus*.

55. GUARINO DA VERONA, humanist (1374–1460).

Obv. Bust to left, aged. Inscription: GVARINVS VERONENSIS

Rev. MATTHEVS DE PASTIS F Within a wreath, a fountain surmounted by nude male figure with mace and shield.

94 mm. A791–55A

Made at Ferrara in or shortly before 1446. The medal is possibly the source for the portrait of Guarino in his MS Strabo at Albi.

Hill has published a mention of an early lead cast of this medal, included in a parcel of lead versions of medals sent by Ulrich Gussenbrot, student at Padua, to his father in Augsburg, 30 Nov. 1459.

Literature: Les Arts, Aug. 1908, p. 10, no. x; cp. Arm. I, 18, 2; *Corpus*, no. 158; Cott, p. 164. Millard Meiss. *Andrea Mantegna as illuminator*, Hamburg, 1957, p. 36, fig. 29, plate facing p. 35 (Guarino portrait in MS).
G. F. Hill, 'A lost medal by Pisanello' in *Pantheon*, 8 (1931), pp. 487–8 (for the mention of the lead specimen of the Guarino. Hill's quotation is fuller than the version in Habich, *Deutsche Schaumünzen*, i. 2, p. xliv).

56. LEONE BATTISTA ALBERTI, architect and writer on art and science (1404–72).

Obv. Bust to left; inscription: LEO BAPTISTA ALBERTVS

Rev. MATTHAEI PASTII VERONENSIS OPVS Wreath of laurel, within which a winged human eye and the motto QVID TVM

93 mm. A792–56A

Dated 1446–1450, because Alberti left Rimini in 1450. A self-portrait plaque of Alberti is also in the Kress collection. The winged eye is variously explained as a reference to Alberti's inventions in optical science, as an adaptation of an Egyptian hieroglyph, and, by identifying the wings on the eye as those of a falcon, as a reference to an omniscient and ubiquitous God.

Literature: Les Arts, Aug. 1908, p. 10, no. ix; cp. Arm. I, 17, 1; *Corpus*, no. 161; Pope-Hennessy, *Kress Bronzes*, no. 1 (self-portrait plaque by Alberti); Wind, p. 186, fig. 65 (the winged eye as a reference to God); K. Badt, 'Drei plastische Arbeiten von Leone Battista Alberti,' in *Mitteilungen des Kunsthistorischen Institutes in Florenz*, 8 (1958), pp. 78–84 (at p. 81 and note 16 on the winged eye).

57. JESUS CHRIST.

Obv. Bust to left, with nimbus. Around, IESVS CHRISTVS DEVS DEI FILIVS HVMANI GENERIS SALVATOR

Rev. Half-figure of the dead Christ supported in the tomb by a winged putto; on the left, another putto weeping; behind, the cross. Signed MATTHAEI PASTII VERONENSIS OPVS

93 mm. A793–57A

Probably contemporary with the Alberti medal. Hill believed a drawing of the obverse in the Louvre to be by the medallist. Degenhart gave the drawing to Pisanello himself, Fossi Todorow classes it as a product of Pisanello's workshop.

Literature. Arm. I, 18, 3; Heiss, *Alberti*, p. 26, no. 3, pl. iii, 3; *Les Arts*, Aug. 1908, p. 10, no. xi; Hill, *Medallic Portrait of Christ*, Oxford, 1920, pp. 12–13, fig. 1, fig. 2 (drawing); *Corpus*, no. 162 *e*; Cott p. 164. Degenhart, *Pisanello*, Turin, 1945, p. 44; Fossi Todorow, no. 263 (for the drawing).

58. SIGISMONDO PANDOLFO MALATESTA, Lord of Rimini and Fano, born 1417, inherited Rimini, 1432, died 1468.

Obv. Bust of Sigismondo to left, in surcoat over mail. Around, SIGISMONDVS P(andulfus) D(e) MALATESTIS S(anctae) R(omanae) ECL(esiae) C(apitaneus) GENERALIS

Rev. O(pus) M(athei) D(e) P(astis) V(eronensis) above, M CCCC XLVI below the achievement of Sigismondo (shield, helmet, elephant-crest, and mantling).

43 mm. A794–58A

Literature: Cp. Arm. I, 20, 15; *Corpus*, no. 165; Cott p. 164; Middeldorf, *Morgenroth*, no. 20.

59. ISOTTA DEGLI ATTI DA RIMINI, mistress (1446), then wife (1456) of Sigismondo Malatesta, died 1474/5.

Obv. Bust to right, hair over high frame, veil fastened with jewel on top of forehead. Around, ISOTE ARIMINENSI FORMA ET VIRTVTE ITALIE DECORI

Rev. The Malatesta elephant to right in a meadow with two rose-bushes. Above, OPVS MATHEI DE PASTIS V(eronensis); below, M CCCC XLVI

84 mm. A795–59A

Hill interpreted the Malatesta elephant as symbolising magnanimity, Tervarent reads it as simply symbolising force.

Literature: Les Arts, Aug. 1908, p. 10, no. viii; cp. Arm. I, 21, 20; *Corpus*, no. 167; Cott p. 164; Middeldorf, *Morgenroth*, no. 21. Tervarent, col. 153 (the Malatesta elephant).

60. SIGISMONDO PANDOLFO MALATESTA.

Obv. Bust of Sigismondo to left, in cuirass and surcoat, Around, SIGISMONDVS PANDVLFVS DE MALATESTIS S(anctae) RO(manae) ECLESIE C(apitaneus) GENERALIS

Rev. The Castle of Rimini. Around, CASTELLVM SISMONDVM ARIMINENSE M CCCC XLVI

83 mm. A796–60A

Literature: Cp. *Corpus*, no. 174; Cott p. 164; Middeldorf *Morgenroth*, no. 22 (from the foundations of a house in Rimini).

61. *Obv*. Same as no. 60, but SIGISMVNDVS for SIGISMONDVS

Rev. Fortitude, wearing crown, cuirass, and long tunic, seated to front on a seat, the sides of which are formed by foreparts of Malatesta elephants; she holds in both hands a broken column; below, MCCCCXLVI

82 mm. A rather rough cast. A797–61A

Literature: Cp. Arm. I, 20, 9; *Corpus*, no. 178; Cott p. 164.

62. *Obv.* Bust to left, in plate-armour over mail. Around, SIGISMVNDVS PANDVLFVS MALATESTA PAN(dulfi) F(ilius).

Rev. Similar to no. 60, but SISMVNDVM

81 mm. A798–62A

Literature: Cp. *Corpus*, no. 186; Cott p. 164.

63. ISOTTA DEGLI ATTI.

Obv. Bust to right, hair over high frame, confined by crossing band, fastened with jewel on top and falling in two pointed masses behind. Inscription: D(ominae) ISOTTAE ARIMINENSI

Rev. The same as no. 59, but signature and two rose-bushes taken out.

83 mm. A799–63A

Literature: Les Arts, Aug. 1908, p. 10, no. vii; cp. Arm. I, 21, 19; *Corpus*, no. 187; Cott p. 164; Middeldorf; *Morgenroth*, no. 29.

64. *Obv.* Bust of Isotta to right, as on no. 63. Around, D(ominae) ISOTTAE ARIMINENSI

Rev. A closed book. Around, ELEGIAE

40 mm. A800–64A

Literature: Cp. Arm. I, 22, 23; *Corpus*, no. 188; Cott p. 164; Middeldorf, *Morgenroth*, no. 30.

65. *Obv.* Bust of Isotta to right, veiled, as on no. 59. Around, D(ominae) ISOTTAE ARIMINEN(si) M CCCCXLVI

Rev. The same as no. 64, but inscription reworked and increased in size.

42 mm. A801–65A

Literature: Cp. Arm. I, 22, 24; *Corpus*, no. 189; Cott p. 165; Middeldorf, *Morgenroth*, no. 31.

AFTER MATTEO DE' PASTI

66. SIGISMONDO PANDOLFO MALATESTA.

Obv. Bust to left, laureate, in armour. Around, SIGISMVNDVS PANDVLFVS MALATESTA PAN(dulfi) F(ilius).

Rev. Front view of San Francesco at Rimini, according to Alberti's proposed reconstruction. Around, PRAECL(arum) ARIMINI TEMPLVM AN(no) GRATIAE V(otum) F(ecit) M CCCC L

40 mm. A802–66A

This is a 'foundation medal' for the church which was dedicated in 1450, though never finished. The medal is generally placed with those by Pasti, although Hill repeated in his *Corpus* his view in *Num. Chron.*, 17 (1917), p. 310, no. 22, that the medal is not by Pasti. Specimens have been excavated in Rimini.

Literature: Cp. Arm. I, 21, 17; *Corpus*, no. 183; Cott p. 165 (as after Pasti); Middeldorf, *Morgenroth*, no. 28 (as Pasti); Münzen und Medaillen, Basel, auction catalogue XVII, 2 Dec. 1957, lot 88 (excavated specimen). C. Ricci, *Il Tempio Malatestiano*, Milan/Rome, 1924, chapter X; C. Brandi, *Il Tempio Malatestiano,* Turin, 1956 pp. 14–20 (for the facade of S. Francesco).

67. *Obv.* Bust to left, laureate, in armour. Around, SIGISMVNDVS PANDVLFVS MALATESTA PAN(dulfi) F(ilius) POLIORCITES ET IMP(erator) SEMPER INVICT(us).

Without reverse, pierced, and plugged with wax.

91 mm. A803–67A

Probably a later work, based on the portraits by Pasti. Other specimens are at Berlin and Cracow.

Literature: Les Arts, Aug. 1908, p. 10, no. vi; *Corpus*, no. 190 *c*; cp. Arm. I, 20, 13; Cott p. 165 (as after Pasti).

BARTOLOMMEO MELIOLI
(b. 1448; d. 1514)

Melioli appears to have spent the whole of his career in Mantua as goldsmith, coin engraver, and medallist. He was possibly succeeded as master of the mint by Gianfrancesco Ruberti in 1500. For plaquettes formerly ascribed to Melioli, see Pope-Hennessy, *Kress Bronzes*, nos. 190–202.

68. LODOVICO III GONZAGA, born 1414, succeeded as second marquess of Mantua, 1444, died 1478.

Obv. Bust to right, wearing mortier, armour, and cloak; on the breast-plate a seven-headed dragon; below, a helmet bearing a device of a bird perched on a curved spray; to right and left of the helmet, shields, one with the Gonzaga arms; around, LVDOVICVS II MARCHIO MANTVAE QVAM PRECIOSVS XPI SANGVIS ILLVSTRAT

Rev. The Marquess seated to right, on a seat adorned with the Gonzaga hound; before him Faith and Pallas, with spear, shield, and helmet. Around, FIDO ET SAPIENTI PRINCIPI FIDES ET PALLAS ASSISTVNT Signed and dated MELIOLVS SACRAVIT ANNO MCCCCLXXV

79 mm. A804–68A

The reliquary of the blood of Christ was preserved in the church of S. Andrea at Mantua. The design of the reverse shows the influence of Mantegna.

Literature: Les Arts, Aug. 1908, p. 11, no. xiv; *Corpus*, no. 194; cp. Armand. I, 80, 2; Cott, p. 165; Middeldorf, *Morgenroth*, no. 32 (specimen from the Dreyfus sale, July 1909, and Oppenheimer sale, lot 23).

69. FRANCESCO II GONZAGA, afterwards fourth Marquess of Mantua (1466–84–1519).

Obv. Bust to right as a boy, wearing cap and richly decorated breast-plate. Around, D(ivus) FRANCISCVS GON(zaga) D(ivi) FRED(erici) III M(archionis) MANTVAE F(ilius) SPES PVB(lica) SALVSQ(ue) P(ublica) REDIVI(va).

Rev. Health standing between a sea and a fire, resting on staff, holding ears of corn and a medicine basket with a scroll inscribed CAVTIVS. Around, ADOLESCENTIAE AVGVSTAE and, under groundline, MELIOLVS DICAVIT

71 mm. A805–69A

Hill dated the medal to 1481, before the death of Federigo I, and identified the reverse type as probably Pandora. Panofsky identifies the figure as Health, holding a basket of medicines, indicating that the medal was made to commemorate the recovery of Francesco from a dangerous illness, in 1484.

Literature: Cp. Arm. I, 80, 4; *Corpus*, no. 196; Cott, p. 165; D. and E. Panofsky, *Pandora's Box*, London, 1956, pp. 22–3, n. 20.

70. CHIARA GONZAGA, wife of Gilbert de Bourbon, Comte de Montpensier and Dauphin d'Auvergne, married 1481, died 1503.

Obv. Bust to right, hair in coif and veil. Around, CLARA DE GONZ(aga) COMITI(ssa) MONT(is)PENSERII ET DELPHINA ALV(ern)IE

Rev. cast hollow, and ornamented with cast impressions of various goldsmith's ornaments.

58 mm. A806–70A

Closely resembling Melioli's signed medal of Maddalena Gonzaga, and dating from or after 1481 (when Chiara married the Comte de Montpensier).

Collection: either from the His de la Salle (sale London, Sotheby, 22 Nov. 1880, lot 8) or Joseph Fau (sale Paris, 3 March 1884, lot 563) collections, although neither catalogue mentions the curious ornaments on the reverse.

Literature: Les Arts, Aug. 1908, p. 12, no. viii; *Corpus*, no. 200*g*; cp. Arm. II, 85, 5; Cott p. 165.

GIANFRANCESCO RUBERTI

(Active 1483–1526)

Ruberti is known as a goldsmith and die-engraver at Mantua from 1483 to 1526. In 1492 he was engaged in striking coins by a new process, and he seems also to have been an armourer to the Mantuan court. He was sent to Milan in 1517, and to Venice in 1497 and 1526. A large group of plaquettes signed IO. F. F. has been ascribed to Ruberti. See Thieme-Becker 29 (1935) p. 147; Forrer, 5, p. 264; Pope-Hennessy, *Kress Bronzes*, nos. 97–110 (plaquettes by IO. F. F.).

71. FRANCESCO II GONZAGA, Marquess of Mantua (1466–84–1519).

Obv. Bust to left, in armour; on the breast-plate, a dove on a curling spray; below, two leaves. Around, FRANCISCVS MARCHIO MANTVAE IIII

Rev. Battle-scene; below, weapons and armour, including a shield with EPO engraved on it. Above, FAVEAT FOR(tuna) VOTIS and, engraved under ground-line, IO(annis) FR(ancisci) RVBERTO OPVS

50 mm. A807–71A

Literature: Cp. Arm. I, 81, 1; *Corpus*, no. 203; Cott p. 165.

ANTICO

(b. *ca.* 1460; d. 1528)

Pier Jacopo di Antonio Alari Bonacolsi, called Antico, was a celebrated Mantuan bronze-worker, under the influence of Mantegna. He worked especially for Gianfrancesco Gonzaga of Ròdigo, and for the Marquess of Mantua. For a plaquette dependent on a medal by Antico see Pope-Hennessy, *Kress Bronzes*, no. 2.

71 *bis*. GIANFRANCESCO GONZAGA DI RÒDIGO, born 1443, Lord of Sabbioneta, etc., 1479, died 1496.

Obv. Bust to left, wearing cloak. Around, IOHANNES FRANCISCVS GONZ(aga).

Rev. Fortune on a starry sphere on a ship's prow; Mars tied to a tree bearing a trophy which includes a shield charged with thunderbolt; Minerva holding spear and resting on another trophy. Above, FORVICTRICI; in exergue ANTI.

40 mm. A808–71 *bis* A

The thunderbolt was an *impresa* of Gianfrancesco.

Literature: Cp. Arm. I, 62, 1; *Corpus*, no. 206; Cott p. 165.

72. ANTONIA DEL BALZO, wife of Gianfrancesco Gonzaga di Ròdigo, born 1441, married 1479, died 1538.

Obv. Bust to right, hair in net, ferronnière on forehead. Around, DIVA ANTONIA BAVTIA DE GONZ(aga) MAR(chionissa).

Rev. Hope, nude, winged, holding broken anchor and tattered sail, standing on prow of a broken-masted vessel drawn by two Pegasi, over which flies a small Cupid; engraved on side of vessel MAI PIV. Around, SVPEREST M(ihi) SPES. In exergue, ANTI

40 mm. A809–72A

Mai più was the motto of Antonia and her husband, and is found also on the bronze vase in the Modena Museum attributed to l'Antico.

Literature: Corpus, no. 212 *l*; cp. Arm. I, 62, 5; Pope-Hennessy, *Kress Bronzes*, no. 2 (for a related plaquette); Middeldorf, *Morgenroth*, no. 33 (of reverse only); Cott p. 165.

73. DIVA JULIA, unknown.

Obv. Bust to right; around, DIVAI IVLIA PRIMVM FELIX

Rev. Battle-scene; below, military and naval arms. Above, DVBIA FORTV(n)A and, engraved on ground-line, ANTICVS

34 mm. A810–73A

The identification of the lady is uncertain; she is too old to be the famous Giulia daughter of Lodovico Gonzaga of Bozzolo.

Collection: His de la Salle (sale London, Sotheby, 22 November 1880 no. 174).

Literature: Corpus, no. 214 *f*; cp. Arm. I, 81, 2; Pope-Hennessy, *Kress Bronzes*, no. 186 (for a plaquette, style of Moderno, with same legend as the medal reverse); Cott p. 165.

IN THE MANNER OF ANTICO

73*a*. MADDALENA OF MANTUA.

Obv. Bust to right. Around, MAGDALENA MANTVANA DIE XX NO M̊CCCCCIIII. Pearled border.

Rev. Occasion, as a female figure, running to right in pursuit of Time, also as a female figure, and holding the verge of a folliot balance (?) and an hour-glass. Around, BENE HANC CAPIAS ET CAPTAN TENETO Pearled border.

46 mm. A1465–725A

Literature: Cp. Arm. II, 100, 11; III, 195, *c*; *Corpus*, 215 *h*; Cott p. 165.

74. LUCA DE' ZUHARI, provost of Pomponesco.

Obv. Bust to left, in cap. Around, LVCAS D(e) ZVHARIS PREPOSITVS PONPONESCHI

Rev. Venus and Mars running to right; below, armour; around, VENER ET MARS VICTOR

40 mm. Gilt on the reverse, and formerly on obverse also. A811–74A

This has been attributed to Ruberti, but is nearer to Antico. VENER should be VENVS. The name Zuhari is perhaps the same as Zuccari. Pomponesco is in Mantuan territory, on the Po.

Literature: Corpus, no. 217 *g*; cp. Arm. II, 101, 15; Cott p. 165. Pope-Hennessy, *Kress Bronzes*, no. 159 (for a plaquette with a related composition, by Moderno).

75. GIULIA ASTALLIA

Obv. Half-figure to left. Around, DIVA IVLIA ASTALLIA.

Rev. Phoenix on pyre, looking up at sun. Around, EXEMPLVM VNICVM FOR(mae) ET PVD(icitiae)

61 mm. Later cast. A812–75A

Perhaps Giulia of Gazzuolo, the victim of an outrage recorded in Bandello's *Novella*, i, 8.

Literature: Les Arts, Aug. 1908, p. 13, no. xxii; *Corpus*, no. 218 *k*; cp. Arm. I, 83, 3; Middeldorf, *Morgenroth*, no. 34 ('the identity of the sitter is a puzzle'); Cott p. 165. Tervarent, col. 306, vi (Phoenix as symbol of a unique being).

GIANCRISTOFORO ROMANO
(b. *ca.* 1485; d. 1512)

Giancristoforo was sculptor, medallist and die engraver. Early in his career he worked in Milan and Rome, then in Mantua, 1497–1505, as the favourite sculptor of Isabella d'Este. He later worked again in Rome, in Naples and in Loreto, where he died. To the bibliography in *Corpus* p. 55 add: R. Weiss, 'The medals of Pope Julius II (1503–1513)', in Warburg *Journal*, 28 (1965) pp. 163–182 (at p. 172, n. 86; re-attributions of medals between Giancristoforo and Serbaldi).

76. ISABELLA D'ESTE, wife of Francesco II Gonzaga, born 1474, married 1490, died 1539.

Obv. Bust to right, hair tied in knot at back of head. Around, ISABELLA ESTEN(sis) MARCH(ionissa) MA(ntuae).

Rev. Astrology, winged, with wand; before her, serpent rearing; above, sign of Sagittarius. Around, BENE MERENTIVM ERGO

39 mm. A813–76A

Giancristoforo completed a medal of Isabella in August 1498. Another one by him, mentioned in November 1505, was probably only a new casting of the old one, though Jacopo d'Atri wrote of it as if it were a new thing. The finely mounted gold specimen at Vienna is merely a much-chased recasting, not worthy of its mount. The medal was very popular, and many copies, varying in the amount of the lettering preserved, exist. The original read BENE MOERENTIVM, an unfortunate mistake which was corrected by omitting the O.

Literature: Cp. Arm. III, 49, A; *Corpus*, no. 221 (with discussion of documents, and source for the reverse legend); Cott p. 165.

77. See Appendix.

IN THE NEIGHBOURHOOD OF GIANCRISTOFORO ROMANO

78. LUCREZIA BORGIA, wife of Alfonso I d'Este, born 1480, married 1502, died 1519.

Obv. Bust to left, hair in jewelled net and continued in queue, ferronnière across forehead. Around, LVCRETIA ESTEN(sis) BORGIA DVC(I)SSA

Without reverse.

60 mm. Four times pierced. A815–78A

Mantuan work, in the neighbourhood of Giancristoforo Romano. This specimen is one of three cited in the *Corpus*, the others being at Paris (Luynes collection), and at Vienna (late chasing).

Literature: Arm. II, 90, 3; 293, 3; III, 190, *b*; Heiss, *Niccolò Spinelli*, p. 43, no. 7, pl. iv, 8; Rodocanachi, *La femme italienne*, p. 220; *Les Arts*, Aug. 1908, p. 13, no. iii; *Corpus*, no. 231 *c*; Cott p. 165.

79. *Obv.* Bust to left, heavy hair down her back in a queue, a braid drawn across from temple and tied behind; dress fastened on left shoulder. Around, LVCRETIA EST(e)N(sis) DE BORGIA DVC(issa).

Without reverse.

59 mm. A816–79A

This portrait was doubtless made for the marriage in 1502; Lucrezia is here Duchess of Bisceglie, not yet of Ferrara. It is often found attached to a portrait of Alfonso d'Este by another hand. Later, the present bust was re-used with a new inscription describing her as Duchess of Ferrara, etc. As to the authorship, all that can be said is that it is Mantuan, in the neighbourhood of Giancristoforo Romano.

Literature: Corpus, no. 232 *j*; cp. Arm. II, 89, 2; 293, 2; Cott p. 165.

80. JACOBA CORREGGIA, unknown.

Obv. Bust to right; behind, a lily and branches of oak and laurel fastened with a strap (*correggia*). Around, IACOBA CORRIGIA FORME AC MORVM DOMINA

Rev. Captive Love bound with a strap to a tree. Around, CESSI DEA MILITAT ISTAT and, in field, P M

53 mm. Five times pierced, but otherwise a fine specimen. Gilt on obverse and reverse. A817–80A

The medal is of Mantuan origin, about 1500. The sitter is unknown, the artist uncertain. Hill suggested that the letters in the field may stand for *P . . . Mantuanus*. Hill noted that the reverse legend had been interpreted to indicate that Cupid was speaking: 'I have had to yield, and leave your goddess in the field'. Tervarent accepts this interpretation.

Collection: Joseph Fau (sale Paris, 3 March 1884, lot 440).

Literature: Les Arts, Aug. 1908, p. 12, no. iv; cp. Arm. I, 118, 1; III, 48 *a*; *Corpus*, no. 234 *h*; Cott p. 166; Tervarent, cols. 19, v; 40–1; Panofsky, pp. 95–128 (Blind Cupid).

81. See Appendix.

82. MADDALENA OF MANTUA, unknown.

Obv. Bust to right, hair in net. Around, MADALENE MANTVANE PM

Rev. Swan, wounded with an arrow in its breast, standing on a bow and quiver; above, a radiant cloud. Around, NON SANA

37 mm. A819–82A

The artist of this dainty medal is unidentified; that he is Mantuan is certain from the style; possibly, as suggested above, the letters P M, which occur also on the medal of Jacoba Correggia (no. 80), are for *P . . . Mantuanus*.

Literature: Les Arts, Aug. 1908, p. 12, no. ix; *Corpus*, no. 236 *d*; cp. Arm. II, 101, 12; Cott p. 166. Tervarent, cols. 140–1, viii.

83. BEATRICE OF ARAGON, wife of Matthias, King of Hungary, born 1457, married 1476, widowed 1490, died 1508.

Obv. Bust to right, veiled. Around, DIVA BEATRIX HVNGARIAE REGINA

Without reverse.

44 mm. A820–83A

One other specimen is recorded, at Budapest.

Hill believed the style of the medal to be that of Melioli, who might have seen Beatrice on her way to Naples in 1501. Huszár attributed the medal to Giancristoforo Romano, explaining that it was modelled in Naples, but finished in Rome, thus avoiding the problem mentioned by Hill of why the medal was not recorded in the letters of the Mantuan ambassador at Naples. Gerevich accepts the attribution to Giancristoforo, observing that the sitter is aged thirty rather than fifty, and not depicted as a widow. He claims the marble portrait relief of her at Budapest as a work of Giancristoforo because the profiles are identical.

Literature: Rodocanachi, *La femme italienne*, p. 220; *Les Arts*, Aug. 1908, p. 13, no. I; Arm. II, 82, 10; *Corpus*, no. 238 *b*; Cott p. 166. L. Huszár, 'Una medaglia della Regina Beatrice', in *Corvina*, XXV–XXVIII (1933–34), pp. 35–44; L. Gerevich, 'Le maître des reliefs en marbre du roi Mathias et sa femme Béatrice', in *Bulletin du Musée Hongrois des Beaux-Arts*, 27 (1965) pp. 15–32 (at p. 30).

GIAN MARCO CAVALLI

(d. after 1508)

Die-engraver and metal-worker, in the employ of the Mantuan court from 1481; at Hall in Tyrol in 1506; died after 1508.

84. FRANCESCO II GONZAGA (1466–84–1519), fourth Marquess of Mantua.

Obv. Bust to left, with long hair, in cuirass. Around, FRANCISCVS MAR(chio) MANTVE IIII

Rev. The Marquess, in armour, standing on garlanded basis, gives ears of corn to a man on his right, behind whom is a helmeted woman with palm-branch; on his left another man approaches to receive alms. Around, DIVINVM DARE HVMANVM ACCIP(ere) and, below, LIBERALITAS

32 mm. Struck. A821–84A

Literature: Cp. Arm. II, 99, 3; *Corpus*, no. 241; Cott p. 166.

85. *Obv.* Bust to left, with long hair, in cuirass. Around, FRANCISCVS MAR(chio) MANTVE IIII

Rev. The Marquess in armour, standing on basis, holding sceptre, giving alms to three men. Around, NON IGNARA MALI MISERIS SVCCVRRERE DISCO

32 mm. Struck. A822–85A

The motto is from Virgil, *Aen.* i. 630. These two belong to a small group of medals—or patterns for coins—illustrating the Marquess's charity.

Literature: Cp. Arm. II, 99, 4; *Corpus*, no. 243; Cott p. 166.

MEA

(Active *ca.* 1510)

A Mantuan artist of whom nothing is known except that he signed a medal of Pietro Pomponazzo, *Corpus*, no. 250, which makes it possible to assign to him a few other medals about 1510.

86. FRANCESCO BONATTI of Mantua, jurisconsult.

Obv. Bust to right, in cap and robe. Around, FRAN(ciscus) BONATTVS MANT(uanus) IVR(is) CO(n)S(ultus) EQ(ues) AC MAR(chiae) AVD(itor).

Rev. A book, from which escapes Truth, naked, holding compasses; on left, a lighted candle. Around, VERITATIS INTERPRES

49 mm. A823–86A

Literature: Cp. Arm. II, 100, 9; *Corpus*, no. 251; Cott p. 166.

87. BATTISTA SPAGNOLI of Mantua, Carmelite, poet (1448–1516).

Obv. Bust to left, wearing habit. Around, BAPT(ista) SPANIOLVS

Rev. On three pedestals, a cherub, a swan, and an eagle; below, TER MAX(imus).

40 mm. A824–87A

About 1513, when Spagnoli became General of his Order.

Literature: Les Arts, Aug. 1908, p. 13, no. v; *Corpus*, no. 253 *g*; cp. Arm. II, 101, 14; Cott p. 166; Middeldorf, *Morgenroth*, no. 36.

88. GIOVANNI GONZAGA, Marquess of Ariano (?).

Obv. Bust to right, with long hair, wearing cuirass. Around, IO(annes) GONZAGA MARCHIO AR(iani).

Rev. Port view of a galley in full sail; above, two flames (St. Elmo's fire ?).

35 mm. A825–88A

The treatment suggests the attribution to Mea. This Giovanni is presumably the son of Federigo (1474–1525); on this and another medal he is called Marquess of Ariano (?) although there is no record of a Gonzaga connexion with that place in the Regno at so early a date. Other specimens in the British and Parma Museums.

Literature: Corpus, no. 254 *c*; cp. Arm. II, 100, 8; Magnaguti, no. 158; Cott p. 166.

MANTUAN SCHOOL

Early Sixteenth Century

89. ORTENSIA PICCOLOMINI.

Obv. Bust to right, wearing long coif. Around, HORTENSIAI PICOLOMINEAI M(ontis) P(escatae) D(ominae).

Rev. The Judgement of Paris. Around, PVLCRAE OPES ET ARMA S(e)D AMOR PVICRIOR

56 mm. A826–89A

The treatment recalls Melioli; the genitives in AI recall Antico's Julia (no. 73). Monte Pescata was a Piccolomini fief near Siena, but the filling out of the abbreviations M P D is not certain. The medal dates from about 1500.

Two other complete specimens and one of the reverse alone are recorded.

Collection: Joseph Fau (sale Paris, 3 March 1884, lot 490).

Literature: Arm. II, 98, 22; Heiss, *Florence*, ii, p. 241, pl. xxii, 5; *Les Arts*, Aug. 1908, p. 12, no. x; *Corpus*, no. 265 *a*; Cott p. 166.

90. FEDERIGO II GONZAGA, fifth Marquess and

first Duke of Mantua, born 1500, marquess 1519, duke 1530, died 1540.

Obv. Bust to front, head to left, wearing cuirass. Around, FEDERICVS II MAR(chio) V MANTVAE

Rev. St Catherine standing, holding palm and resting on wheel.

35 mm. A827–90A

Perhaps a pattern for a coin. Between 1513, when Federigo succeeded, and 1530 when he was created Duke. Other specimens are recorded at Milan (2) and Vienna by the *Corpus*, and in commerce, 1957.

Literature: Cp. Arm. II, 155, 2; *Corpus*, no. 269; Cott p. 166; Münzen und Medaillen, Basel, auction catalogue XVII, 2 Dec. 1957, lot 93, pl. 10 (a fifth specimen, 34 mm).

91. CORRADO (of the Nobili GONZAGA), fourteenth century.

Obv. Bust to right, in cap and cuirass. Around, CORADVS GONZAGA ALOISII FIL(ius).

Without reverse.

80 mm. A828–91A

This portrait of Corrado (doubtless fictitious) is found attached to one of his wife Paola Beccaria, whom he married in 1340. The medal is a restitution of uncertain date, possibly of the sixteenth century.

Literature: Arm. II, 14, 14; *Corpus*, no. 274; Cott p. 166.

GIANFRANCESCO ENZOLA

Gianfrancesco Enzola of Parma, goldsmith, medallist, and die-engraver, working 1455–78. Employed at first especially by Francesco Sforza and Pier Maria Rossi of Berceto, for whom he engraved dies; after about 1471 he took to casting large medals, especially for Costanzo Sforza of Pesaro. For plaquettes by Enzola see Pope-Hennessy, *Kress Bronzes*, nos. 62–68.

92. FRANCESCO SFORZA, 1401–66, fourth Duke of Milan, 1450.

Obv. Bust to right, in armour. Around (Sforza biscione) FR(anciscus) SFORTIA VICECOMES M(edio)L(an)I DVX IIII BELLI PATER ET PACIS AVTOR MCCCCLVI Across field, V F

Rev. Under a tree, a greyhound seated; a hand issuing from a radiant cloud touches him; a bridle on the ground tied to the tree by a chain. Around, IO(annis) FR(ancisci) ENZOLAE PARMENSIS OPVS

42 mm. A829–92A

This, like all existing specimens, is cast, although the original was undoubtedly struck from dies. The letters V F on this and other medals by Enzola are unexplained; they may be the dedicatory formula *votum fecit*. The reverse type was an *impresa* of the Duke, to the motto *Quietum nemo me impune lacesset.*

Literature: Cp. Arm. I, 44, 6; *Corpus*, no. 281; Cott p. 166; Middledorf, *Morgenroth*, no. 38; Terrarent, col. 258.

93. FRANCESCO I and GALEAZZO MARIA SFORZA, fourth and fifth Dukes of Milan, 1459.

Obv. Bust of Francesco Sforza and inscription, as on no. 92.

Rev. Bust of Galeazzo Maria to left in mail; around, (Sforza biscione) GALEAZ(ius) MARIA SFORTIA VICECOMES FR(ancisci) SFORTIAE M(edio)L(an)I DVCIS IIII PRIMOGEN(i)T(u)S; across field, V F and MCCCCLVIIII

44 mm. A830–93A

A good cast, but the original, like no. 92, was struck from dies; it is doubtful if any of the original strikes survive.

Literature: Cp. Arm. I, 44, 7; *Corpus*, no. 284; Cott p. 166.

94. TADDEO DI GUIDACCI MANFREDI, Count of Faenza and Lord of Imola 1449, living in 1493.

Obv. Bust to left, in armour. Around, TADEVS MANFREDVS COMES FAVENTIE IMOLEQ(ue) D(ivi) AC INCLITI GVIDATII and, in field, VNICVS GENITVS; to left and right, V F, and, on right, 1461

Rev. Nearly nude female figure seated, with sword and wheel; behind her, putto holding caduceus; on the seat, ACCEDA and, below, OPVS IO(annis) FR(ancisci) PARMENSIS Around, SOLA VIRTVS HOMINEM FELICITAT

45 mm. Rough cast. A831–94A

Literature: Cp. Arm. I, 43, 1; *Corpus*, no. 285; Cott p. 166.

95. COSTANZO SFORZA, Lord of Pesaro (1447–73–83).

Obv. Bust to left, in cuirass. Around, CONSTANTIVS SFORTIA DE ARAGONIA DI(vi) ALEXAN(dri) SFOR(tiae) FIL(ius) PISAVRENS(is) PRINCEPS AETATIS AN(no) XXVII

Rev. Costanzo riding to left, fully armed (crest: dragon with head of an old man holding a ring), sword erect in right hand, shield with his arms on his left arm; under the horse, a hound running; flowery foreground, landscape with scenes of agriculture in background. Around, QVIES SECVRITAS COPIA MARTIS HONOS 7(et) SALVS PATRIAE MCCCCLXXV; under ground-line, IO(annis) FR(ancisci) PARMEN(sis).

Lead, 80 mm. After-cast. A832–95A

Only two early examples are known, at Berlin and Pesaro.

Literature: Cp. Arm. I, 45, 10; *Corpus*, no. 292; Cott p. 166. Pope-Hennessy, *Kress Bronzes*, no. 67 (for a plaquette related to the reverse).

96. COSTANZO SFORZA, Lord of Pesaro, and his father ALESSANDRO (1409–45–68).

Obv. Bust of Costanzo to left, as on no. 95. Around, CONSTANTIVS SFORTIA DE ARAGONIA FILIVS BENEMERITO PARENTI D(icat) D(edicat) MCCCCLXXV

Rev. Bust of Alessandro to left, in plate-armour over mail. Around, ALEXANDRO SFORTIAE DIVI SFORTIAE FILIO IMPERATORI INVICTISS(imo).

80 mm. A833–96A

Literature: Les Arts, Aug. 1908, p. 8, no. x; cp. Arm. I, 45, 11; *Corpus*, no. 293; Cott p. 166.

97. COSTANZO SFORZA, Lord of Pesaro.

Obv. Bust to left, in plate-armour. Around, CONSTANTIVS SFORTIA DE ARAGONIA DI(vi) ALEXAN(dri) SFOR(tiae) FIL(ius) PISAVRENS(is) PRINCEPS AETATIS AN(no) XXVII

Rev. The Castle of Pesaro. Around, INEXPVGNABILE CASTELLVM CONSTANTIVM PISAVRENSE SALVTI PVBILICAE M CCCC LXXV; below, IO(annes) FR(anciscus) PARMEN(sis).

83 mm. Old cast, untrimmed, traces of gilding on reverse. A834–97A

Literature: Les Arts, Aug. 1908, p. 8, no. xi; cp. Arm. I, 45, 9; *Corpus*, no. 294; Cott p. 167.

98. FRANCESCO SFORZA (1401–66), fourth Duke of Milan, 1450.

Obv. Bust of Sforza to right as on no. 92, on a slightly larger scale.

Without reverse.

Oval, 42 × 31 mm. A835–98A

Other specimens in the Milan (Ambrosiana) and formerly Henry Oppenheimer Collections (although not in the Oppenheimer sale).

Literature: Cp. *Corpus*, no. 298; Cott p. 167.

99. COSTANZO SFORZA (see no. 95).

Obv. Bust to left, in cuirass. Around, CONSTANTIVS SF(ortia) DE ARAGO(nia) PISAV(ri) D(ominus).

Rev. The Castle of Pesaro. Around, SALVTI ET MEMORIAE CONDIDIT

30 mm. Struck. A836–99A

This may with confidence be attributed to Enzola. It was a foundation medal for the Castle of Pesaro.

Literature: Cp. Arm, II, 68, 37; *Corpus*, no. 299 *k*; Cott p. 167.

CLEMENTE DA URBINO

A bronze-caster and medallist, whose only authenticated work is the medal of 1468 described below.

100. FEDERIGO DA MONTEFELTRO, Count of Urbino, born 1422, count 1444, duke 1474, died 1482.

Obv. Bust to left, in mortier, cuirass, and mantle; on the breast-plate a Lapith fighting a Centaur, and two Victories. Around, ALTER ADEST CESAR SCIPIO ROMAN(us) ET ALTER SEV PACEM POPVLIS SEV FERA BELLA DEDIT

Rev. An eagle on a fulmen, supporting with spread wings a plate on which are cuirass, shield, sword, globe, brush, and olive-branch; above, the stars of Jupiter, Mars, and Venus. Around and in field, MARS FERVS ET SVMHVM TANGENS CYTHEREA TONANTEM DANT TIBI REGNA PARES ET TVA FATA MOVENT; INVICTVS FEDERICVS C(omes) V(r)BINI ANNO D(omini) MCCCCLXVIII and, below, OPVS CLEMENTIS V(r)BINATIS

94 mm. A837–100A

The details of the bust are copied from Cristoforo di Geremia's medal of Alfonso of Aragon (no. 210). Of the objects on the reverse, the brush is the *scopetta* device which may be seen on the buildings at Urbino. Wind explains the reverse as symbolizing the balance of Mars and Venus under Jupiter.

Collection: Probably from the J. C. Robinson collection (sale Paris, 19 May, 1884, lot 29).

Literature: Les Arts, Aug. 1908, p. 13, no. xiii; *Corpus*, no. 304 *g*; cp. Arm. I, p. 47; Cott p. 167. Wind, p. 88; Tervarent, col. 5.

FRANCESCO DI GIORGIO MARTINI (b. 1439; d. 1501/2)

Born in Siena, and active as architect, painter, and metalworker. Sometime between 1475 and 1477 he left Siena to work for Federigo da Montefeltro in Urbino, returning to Siena after about 1485, and then active concurrently in Urbino, Gubbio, Naples and Milan. For his career see A. S. Weller, *Francesco di Giorgio*, Chicago, 1943. For plaquettes by the artist see Pope-Hennessy, *Kress Bronzes* nos. 71–74.

101. BORGHESE BORGHESI, jurisconsult of Siena (1414–90).

Obv. Bust to left, wearing flat cap. Around, BVRGHESIVS SENEN(sis) (EQ) VES IVRIS VTR(iusque) CONSVLTIS[S] (imus) P(ater) P(atriae).

Rev. Minerva to left, holding spear and shield. Around, [IN]GENIO MORTALI INGENIVM PRAEB[VI]T IMMORTALI DEA ORTA

64 mm. Four times pierced, and battered, but old. A838–101A

Borghesi was knighted after the battle of Poggio Imperiale (near Poggibonsi) in 1479 by the Duke of Calabria for his help against the Florentines, in the war against Lorenzo de'Medici conducted by King Ferdinand of Naples and Pope Sixtus IV. Borghesi was given the title of *Pater Patriae* by the Sienese.

Literature: Cp. Arm. II, 154, 16; *Corpus*, no. 310; Cott p. 167; Middeldorf, *Morgenroth*, no. 39; A. S. Weller, *Francesco di Giorgio*, Chicago, 1943, p. 177, fig. 70.

COSTANZO DA FERRARA

Painter and medallist, who worked chiefly at Naples. He was summoned to Constantinople, to paint the Sultan's portrait, and doubtless returned after the Sultan's death on 3 May 1481. Meanwhile he had made the following medal, which is easily the finest presentation of Mohammad II extant. Those who are looking for traces of Gentile Bellini's work at Constantinople would do well to remember Costanzo, of whose painting traces may perhaps remain there.

102. MOHAMMAD II, Sultan of the Turks (1430–51–81).

Obv. Bust to left, in turban and cape. Around, SVITANVS MOHAMETH OTHOMANVS TVRCORVM IMPERATOR

Rev. The Sultan riding to left; trees and building in background. Around, HIC BELLI FVLMEN POPVLOS PROSTRAVIT ET VRBES Below, on tablet, CONSTANTIVS F(ecit).

123 mm. A839–102A

Doubtless early in 1481 or somewhat before. This specimen, which is unique, is the earlier version of the medal, which is well known from later, much inferior, versions, on which the inscription was remodelled and a heavy double circular border and the date 1481 added. Possibly only this earlier version is from the hand of the artist. In spite of a slight roughness in the casting of the reverse, it is the most outstanding medal in the whole of the present collection. Babinger suggests that the Bertoldo portrait of Mohammad (no. 248) depends either on this piece by Costanzo, or on another untraced model which was also used by Bellini.

Literature: Arm. I, 79, 2; Heiss, *Niccolò Spinelli*, pp. 81–2, pl. x, 1; *Les Arts*, Aug. 1908, p. 8, no. viii; *Corpus*, no. 321 *a*; Cott p. 167. F. Babinger, *Mehmed der Eroberer und seine Zeit*, Munich, 1953 p. 554 (Costanzo and Bertoldo), pp. 425–6 (Bertoldo and Bellini).

NEAPOLITAN SCHOOL

Late Fifteenth Century

103. ANDREA MATTEO III D'ACQUAVIVA, Duke of Atri and Teramo (1457–81–1528).

Obv. Bust to right with long hair, in cuirass. Around, ANDREAS MATTHEVS III DE AQVAVIVA

Rev. Crowned shield of arms. Around, DVX HADRIE TERAMIQVE

44 mm. Broken at edge. A840–103A

Andrea Matteo was born in 1457; the medal is doubtless earlier than 1500, and was probably made at Naples. Other specimens are at Milan (Brera collection in the Castello) and Vienna (a bad cast).

Literature: *Corpus*, no. 332 *c*; cp. Arm. II, 106, 1; Cott p. 167.

ADRIANO FIORENTINO

(Active 1488–1499 or later)

Adriano de' Maestri, sculptor and bronze-caster, greatly influenced by Bertoldo. A large number of strongly mannered medals made at Rome, Naples, Urbino, and in Germany are attributed to him, because of their likeness to the medal no. 107 and to a similar one of Emilia Pio, for his authorship of which there is some documentary evidence. First heard of in 1488; a sculptor of his name died in 1499, but the two medals just mentioned seem to refer to later events.

104. FERDINAND OF ARAGON, Prince of Capua, afterwards King Ferdinand II (1495–6).

Obv. Bust to right, with long hair, wearing cap with mark W on edge. Around, FERDINANDVS ALFONSI DVC(is) CALAB(riae) F(ilius) FERD(inandi) REG(is) N(epos) DIVI ALFON(si) PRON(epos) ARAGONEVS and, across field, CAPVE PRINCEPS

Rev. Felicitas seated to left, holding ears of corn and waving cornucopiae over her head; in field left, eagle; below her chair, W; around, PVBLICAE FELICITATIS SPES

75 mm. A841–104A

The only one of the three known examples that has any claim to be of the time. The medal must have been made before the death of Ferdinand I, 25 Jan. 1494. The W, which used to be taken for an artist's mark, is an unexplained personal device.

Literature: *Corpus*, no. 335 *b*; cp. Arm. I, 101, 1; Cott p. 167.

105. FERDINAND II OF ARAGON, King of Naples (1495–6).

Obv. Bust to right, wearing cap, on the edge of which the letter W. Around, FERDINANDVS II DE ARAGONIA REX SICILIAE VNGARIAE HIERVSALEM

Rev. Janiform head (bearded male to left, female to right); on right, a sword. Around, LIBERATORI VRBIVM

52 mm. A842–105A

Another specimen is in the Louvre, and a poor one at Bologna.

Literature: Corpus, no. 337 *c*; cp. Arm. I, 101, 2; Cott p. 167.

106. GIOVANNI GIOVIANO PONTANO, poet (1426–1503).

Obv. Bust to right, bald, unclothed. Around IOANNES IOVIANVS PONTANVS

Rev. Urania walking to right, holding globe and lyre. Below, VRANIA

84 mm. A843–106A

The reference of the reverse is to Pontano's astronomical poem *Urania*, the personification being that of the poet's inspiration, combined with astronomy.

Literature: Corpus, no. 340 *j*; cp. Arm. II, 30, 10; Cott p. 167. Tervarent, cols. 256, 359, iii.

107. ELISABETTA GONZAGA, Duchess of Urbino, married Guidobaldo I 1489, widowed 1508, died 1528.

Obv. Bust to right, hair in coif and hanging in long queue behind. Around, ELISABET(ta) GONZAGA FELTRIA DVCIS(sa) VRBINI

Rev. Female figure lying on a rock, her head against a closed gate (?), holding a bridle; in the air, a mass of flame projecting sparks. Around, HOC FVGIENTI FORTVNAE DICATIS

85 mm. A844–107A

This appears to be the medal by Adriano Fiorentino mentioned by the Duchess in a letter of 1495; yet the reverse, with its allusion to the flight of Fortune, would seem to refer to a later period, when Adriano is supposed to have been dead. The flame is a symbol of the soul; but the whole allegory is obscure. The object against which the figure reclines may perhaps be not a gate but that frame-work which appears in certain *memento mori* designs (e.g. no. 272).

Literature: Les Arts, Aug. 1908, p. 13, no. xi; *Corpus*, no. 344 *i*; cp. Arm. II, 118, 54; Cott p. 167.

108. UNKNOWN BOY.

Obv. Bust to right with long hair, wearing cap. The original inscription removed, and the following engraved: SIGISMVNDO SCOTTO MAGNO MILITI ANNO THEOGONIAE MCCV

Without reverse.

85 mm. The only specimen known. A845–108A

The treatment of the bust leaves no doubt that this is by the author of the present group, of which it is one of the most charming examples. Sigismondo Scotto appears to be unknown, and the inscription cannot refer to this boy. He resembles a young Gonzaga (?) in a well-known drawing by Bonsignori in the Albertina at Vienna.

Literature: Arm. III, 151, *L*; *Corpus*, no. 346 *a*; Cott p. 167.

GIROLAMO SANTACROCE
(b. 1502; d. 1537)

The Neapolitan sculptor Girolamo Santacroce is mentioned as having made a medal of Jacopo Sannazaro, the poet, in about 1524. The medal of Andrea Caraffa is by the same hand as that medal. See *Corpus*, p. 87; Thieme-Becker, 29 (1935) pp. 424–5.

109. ANDREA CARAFFA, Count of Santa Severina 1496, Viceroy of Naples, 1524, died 1526.

Obv. Bust to left in helmet with winged monster as crest. Around, ANDREAS CARRAFA S(anctae) SEVERINAE COMES

Rev. Prudence seated, holding in right hand a double-faced (male and female) head on a staff, and serpent in left hand. Below, NIL ABEST

38 mm. A846–109A

The reverse legend is an allusion to Juvenal, x, 365.

Literature: Corpus, no. 349 *k*; cp. Arm. II, 108, 13; Cott p. 167; Middeldorf, *Morgenroth*, no. 41. Tervarent, col. 407.

NEAPOLITAN SCHOOL
Early Sixteenth Century

110. ANDREA CARAFFA, Count of Santa Severina (1496–1526).

Obv. Bust to right, wearing crested helmet and cuirass. Around, AND(reas) CARAFA S(ante) SEVERINE COMES

Rev. Shield of Caraffa arms, between a steel-yard on left and a screw-jack with scroll on right. Around, CONTERET CONTRARIA VIRTVS

63 mm. A847–110A

Literature: Cp. Arm. II, 108, 12; *Corpus*, no. 351; Middeldorf, *Morgenroth*, no. 43 (*Corpus* 351 *d*); Cott p. 167. Tervarent, col. 304 (steelyard).

111. *Obv.* Bust to right, wearing helmet with small plumes, and cuirass. Around, ANDREAS CARRAFA SANTE SEVERINE COMES

Rev. Similar to preceding.

66 mm. A848–111A

The larger of these two varieties seems to be the later, the details being remodelled. The earlier variety corresponds closely to a sardonyx cameo formerly in the Henry Oppenheimer Collection. The steel-yard is the symbol of the *della Stadera* branch of the family, although Andrea belonged to the other branch, *della Spina*. The obverse portrait so closely resembles the medallion portrait of Galeotto Caraffa, on his monument erected in 1513 by

Andrea in San Domenico Maggiore in Naples, and attributed to Romolo da Settignano, that there must be some connexion in origin between the two. The extreme dates possible for the medals are 1496 and 1525.

Literature: Cp. Arm. II, 108, 11; *Corpus*, no. 352; Cott p. 168; B.F.A.C. exhibition, 1912, pp. 138–9, no. 6, pl. lxix (for the Oppenheimer cameo).

SPERANDIO OF MANTUA
(b. *ca.* 1431; d. 1504)

Sperandio was the son of a Mantuan goldsmith, Bartolommeo di Sperandio Savelli, and was active not only in his native town, to which he remained attached, but in Ferrara (1463–1477), Bologna (1478–90), Milan, Faenza, and Venice, where he died, past work, in 1504. He is the most prolific of fifteenth-century medallists, masterly in his portraits but careless both in composition and execution and unoriginal in conception. To the bibliography in the *Corpus* pp. 90–1 may be added: Hill in Thieme-Becker, 31 (1937) pp. 359–360; Pope-Hennessy, *Kress Bronzes* no. 235 (for a plaquette by Sperandio).

112. BARTOLOMMEO PENDALIA, merchant of Ferrara.

Obv. Bust to left in flat-topped cap and robe. Around, BARTHOLOMAEVS PENDALIA INSIGNE LIBERALITATIS ET MVNIFICENTIAE EXEMPLV(m).

Rev. Nude male figure seated on a cuirass, holding globe and spear, his left foot on a bag from which money flows; behind, two shields; above, CAESARIANA LIBERALITAS; below, OPVS SPERANDEI

84 mm. A849–112A

The reverse alludes to the knighthood conferred on Pendalia in 1452 by the Emperor Frederick III. The medal belongs to about 1462, before 1 March of which year Pendalia died.

Literature: Les Arts, Aug. 1908, p. 9, no. vii; *Corpus*, no. 356 *h*; cp. Arm. I, 71, 32; Cott p. 168; Middeldorf, *Morgenroth*, no. 45.

113. ANTONIO SARZANELLA DE' MANFREDI of Faenza, diplomatist.

Obv. Bust to right, wearing flat-topped cap and gown with a small animal's fur round neck. Around, ANTONIVS SARZANELLA DE MANFREDIS SAPIENTIAE PATER

Rev. Prudence (double-headed) seated on seat formed by two hounds (for trustworthiness) holding the Manfredi shield, a pair of compasses, and a mirror. Around, IN TE CANA FIDES PRVDENTIA SVMMA REFVLGET; in the field to right, OPVS SPERANDEI

73 mm. A850–113A

Probably about 1463, at Ferrara, where the sitter was then present, being in the diplomatic service of the Estensi.

Literature: Les Arts, Aug. 1908, p. 9, nos. v, vi; cp. Arm. I, 74, 41; *Corpus*, nos. 358; Cott p. 168; Tervarent, cols. 94 v (the hound); 407 (Prudence).

114. LODOVICO CARBONE of Ferrara, poet (about 1436–82).

Obv. Bust to left, in tall cap and gown. Around, CANDIDIOR PVRA CARBO POETA NIVE

Rev. Carbone receiving a wreath from the seated Muse Calliope; in background, a fountain. Around, HANC TIBI CALLIOPE SERVAT LODOVICE CORONAM; in field to left, OPVS SPERANDEI

70 mm. A851–114A

About 1462–3, at Ferrara. The verse round the head, with its pun on the name of 'Carbo whiter than pure snow', comes from a poem addressed to him by Tito Vespasiano Strozzi.

Literature: Les Arts, Aug. 1908, p. 9, no. ix; *Corpus*, no. 359 *i*; cp. Arm. I, 66, 13; Cott p. 168.

115. FRANCESCO SFORZA, (1401–66) Duke of Milan.

Obv. Bust three-quarters to right, in armour. Around, FRANCISCVS SFORTIA VICECOMES DVX MEDIOLANI QVARTVS

Rev. OPVS SPERANDEI Renaissance building with four cupolas.

86 mm. A852–115A

Probably about 1466, the building being intended for a memorial of the Duke. The portrait is doubtless not from life, but copied from some painting.

Literature: Cp. Arm. I, 74, 42; *Corpus*, no. 361; Cott p. 168.

115*a*. FRA CESARIO CONTUGHI, a Servite of Ferrara.

Obv. Bust left, elderly, wearing habit with hood over head. Around, FR(ater) CESARIVS FER(rariensis) ORDINIS SER(vorum) B(eatae) M(ariae) V(irginis) DIVIN(arum) LIT(erarum) EXCELLEN(tissimus) DOC(tor) AC DIVI(nae) VER(itatis) FAMOSIS(simus) PREDICATOR

Rev. Fra Cesario seated on a rock, resting his head on left hand, and contemplating a skull on the ground. Around, INSPICE MORTALE GENVS MORS OMNIA DELTE, and below OPVS SPERANDEI

83 mm. A1417–677A

ca. 1467.

Literature: Arm. I, 67, 16; Heiss, *Sperandio*, p. 36, no. 16, pl. v, 3; *Corpus*, no. 363 *g*; Cott p. 168.

116. ERCOLE I D'ESTE (1471–1505) and his wife ELEONORA OF ARAGON (married 1473, died 1493).

Obv. Busts confronted; on right, Ercole, in tall cap, chain with pendant over his dress; on left, Eleonora wearing coif, and chain with pendant; above, a four-winged cherub's head; below, OPVS SPERANDEI All in wreath.

Without reverse.

Lead, 112 mm. A853–116A

This doubtless commemorates the marriage of 3 July 1473. There are various versions, some without the cherub's head or signature (an octagonal specimen at Berlin with HER DVX engraved below); and the bust of Eleonora also occurs separately as a rectangular plaquette (e.g. in the Victoria and Albert Museum).

Literature: Cp. Arm. I, 68, 21; *Corpus*, no. 366; Cott p. 168.

117. SIGISMONDO, son of Niccolò III d'Este (1433–1507).

Obv. Bust to left, with long hair, dress with high collar and chain (?). Around, ILLVSTRISSIMVS SIGISMVNDVS ESTENSIS

Rev. Nude winged Cupid to front, holding palm-branch and balance, leaning on a sword. Around, OPVS SPERANDEI

Lead, 87 mm. A854–117A

If the Cupid refers to Sigismondo's mission to Naples to escort Eleonora to Ferrara, the medal dates from 1473. It is in any case in Sperandio's first Ferrarese period.

Literature: Cp. Arm. I, 68, 19; *Corpus*, no. 367; Cott p. 168; Tervarent, col. 16.

118. *Obv.* The bust alone, from the preceding medal.

Without reverse.

71 × 44 mm. A855–118A

Literature: Les Arts, Aug. 1908, p. 13, no. ix; *Corpus,* no. 367 note; Cott p. 168.

119. PIETRO BONO AVOGARIO, physician and astrologer of Ferrara (died in 1506).

Obv. Bust to left, in truncated conical cap. Around, PETRVS BONVS AVOGARIVS FERRARIENSIS MEDICVS INSIGNIS ASTROLOGVS INSIGNIOR

Rev. Aesculapius (AESCVLAPIVS) standing on a dragon, holding phial and branch, and Urania (VRANIE) on a globe engraved with names of ASIA, EVRO(pa), AFRICA, and holding an astrolabe and a book containing astrological diagrams. Below, OPVS SPERANDEI

90 mm. Later cast. A856–119A

About 1472. The three continents on the globe are divided on the system of the so-called T–O maps of the world.

Literature: Cp. Arm. I, 64, 3; *Corpus*, no. 371 (misread *Astrologicus*); Cott p. 168. Tervarent, cols. 250, vi; 359, iii.

120. AGOSTINO BUONFRANCESCO of Rimini, Councillor of Ercole I d'Este.

Obv. Bust to left, with long hair, conical cap, robe with chain.

Without reverse.

Height 68 mm. Cut out from the medal. A857–120A

The only good specimen of the whole obverse is at Berlin, and that specimen lacks the reverse. The medal dates between 1471 and 1477.

Literature: Les Arts, Aug. 1908, p. 9, no. viii; *Corpus*, no. 372 *d*; Cott p. 168.

121. See Appendix.

122. See Appendix.

123. CARLO MANFREDI, Lord of Faenza (1439–84).

Obv. Bust to left, wearing tall conical cap and cuirass. Around, incised, KROLVS SECVNDVS DE MANFREDIS FAVEN(tinus).

Without reverse.

Lead, 74 mm. A860–123A

An unfinished piece; the reverse would doubtless have been signed, but as it is Sperandio's authorship is unmistakable. Carlo Manfredi's rule at Faenza came to a sudden end only four months after Sperandio went to work for him there, in 1477. The piece is only known from this specimen and an after-cast at Paris.

Literature: Corpus, no. 379 *b*; Arm. II, 68, 35; III, 16, A; Argnani, *Cenni storici sulla zecca . . . de' Manfredi* (Faenza 1886), pl. ii, 2; J. de Foville, *Sperandio de Mantoue*, Paris, 1910, p. 47. Cott p. 168.

124. ALESSANDRO TARTAGNI, jurisconsult of Imola (died 1477 aged 56).

Obv. Bust to left, wearing chaperon and gown. Around, ALEXANDER TARTAGNVS IVRE CONSVLTISSIMVS AC VERITATIS INTERPRES

Rev. On the summit of a hill (PARNASVS) Mercury seated on a dragon, from whose mouth issues the motto VIGILANTIA FLORVI; across the field, OPV(S) SPERA(n)DEI

90 mm. A861–124A

The final of three states of this medal, which was made at Bologna, probably after the subject's death, about 1478.

Literature: Heiss, *Sperandio*, p. 71, no. 42, pl. xiv, 2; *Corpus,* no. 381 *C*, c, *c*; Cott p. 169.

125. ANDREA BARBAZZA of Messina, legist (died 1479).

Obv. Bust to left, in conical fluted cap and brocaded gown, edge of which left hand clasps. Around, ANDREAS BARBATIA MESANIVS EQVES ARAGONV(m) Q(ue) REGIS CONSILIARIVSIVRISVTRIVSQ(ue) SP(LEN)DIDISSIMV(m) IVBAR

Rev. Fame, body covered with feathers, having three pairs of wings, standing to front, holding up a closed and an open book; at her feet, other books. Around, FAMA SVPER AETHERA NOTVS and, below, OPVS SPERANDEI

Lead, 114 mm. A862–125A

The motto is from Virgil, *Aen.* i. 379. The medal is said to have been made on the death of Barbazza at Bologna, 20 July 1479. There is a bust of him in San Petronio at Bologna, attributed to Sperandio.

Literature: Cp. Arm. I, 64, 4; *Corpus*, no. 384; Cott p. 169. Tervarent, col. 10, iv (winged Fame).

126. NICCOLÒ DA CORREGGIO, Count of Brescello (1450–80–1508).

Obv. Bust to left, in cap and cuirass. Around, NICOLAVS CORIGIENS(is) BRIXILI AC CORIGIAE COMES ARMORVM DVCTOR ETC

Rev. Niccolò, in full armour, riding three-quarters to left, reaches his hand to a bearded and cowled friar; on either side, leafless tree. Around, IVSTICIA AMBVLABIT ANTE TE VT PONAT IN VIA GRESSVS TVOS Below, OPVS SPERANDEI

Lead, 79 mm. A863–126A

Niccolò (born 1450) assumed the title of Count of Brescello in 1480, from about which time the medal may date.

Literature: Arm. I, 67, 17; Heiss, *Sperandio*, p. 38, no. 17, pl. vi, 1; *Corpus*, no. 386 *c*; Cott p. 169.

127. NICCOLÒ SANUTI, noble of Bologna (1407–82).

Obv. Bust to right, in flat-topped cap and flowered robe. Above, his arms. Around, NICOLAVS SANVTVS EQVES DO · CO · SENATORQ(ue) BONON(iensis) I(n)TEGERIMVS and OPVS SPERA(n)DEI

Rev. Long spiral inscription, recording his services to his city, the bequest of all his goods to pious purposes, and his death on 26 June 1482. In centre, Pelican in her piety.

Bronze gilt, 93 mm. A864–127A

1482 or soon after. There is no reason to doubt the signature, although the lettering and the treatment of the contour of the bust are not very characteristic of Sperandio.

Collection: From the Stroganoff collection.

Literature: Corpus, no. 388 *e*; cp. Arm. I, 73, 40; Cott p. 169.

128. GIOVANNI II BENTIVOGLIO (born 1443, Lord of Bologna 1462–1506, died 1509).

Obv. Bust to right, in tall cap and plate-armour. Around, IO(annes) BENT(ivolus) II HAN(n)IB(alis) FILIVS EQVES AC COMES PATRIAE PRINCEPS AC LIBERTATIS COLVMEN

Rev. Giovanni in armour riding to left; trapper of the horse adorned with Bentivoglio arms. Behind him, seen from the front, mounted squire. Above, OPVS SPERANDEI

98 mm. With loop for suspension. A865–128A

The reverse is a pastiche from two medals of Pisanello (nos. 2 and 3). About 1478–82.

Literature: Heiss, *Sperandio*, p. 24, no. 8, pl. iii, 2; *Les Arts*, Aug. 1908, p. 9, nos. i, ii; *Corpus*, no. 391 *n*; cp. Arm. I, 65, 6; Cott p. 169; Middeldorf, *Morgenroth*, no. 48 (lead, 97 mm).

129. See Appendix.

130. See Appendix.

131. FRANCESCO II GONZAGA, fourth Marquess of Mantua (1466–84–1519).

Obv. Bust to left, wearing cap and plate-armour. Around, FRANCISCVS GONZAGA MANTVAE MARCHIO AC VENETI EXERC(itus) IMP(erator).

Rev. The Marquess on horseback accompanied by a number of horsemen and foot-soldiers. Around, OB RESTITVTAM ITALIAE LIBERTATEM; below, OPVS SPERANDEI

95 mm. A868–131A

Francesco commanded on the Italian side at the battle against the French at Fornovo in 1495. The medal commemorates this event.

Literature: Les Arts, Aug. 1908, p. 9, nos. iii, iv; *Corpus*, no. 400 *f*; cp. Arm. I, 69, 23; Cott p. 169.

132. See Appendix.

133. See Appendix.

134. See Appendix.

PIETRO DA FANO

Known to have been working from about 1452 until 1464; his few medals, which have a certain clumsy dignity, represent Lodovico Gonzaga and the ducal pair described below.

135. PASQUALE MALIPIERI, born 1385, Doge of Venice (1457–62), and his wife GIOVANNA DANDOLO.

Obv. Bust of the Doge to left, in cap and robes. Below, a crown. Around, PASQVALIS MARIPETRVS VENETVM D(ignissimus) DVX

Rev. Bust of the Dogaressa to left, in flat cap and veil. Around, INCLITE IOHANNE ALME VRBIS VENEZIAR(um) DVCISE

93 mm. A872–135A

The authorship of these portraits is fixed by another medal which has exactly the same portrait of the lady, combined with a reverse bearing the artist's signature.

Literature: Cp. Arm. I, 35, 4; III, 5, B; *Corpus*, no. 409; Cott p. 169; Middeldorf, *Morgenroth*, no. 51.

ANTONIO GAMBELLO DA SAN ZACCARIA

Architect working from 1458 to after 1479. The following medal, signed A N, is attributed to him.

136. FRANCESCO FOSCARI, Doge of Venice (1423–57).

Obv. Bust to right in ducal cap and robe. Around, FRANCISCVS FOSCARI DVX

Rev. Venetia seated holding sword and shield, two Furies at her feet. Around, VENETIA MAGNA; below, A N

47 mm. A873–136A

The figure of Venetia reproduces the relief on the façade of the Ducal Palace.

Literature: Cp. Arm. I, p. 25; *Corpus*, no. 410; Cott p. 170.

137. See Appendix.

MARCO GUIDIZANI

Known, from his medals, to have been working at Venice about 1454–62.

138. BARTOLOMMEO COLLEONE of Bergamo, condottiere (1400–75).

Obv. Bust to left, wearing cap and cuirass. Around, BARTHOL(omeus) CAPVT LEONIS MA(gnus) C(apitaneus) VE(neti) SE(natus).

Rev. Laureate nude male figure seated on a cuirass; with the left hand he holds above his head the end of a plummet line which passes through a ring, the plummet by his knee, and with the right hand he points to the vertical line; around IVSTIZIA AVGVSTA ET BENIGNITAS PVBLICA and, in field to right, OPVS M(arci) GVIDIZANI

Lead, 83 mm. A875–138A

The plummet is the symbol of Justice. The titles date the medal in 1454 or later.

Literature: Cp. Arm. I, 34, 86; *Corpus*, no. 412; Cott p. 170.

GIOVANNI BOLDÙ
(d. before 1477)

A Venetian painter and medallist, distinguished by a wiry precision of style, much influenced by antique gem-engraving. He is mentioned in documents from 1454 to 1473; his medals (excluding one of doubtful attribution) are dated 1457 and 1458.

139. FILIPPO MASERANO, of Venice.

Obv. Bust to left, in embroidered dress. Around, PHILIPPO MASERANO VENETO MVSIS DILECTO

Rev. Arion (ARIONI) to left riding on dolphin; above, VIRTVTI OMNIA PARENT; below, MCCCCLVII OPVS IOANIS BOLDV PICTORIS

71 mm. A876–139A

Nothing is known of Maserano, except that, as the medal by type and inscription indicates, he was a poet or musician.

Literature: Les Arts, Aug. 1908, p. 10, nos. iv, v; *Corpus*, no. 417 *h*; cp. Arm. I, 37, 5; Cott p. 170; Middeldorf, *Morgenroth* no. 53 (*Corpus* 417 *j*).

140. NICOLAUS SCHLIFER, German musician.

Obv. Bust to left; around, NICOLAVS SCHLIFER GERMANVS VIR MODESTVS ALTERQ(ue) ORPEHEV(s) (for ORPHEVS)

Rev. Apollo, with lyre and long scroll. Around, MCCCCLVII OPVS IOANIS BOLDV PICTORIS

81 mm. A877–140A

The reverse is inspired by a sard intaglio at Naples of Apollo and Marsyas, formerly in the Medici Collection. The sitter is otherwise unknown.

Literature: Les Arts, Aug. 1908, p. 10, no. i; *Corpus*, no. 418 *f*; cp. Arm. I, 37, 6; Cott p. 170. For the gem see A. Furtwängler, *Die antiken Gemmen*, Leipzig/Berlin, 1900, vol. I, pl. xlii, no. 28; M-L. Vollenweider, *Die Steinschneidekunst und ihre Künstler in spätrepublikanischer und augusteischer Zeit*, Baden-Baden, 1966, p. 61, pl. 63, fig. 2.

141. GIOVANNI BOLDÙ, the medallist.

Obv. Bust to left, in tall soft cap. Around, ΙΩΑΝΗΣ צייר ΜΠΩΛΝΤΥ יוחנו בולדו מונ יציייא ΖΩΓΡΑΦΟΥ

Rev. Boldù seated, pensive, between Faith, holding up a chalice, and Penitence, as an old woman, who scourges him. Around, OPVS IOANIS BOLDV PICTORIS VENETI and, below, MCCCCLVIII

87 mm. A878–141A

The obverse legend reads 'Giovanni Boldù of Venice, painter.' Janson shows that the reverse of this medal and of the following medal indicate a shift in meaning for the artist from Christian allegory to a new interpretation under the influence of Boldù's Humanism, in terms of antiquity. On this medal the skull is Destiny, with personifications of Faith for Salvation and Penitence for Conscience. On no. 142 the re-interpretation of the type is consonant with the new obverse portrait, *all'antica*. On no. 142 also the putto with skull is the first appearance of this conceit in Renaissance iconography.

Collection: His de la Salle (sale London, Sotheby, 22 Nov. 1880, lot 32).

Literature: Les Arts, Aug. 1908, p. 10, no. ii; cp. Arm. I, 36, 2: *Corpus*, no. 420*f*; Cott p. 170. H. Janson, 'The putto with the Death's Head', in *The Art Bulletin*, 19 (1937) pp. 423–449.

142. *Obv*. Bust to left, unclothed, wearing ivy-wreath. Around, ΙΩΑΝΗΣ ΜΠΩΛΝΤΟΥ ΖΩΓΡΑΦΟΥ ΒΕΝΑΙΤΙΑ

Rev. The artist seated, his head in his hands; before him, a putto (genius of Death) holding a flame and resting on a skull. Above, OPVS IOANIS BOLDV PICTORIS VENETVS XOGRAFI and, below, MCCCCLVIII

85 mm. A879–142A

It is not certain whether this reverse was originally made for this obverse, the two designs not being of quite the same size. The reverse is copied in one of the marble medallions of the Certosa of Pavia and in a decorative roundel on the tomb of Marc Antonio Martinengo by Maffeo Olivieri now in the Museo Cristiano, Brescia. See the note to no. 141.

Collection: His de la Salle (sale, London, Sotheby, 22 Nov. 1880, lot 31).

Literature: Les Arts, Aug. 1908, p. 10, no. iii; cp. Arm. I, 36, 1; *Corpus*, no. 421 *h*; Cott p. 170; H. Janson, 'The Putto with the Death's Head', in *The Art Bulletin*, 19 (1937) pp. 423–449; Antonio Morassi, 'Per la ricostruzione di Maffeo Olivieri', in *Bollettino d'Arte*, 30 (1936) pp. 237–249 (at p. 242 for the roundel on the Martinengo monument). Tervarent, col. 184, v (the flame as funerary motif); col. 374, iii (Death's head) and figs. 69 (roundel at Pavia) and 70 (Martinengo roundel).

ATTRIBUTED TO BOLDÙ

143. THE EMPEROR CARACALLA.

Obv. Bust of the young Caracalla to left, laureate. Around, ANTONINVS PIVS AVGVSTVS

Rev. The same design as on no. 142. Above, IO SON FINE and, below, MCCCCLXVI

62 mm. A880–143A

This attractive medal is generally attributed to Boldù, because of the identity of the reverse composition with that of the medal of himself (no. 142). But this reverse has only been adapted by the artist responsible for the head on the obverse, whose style is not that of Boldù. The head itself is loosely copied from a Roman coin.

Literature: Cp. Arm. I, 37, 4; *Corpus*, no. 423; Cott p. 170; Middeldorf, *Morgenroth*, no. 54 ('Attribution and real date are uncertain'); H. Janson, 'The Putto with the Death's Head', in *The Art Bulletin* 19 (1937) pp. 423–449; Planiscig, 'Bronzi inediti di autori ignoti', in *Dedalo*, 12 (1932) pp. 739–752 (at p. 745, for an infant Bacchus, seated astride a barrel decorated with the obverse of this medal). Tervarent, cols. 184, v; 374, iii.

GENTILE BELLINI
(b. *ca*. 1429/30; d. 1507)

The famous painter was in Constantinople, 1479–80. The portrait of Mohammad ascribed to him and now in the National Gallery, London, is dated 25 November 1480. His medal was more probably inspired by the example of Costanzo da Ferrara (no. 102).

144. MOHAMMAD II, Sultan of the Turks (1430–51–81)

Obv. Bust to left, in turban and gown. Around, MAGNI SOVLTANI F MOHAMETI IMPERATORIS

Rev. Three crowns: of Constantinople, Iconium, and Trebizond. Around, GENTILIS BELLINVS VENETVS EQVES AVRATVS COMES Q PALATINVS F

92 mm. Later casting. A881–144A

In the original version the F (which is erroneous) was absent from the inscription round the bust. Hill suggested that the medal was designed before the end of November 1480, when Bellini returned from Constantinople. Babinger suggests that the portrait more probably derives from Costanzo da Ferrara's medal, or some other model (which was also used by Bertoldo). The three crowns reappear in the field of the painting.

Literature: Cp. Arm. I, 78; III, 18 *a*; Heiss, *Niccolo Spinelli*, p. 79, pl. ix, 1; *Les Arts*, Aug. 1908, p. 8, no. vi; *Corpus*, no. 432 *i*; Cott, p. 170; Middeldorf, *Morgenroth*, no. 55; F. Babinger, *Mehmed der Eroberer und seine Zeit*, Munich, 1953, pp. 425–6 (Bertoldo and Bellini). M. Davies, *The earlier Italian Schools*, National Gallery catalogue, London, 1961, pp. 51–2, no. 3099 (for the painting, ascribed to Gentile Bellini).

CAMELIO
(b. *ca.* 1455/60; d. 1537)

Vettor di Antonio Gambello, known as Camelio, was a medallist, die-engraver, jeweller and armourer. He is first mentioned in 1484 as master of the dies in the Venetian mint, and worked there until 1510. Possibly before 1484, and certainly between 1513–1516, he worked as an engraver at the papal mint, concluding his career in Venice, 1516–1537. Like Enzola he experimented with the striking of medals from dies, and he was probably in touch with Caradosso in Rome. For a signed plaquette by him, see Pope-Hennessy, *Kress Bronzes*, no. 46.
To the bibliography in the *Corpus* pp. 115–6, may be added P. Grotemeyer, 'Drei Medaillen von Camelio', in *Münchner Jahrbuch der Bildenden Kunst*, 12 (1937–8) pp. x–xi; and W. Schwabacher, 'En unkendt Renaissancemedaille af Camelio', in *Konsthistorisk Tidskrift*, 13, (3) (Oct. 1944), pp. 92–5.

145. SIXTUS IV, Pope, 1471–84.

Obv. Bust to left, wearing tiara over skull-cap, and cope. Around, SIXTVS IIII PONTIFEX MAXIMVS VRBE RESTAVRATA

Rev. The Pope in audience. Below, OP(us) VICTORIS CAMELIO VE(neti).

51 mm. A882–145A

The reverse is adapted from a medal of Paul II.

Literature: Cp. Arm. I, 116, 9; *Corpus*, no. 437; Cott p. 170.

146. GIOVANNI BELLINI, the painter (*ca.* 1430–1516).

Obv. Bust to left in cap and robe with stole over shoulder. Around, IOANNES BELLINVS VENET(us) PICTOR(um) OP(timus)

Rev. An owl. Above, VIRTVTIS ET INGENII and, below, VICTOR CAMELIVS FACIEBAT

58 mm. A late cast. A883–146A

The *Corpus* records only the specimen at Venice (Museo Archaeologico) as an original, with a reverse spoiled by tooling. A second good specimen went from the Oppenheimer collection to the British Museum.

Literature: Cp. Arm. I, 115, 2; Heiss, *Venise*, p. 123, pl. vii, 2; *Les Arts*, Aug. 1908, p. 12, no. xii; *Corpus*, no. 438 *c*; Cott p. 170; *National Art-Collections Fund Thirty Third Annual Report*, 1936 (London 1937) p. 28, no. 1006 and facing plate; and Oppenheimer collection (sale, London, Christie, 27 July 1936, lot 48, illustrated) for the specimen now in the British Museum.

147. GENTILE BELLINI, the painter (1429–1507).

Obv. Bust to left in cap, wearing chain with medallion. Around, GENTILIS BELINVS VENETVS EQVES COMESQ(ue).

Rev. Incised across field, GENTILI TRIBVIT QVOD POTVIT VIRO NATVRA HOC POTVIT VICTOR ET ADDIDIT

64 mm. Late cast. A884–147A

The titles borne by Gentile were granted by Frederick III. The medal is doubtless not much earlier than 1500, when when the sitter was 70 years old.

Literature: Corpus, no. 439 *e*; cp. Arm. I, 114, 1; Cott p. 170.

148. VETTOR GAMBELLO, the medallist, 1508.

Obv. Head to right. Around, VICTOR CAMELIVS SVI IPSIVS EFFIGIATOR MDVIII

Rev. Sacrificial scene in antique manner. Above, FAVE FOR(tuna); below, SACRIF(icio).

37 mm. Struck. A885–148A

Literature: Les Arts, Aug. 1908, p. 12, no. xiv; cp. Arm. I, 115, 3; *Corpus*, no. 446; Cott p. 170. J. Pope-Hennessy, 'Italian Bronze statuettes-I,' in *Burl. Mag.* 105 (1963) pp. 14–23 (at pp. 22–3, for the significance of this reverse type as a relief by Camelio in attributing figure bronzes to the artist); F. Saxl, in Warbwig Journal, 2 (1938-9) at p. 366 n. 2 (for the context of the medal reverse).

149. (See 150*a*).

150. VETTOR GAMBELLO, the medallist.

Obv. Youthful head to right.

Rev. Nude male figure seated on stump under a sapling in the attitude of the Ludovisi Ares; before him, winged caduceus rising out of cuirass, with spear, helmet, and shield leaning against it; behind him, an owl. Below, V CAMELIO

29 mm. Struck. A887–150A

Hill believed the portrait type to be Augustus. Schwabacher however, in publishing for the first time a companion piece of a woman inscribed DIVA IVSTINA which has the same reverse type, suggests that this 'Augustus' is probably a self-portrait. The woman depicted was perhaps a friend of the artist, Giustina. The 'Augustus' profile may be compared with no. 148. The type of the reverse suggests that the Ludovisi Ares was discovered at the time when Gambello was in Rome, i.e. 1513–16.

Literature: Arm. I, 115, 4. Heiss, *Venise*, p. 124, pl. vii, 4; *Les Arts*, Aug. 1908, p. 12, no. xiii; *Corpus*, no. 448 *b*; cp. Arm. III, 45, *a*; Cott p. 171; W. Schwabacher, 'En unkendt Renaissancemedaille af Camelio,' in *Konsthistorisk Tidskrift*, year 13, part 3 (Oct. 1944), pp. 92–5 (for the medal of Giustina).

150*a*. CLASSICAL SUBJECTS.

Obv. Nude male figure carrying dead stag; behind him, Pan seated and two other satyrs in the background; on left, two putti playing and a seated female (?) figure.

Rev. Flaming tripod on a square altar, on its front a blank tablet; on right, wine-skin at foot of a tree; on left, ram tied to the altar and a goat; axe, torch, etc., lying on the ground. Below, V CAMELIO

30 mm. A886–149A

This is cast; the original was struck.

Literature: Cp. Arm. I, 117, 13; Molinier, i, p. 111, no. 156; *Corpus*, no. 447; Cott p. 170.

IN THE MANNER OF CAMELIO

151. MARCO BARBADIGO, Doge of Venice 1485–6.

Obv. Bust to right, in ducal cap and robes. Around, MARCVS BARBADICO DVX VENECIAR(um).

Rev. In wreath of ivy, inscription: SERVAVI BELLO PATRIAM &C., similar to the *breve* attached to the portrait of the Doge in the Sala del Gran Consiglio.

Collection: His de la Salle (sale, London, Sotheby, 22 Nov. 1880, lot 97).

Literature: Cp. Arm. II, 70, 1; *Corpus*, no. 449; Cott p. 171.

152. LEONARDO LOREDANO, Doge of Venice 1501–21.

Obv. Bust to left, wearing ducal cap and robe. Around, LEONAR(dus) LAVREDANVS DVX VENETIAR(um) ETC. Moulded border.

Rev. Equity holding scales and sceptre. Around, AEQVITAS PRINCIPIS Moulded border.

63 mm. A889–152A

The attribution to Gambello, based on style, appears to be sound.

Literature: Corpus, no. 452 *j*; cp. Arm. II, 124, 1; Cott p. 171.

153. ANDREA GRITTI, Doge of Venice 1523–38.

Obv. Bust to left, in ducal cap and robe. Around, ANDREAS GRITI DVX VENETIAR(um) ETC (saltire). Moulded border.

Rev. Venetia seated holding scales and cornucopiae; behind her, arms; in background, galleys at sea. Below, VENET. Moulded border.

66 mm. A890–153A

Somewhat in Gambello's manner, but coarser in execution, and perhaps made at the time of the Doge's death.

Literature: Cp. Arm. II, 174, 3; *Corpus*, no. 456; Cott p. 171.

154. GIULIANO II DE' MEDICI, Duc de Nemours (1478–1516).

Obv. Bust to left. Around, MAGNVS IVLIANVS MEDICES

Rev. Virtue giving her right hand to Fortune. Around, DVCE VIRTVTE COMITE FORTVNA MDXIII

54 mm. A891–154A

Made at Rome, probably by Gambello, after the election of the Medici Pope, Leo X, in March 1513.

Literature: Cp. Arm. II, 94, 2; *Corpus*, no. 456 *bis*; Cott p. 171. Tervarent, col. 267, ii. (on the type of Fortune).

155. AGOSTINO BARBADIGO, Doge of Venice 1486–1501.

Obv. Bust to left in ducal cap and robe. Around, AVGVSTINVS BARBADIC(us) VENETOR(um) DVX

Rev. Venetia seated to left on throne supported by a lion, holding sword erect; about her, arms. Below, VENE(tia).

32 mm. A892–155A

The original was struck from dies. Heiss first suggested the attribution to Gambello.

Literature: Cp. Arm. II, 70, 4; *Corpus*, no. 458; Cott p. 171.

GIOVANNI FALIER

The signature on the following medal probably represents the artist who signs 'Ioannis Faletro' on a medal of the Priest Marcus.

156. ANDREA GRITTI, Procurator of St Mark's, afterwards Doge of Venice.

Obv. Bust to left, in armour and cloak. Around, ANDREAE GRITO PROCVR(atori) D(ivi) MARCI; below, IO F. Moulded border.

Rev. Gritti commanding on horseback before a city the wall of which is breached; before him, a nude man seen from behind. Above, OPT(ime) DE PATRIA MERITO; below, GRAT(ia) CIV(ium).

66 mm. A893–156

Commemorates the services of Gritti at the siege of Brescia (1512 or 1516) or Bergamo (1512). The signature may also be read Φ (for Falier) F(ecit).

Literature: Cp. Arm. I, p. 122; *Corpus*, no. 464; Cott p. 171. Middeldorf, *Morgenroth*, no. 56.

FRA ANTONIO DA BRESCIA
(Active *ca.* 1485–1515)

Working at Padua, Treviso, Verona, and Venice. The following medal, unsigned, is somewhat in his manner. To the *Corpus*, pp. 123–4, may be added G. F. Hill, 'Frate Antonio de Brescia', in *Miscellanea di Storia dell'Arte in onore di Igino Benvenuto Supino,* Florence, 1933, pp. 483–5 For plaquettes formerly ascribed to the artist, see Pope-Hennessy, *Kress Bronzes,* nos. 187–9.

157. NICCOLÒ TEMPESTÀ (?) of Treviso.

Obv. Bust to left. Around, NICOLAVS TEMPE(stà ?) TAR(visius).

Rev. A winged dragon sejant on a rock to right, holding a balance in its jaws.

47 mm. A894–157A

The name of the sitter is probably Tempestà, which was borne by an important family of Treviso. In style the medal bears some resemblance to the signed work of Fra Antonio da Brescia.

Literature: Les Arts, Aug. 1908, p. 13, no. iv; *Corpus,* no. 480; cp. Arm. II, 72, 14; Cott p. 171.

MAFFEO OLIVIERI
(b. 1484; d. after 1534)

A bronze-worker of Brescia, who made in 1527 a pair of candlesticks, now in St Mark's at Venice, for Altobello Averoldo, is probably to be identified with the author of the medal of that prelate (no. 161) and of a group of other medals round about the year 1523. He is distinguished by the pomp and aristocratic air of his portraits, and the fine spacious composition of his reverses, qualities admirably exemplified in the medal of Averoldo himself.

To the materials in the *Corpus* p. 127 may be added: Thieme-Becker, 26 (1932), pp. 6–7; A. Morassi, 'Per la ricostruzione di Maffeo Olivieri,' in *Bollettino d'Arte,* 30 (1936), pp. 237–249.

158. FRANCESCO DI ANDREA MALIPIERI, Venetian, 1523.

Obv. Bust to right. Around, FRANCISCVS MARIPETRO ANDREAE F(ilius) AN(no) XXX

Rev. Pelican in her piety, on stump of a tree growing on a mound. Above, FIRMAE ET PERPETVAE CARITATI and, below, MDXXIII

64 mm. A895–158A

Other specimens in the Victoria and Albert and Correr Museums.

Literature: Arm. I, 125, 3; Heiss, *Venise,* p. 190, pl. xiv, 4; *Corpus,* no. 482 *c*; Cott p. 171.

159. VINCENZO DI ANDREA MALIPIERI (b. 1476) Venetian, 1523.

Obv. Bust to right. Around, VINCENTIVS MARIPETRO AND(reae) F(ilius) AN(no) AET(atis) XLVII

Rev. A crowned eagle, displayed on a mound amidst waters. Above, REGALIS CONSTANTIA; below, MDXXIII

64 mm. A896–159A

Literature: Arm. I, 124, 2; Heiss, *Venise,* p. 189, pl. xiv, 5; *Corpus,* no. 483 *e*; Cott p. 171; Middeldorf, *Morgenroth,* no. 58.

160. AUGUSTO DA UDINE (PUBLIO AUGUSTO GRAZIANI), poet and astrologer.

Obv. Bust to left, with lank hair, laureate. Around, AVGVSTVS VATES

Rev. Nude female figure (VRANIA) with long hair, standing to front, her right hand to her head.

32 mm. A897–160A

The portrait is figured in Augusto's *Odae,* published at Venice in 1529. The medal has been variously attributed: to Adriano Fiorentino, to Fra Antonio da Brescia, to Maffeo Olivieri, of which the last seems most likely. The poet was laureated by Frederick III before 1493, perhaps in 1489. He was still living in 1519, about which time the medal was probably made. The reverse type alludes to his astrological studies.

Literature: Corpus, no. 485 *n*; cp. Arm. II, 72, 15; Cott p. 171.

161. ALTOBELLO AVEROLDO of Brescia, Bishop of Pola (1497), Legate Apostolic at Venice (1526), died 1531.

Obv. Bust to right in berretta and rochet. Around, ALTOBELLVS AVEROLDVS BRIXIEN(sis) POLEN(sis) EP(iscopu)S VEN(etiae) LEG(a)T(u)S APOST(olicus).

Rev. Truth unveiled by two nude men. Below, VERITATI D(icatum).

93 mm. A898–161A

Collection: His de la Salle (sale, London, Sotheby, 22 Nov. 1880, lot 101).

Literature: Les Arts, Aug. 1908, p. 12, no. v; cp. Arm. II, 104, 12; *Corpus,* no. 486; Cott p. 171; Middeldorf, *Morgenroth,* no. 59.

162. SEBASTIANO MONTAGNACCO, Patrician of Venice, died 1540.

Obv. Bust to right. Around, SEBASTIANVS MONTENIAC(us) P(atricius) V(enetus).

Rev. A fortress, with tall tree in background. Below, S(enatus) C(onsulto). Around, CASSIANVM SOL(idatum ?) ET IMPENSA RESTAVRATVM

64 mm. A899–162A

Perhaps refers to the restoration in 1480 of the Castle of Cassacco, although the medal is much later (1520–30).

Literature: Corpus, no. 488 *c*; cp. Arm. III, 215, *d*; Cott p. 171.

VENETIAN SCHOOL
About 1450–1475

163. BEATO LORENZO GIUSTINIAN (1380–1456).

Obv. Bust to left, radiate, wearing cap and rochet. In a raised frame, on which BEATVS LAVRENTIVS IVSTINIANVS PRIMVS PATRIARCHA VENETIARVM

Without reverse.

Rectangular, 90 × 73 mm. A900–163A

Venetian work, after 1472, when Giustinian was beatified. The portrait is based on that by Gentile Bellini of 1465 in the Venice Academy.

Literature: Les Arts, Aug. 1908, p. 13, no. ii. cp. Arm. II, 300, 1 *bis*; Bange, no. 246; *Corpus*, no. 496 *c*; Cott p. 171.

VENETIAN SCHOOL
About 1500–1525

164. ANTONIO GRIMANI, Doge of Venice 1521–3.

Obv. Bust to left, in ducal cap and robe. Around, ANT(onius) GRIMANVS DVX VENETIAR(um).

Rev. Justice and Peace grasping hands. Around, IVSTITIA ET PAX OSCVLATE SVNT

32 mm. A901–164A

The reverse legend is from Ps. lxxxiv, 11.

Literature: Cp. Arm. II, 124, 4; Heiss, *Venise*, p. 155, no. 2, pl. x, 8; *Corpus*, no. 507; Cott p. 171. Tervarent, col. 176 (for literature on the reverse type).

165. GIOVANNI FASIOL.

Obv. Bust to left, in round cap. Around, engraved, IOANNES FASEOLVS V(enetus).

Rev. Nude helmeted figure holding small figure of Victory and branch.

43 mm. The only specimen known. A902–165A

This cannot be the Giov. Fasiol who taught Greek and Latin at Padua, for he was young in 1560. This medal, though cast, shows many affinities with the die-engraver of what Hill has called the Alviano group, who was working about 1500–25. The reverse design was too small for the obverse. The next two medals belong to the same group.

Literature: Arm. II, 125, 8; Heiss, *Venise* p. 187, pl. xiii, 8; *Les Arts*, Aug. 1908, p. 13, no. xviii; *Corpus*, no. 516 *a*; Cott p. 171.

166. SIMONE MICHIEL, Protonotary, afterwards Canon of Verona (1498) and (1510) of Treviso; died 1525.

Obv. Bust to left, wearing cap. Around, incised, SIMON MICHAEL PROTHONOTARIVS

Without reverse.

52 mm. The only known specimen. A903–166A

There are other medals of this man by Fra Antonio da Brescia.

Literature: Arm. II, 175, 11; Heiss, *Venise*, p. 195, pl. xiv, 7; *Corpus*, no. 517 *a*; Cott p. 172.

167. TOMMASO MOCENIGO.

Obv. Bust to left, in cap. Around, THOMAS MOCENICO

Rev. The Toilet of Venus? Around, VIRTVTE DVCE ET COMITE FORTVNA

39 mm. Struck. A904–167A

Probably the man who in 1504 became Procurator of St Mark's, and before that date.

Literature: Cp. Arm. II, 175, 12; Heiss, *Venise*, p. 195, pl. xv, 4; *Corpus*, no. 518 *e*; Cott p. 172.

168. FRA GIOVANNI CORNARO, Benedictine monk.

Obv. Bust to left, wearing habit. Around, +IO(annes) CORNELIVS MONACOR(um) CASIN(ensium) COLVMEN

Rev. Shepherd, carrying a sheep on his shoulders, driving his flock past a palm-tree on which is a pelican in her piety. Around, PIETAS EVANGELICA

43 mm. A905–168A

Giovanni Cornelio or Cornaro, a Venetian Benedictine of the Abbey of Praglia, was abbot of Santa Giustina at Padua, 1507–14. The medal may date from that time, or from just after his death.

Literature: Cp. Arm. II, 70, 5; *Corpus*, no. 527 *k*; Cott p. 172.

169. PAOLO DIEDO.

Obv. Bust to left, in cap and gown, seen slightly from behind. Around, PAVLVS DEDVS VENETVS MCCCCCVII

Without reverse.

45 mm. A906–169A

The Berlin specimen is the only one recorded with a reverse, a triple-faced bust, with an infant's face on top of the head, and the motto SOL PER CHE TROPPO GLIE

Literature: Arm. II, 125, 6; Heiss, *Venise*, p. 186, pl. xiii, 4; *Corpus*, no. 529 *e*; Cott p. 172.

170. GIOVANNI MANNELLI, Florentine.

Obv. Bust to right, wearing cap and coat. Around, IOANNES MANNELLVS FLORENTINVS CI(vis) and, below, XXI Concave field. Moulded border.

Without reverse.

58 mm. Gilt. A907–170A

Giovanni di Niccolò di Lionardo Mannelli was a Prior of Florence in Nov. and Dec. 1508. The medal is probably Venetian; it has been described as near the manner of Giulio della Torre, but it is perhaps still nearer that of Gambello.

Literature: Cp. Arm. I, 134, 23; *Corpus*, no. 535; Cott p. 172.

171. ALVISE DA NOALE, jurist.

Obv. Bust to left, cloak knotted on breast. Moulded border.

Rev. ALOYSIVS ANOALIS IVRECONSVLTVS Moulded border.

37 mm. A908–171A

Alvise was a lawyer prominent in Venetian affairs from 1509 until 1533 or later. The medal must, by its style, be dated about 1512–20.

Literature: Arm. III, 235 F; *Corpus*, no. 538 *e*; Cott p. 172.

BARTOLOMMEO BELLANO
(b. *ca.* 1434; d. 1496/7)

Sculptor and architect in Padua, and a pupil of Donatello. The following medal, attributed to him by Vasari, is in his characteristically uncouth style. For a plaquette by Bellano see Pope-Hennessy, *Kress Bronzes*, no. 3.

172. ANTONIO ROSELLI of Arezzo, jurist (1378–1466).

Obv. ANTONIVS DE ROYZELLIS MONARCHA SAPIENTIE Bust to left, wearing cap and robe; in field behind, 91

Rev. Figure of Roselli, seated on an architectural bracket; in field, C V Above, CELITVM BENIVOLENTIA

47 mm. A909–172A

The title 'Monarch of Wisdom' was given to Roselli in 1460 by the Venetian Senate; if he was at the same time made a Venetian citizen, this would explain the letters C V. The medal may have been made shortly after the conferment of the honour; or it may be posthumous (he died 16 Dec. 1466). The figure 91 may indicate his age; if so, it would appear to be three years out, since he did not reach more than 88 years.

Literature: Les Arts, Aug. 1908, p. 14, no. iii; *Corpus*, no. 540*f*; cp. Arm. I, 47, 3; Cott p. 172.

PADUA, 1515

173. GIROLAMO DI BENEDETTO PESARO, Captain of Padua 1515.

Obv. Bust to left, in cap and robe.

Rev. In a wreath, HIERONYMVS PISAVRVS PADVAE PRAEFECTVS BENEDICTI PROCVRATORIS F(ilius) MDXV

65 mm. A910–173A

Perhaps made at Padua, where Pesaro was captain from 1515 to 1517.

Collections: Samuel Addington (sale, London, Sotheby, 19 May 1886, lot 47) and Baron Heath (sale, London, Sotheby, 7 June 1879, lot 13).

Literature: Corpus, no. 543 *c*; cp. Arm. II, 126, 12; Cott p. 172.

174. *Obv.* Bust to left, in cap and gown. Around, HIERONIMVS PISAVRVS B(enedicti) F(ilius) PROC(uratoris)

Rev. Within a wreath, PADVAE PRAEFECTVS MDXV

32 mm. A911–174A

See the preceding medal.

Literature: Cp. Arm. II, 126, 13; *Corpus*, no. 544; Cott p. 172.

GIOVANNI MARIA POMEDELLI
(b. 1478/9; d. 1537 or later)

Goldsmith, painter, and engraver. His medals were nearly all made at Verona. His mark is an apple with a monogram of ZVAN, flanked by a punch and a graver.

175. STEFANO DI ANDREA MAGNO, 1519 (born soon after 1499, died 1572).

Obv. Bust to left. Around, STEPHANVS MAGNVS DOMINI ANDREAE FILIVS

Rev. Neptune seated on dolphin, his right foot on an urn from which water flows, spearing a lobster with his trident, and holding up a wreath; around, IOANNES MARIA POMEDELVS VERONENSIS F(ecit); in the field, MDXIX; below, the artist's mark.

56 mm. A912–175A

Collection: His de la Salle (sale, London, Sotheby, 22 Nov. 1880, lot 85).

Literature: Arm. I, 127, 7; *Les Arts*, Aug. 1908, p. 12, no. iii; *Corpus*, no. 586 *e*; Cott p. 172.

176. GIOVANNI EMO, Podestà of Verona 1527.

Obv. Bust to left, wearing cap and robe with stole over shoulder. Around, IOANNES AEMO VENET(us) VERONAE PRAETOR

Rev. Pallas, holding palm-branch, plucks a branch from an olive-tree; facing her, Mars, in armour, holding up shield and resting on spear beside his horse. Around, ET PACI ET BELLO MDXXVII; under ground-line and below, IO(annes) MARIA POMEDELLVS VERONENSIS F(ecit).

52 mm. A913–176A

Collection: His de la Salle (sale, London, Sotheby, 22 Nov. 1880, lot 86).

Literature: Les Arts, Aug. 1908, p. 12, no. ii; cp. Arm. I, 126, 4; *Corpus*, no. 588 *h*; Cott p. 172.

177. TOMMASO MORO, Captain of Verona 1527.

Obv. Bust to right, in cap and robe with stole. Around, THOMAS MAVRVS VENETVS VERONAE PRAEFECTVS

Rev. Phoenix on pyre gazing at sun. Around, MORIENS REVIVISCO and IO(annes) MARIA POMEDELVS VERONEN(sis) F(ecit); across field, MDXXVII

52 mm. A914–177A

Other specimens at Berlin and Venice.

Collection: His de la Salle (sale London, Sotheby, 22 Nov. 1880, lot 84).

Literature: Corpus, no. 589 *c*; cp. Arm. I, 128, 11; Cott p. 172. Tervarent, cols. 304–5.

178. CHARLES V, born 1500, King of Spain 1516, Emperor 1519–56, died 1558.

Obv. Bust to right, young, wearing flat cap and robe with collar of the Golden Fleece. Around, KAROLVS REX CATOLICVS

Rev. Young winged genius kneeling, writing on a shield hung on an oak-tree; behind, a vase; above, an eagle flying crowns him; around, VITORIA

35 mm. A915–178A

A later version of a medal inscribed VICTORIA and having the mark of Pomedelli below.

Literature: Cp. *Corpus*, no. 591; cp. Arm. I, 125, 1; Cott p. 172; Bernhart, *Bildnismedaillen Karls des Fünften*, Munich, 1919, p. 33, no. 2, pl. i.

179. FRANCIS I of France (1494–1515–47).

Obv. Bust to left, beardless, in cap and robes, wearing collar of St Michael. Around, FRANCISCVS I CHRISTIANISIMVS REX FRANCOR(um).

Rev. On a large tazza, a salamander in flames; above, crown; around, NVTRISCO EXTINGO; below, the artist's mark.

50 mm. Later casting. A916–179A

The original was made between 1515 (the date of the accession of Francis) and 1518 (when he began to grow a beard). The *Corpus* records only one good specimen of this medal.

Literature: Cp. Arm. I, 127, 5; *Corpus*, no. 592; Cott p. 179. Tervarent, cols. 333–4 (for the salamander device).

180. UNKNOWN LADY

Obv. Bust to left; around, F·B·ET LONGIVS VIVAT SERVATA FIDE

Rev. Naked bearded man kneeling, holding on his head basket of fruits; behind him, Cupid standing on a globe inscribed A S O (*Amor superat omnia*); in the field, caduceus and growing vine. Around, IOANNES MARIA POMEDELLVS VERONE(n)SI(s) F(ecit).

54 mm. Somewhat over-chased. A917–180A

The initials on the obverse perhaps represent the lady's name.

Literature: Les Arts, Aug. 1908, p. 12, no. i; *Corpus*, no. 594 *g*; cp. Arm. I, 129, 13; Cott p. 172.

181. FEDERIGO II GONZAGA (1500–1540), fifth Marquess of Mantua 1519, Duke 1530.

Obv. Bust to left, wearing coat with chain over. Around, FEDERICVS II MARCHIO MANTVAE V

Rev. Altar of FIDES on a mountain (Olympus); below, IOA(n)NES MARIA POMED(ellus) F(ecit); all in wreath.

39 mm. A918–181A

The medal dates between 1523 and 1530.

Literature: Corpus, no. 595 *e*; cp. Arm. I, 127, 6; Cott p. 172. Tervarent, col. 276 (for the mountain as a Gonzaga device).

182. ISABELLA MICHIEL, wife of Giambattista Sesso.

Obv. Bust to left, head swathed in drapery, cloak tied on left shoulder. Around, (vine-spray) ISABELLA SESSA MICHAEL VENETA

Rev. Occasion seated to left, semi-nude, holding bridle and three nails, right foot on a skull; behind her, a leafless tree and a sphinx-crested helmet. Below, the artist's mark. Above, ΕΚ ΠΑΛΑΙ ΜΟΙ ΜΗΝΙΖΟΜΕΝΗ

45 mm. A919–182A

The reverse of this and other medals of Isabella seem to refer to her wartime distresses as governess of Vicenza for the Imperialists against Venice in 1511. In Nov. 1511 she retired to Verona, and probably returned to Vicenza, having sued for pardon, in 1517. She lost her property, and had no reward from Maximilian, so that Fortune is rightly described as 'since long time wroth' with her. The form μηνίζεσθαι is unclassical.

Literature: Corpus, no. 597, l; cp. Arm. I, 127, 8; Cott p. 173; Morsolin, 'Isabella Sesso', in *Rivista Italiana di Numismatica*, iii, 1890, pp. 250–258 (for the career of Isabella). Tervarent, col. 267, ii (on the type of Occasion or Fortune); col. 278 (Bridle and Fortune).

183. FRANCIS I of France (1494–1515–47).

Obv. Bust to right, youthful, wearing plumed hat. Around, FR(ancisco) FR(ancorum) REGI VICTORI MAX(imo) AC VINDICI OPT(imo).

Rev. Diomede seated on cippus, from corner of which

hangs a garland; he holds palladium and dagger. Around, F(rancisci) NIBII NOVAR(iensis) CVRA OB EIVS PATRIAM DOMVMQ(ue) SERVAT(am).

48 mm. Not a contemporary cast. A920–183A

Francesco Nibbia of Novara had this medal made for Francis in gratitude 'for saving his country and his house', doubtless in the campaign of Marignano (1515). The attribution to Pomedelli is not certain, though probable. The reverse is copied either from a well-known Medici gem of which the Kress collection has a bronze version; or from the medallion in the Riccardi Palace which reproduces it.

Literature: Cp. Arm. II, 187, 5; *Corpus*, no. 600; Cott p. 173; Pope-Hennessy, *Kress Bronzes* no. 257 (for the bronze version of the gem, with literature); cp. no. 256; Ursula Wester and Erika Simon, 'Die Reliefmedaillons im Hofe des Palazzo Medici zu Florenz', in *Jahrbuch der Berliner Museen*, 7 (1965), I, pp. 27–8, 34, 50, figs. 2, 3 (for the tondo, gem); B. H. Pollak, 'A Leonardo drawing and the Medici Diomedes gem', in Warburg *Journal*, 14 (1951), pp. 303–4 (for versions of the composition in other media).

FRANCESCO FRANCIA

(b. *ca.* 1450/3; d. 1517)

A famous painter of Bologna. The two following medals are only attributed to him.

184. GIOVANNI II BENTIVOGLIO (Born 1443, Lord of Bologna 1462–1506, died 1509)

Obv. Bust to right, with long hair, in cap, doublet, and coat. Around, IOANNES BENTIVOLVS II BONONIENSIS

Rev. MAXIMILIANI IMPERATORIS MVNVS MCCCCLXXXXIIII

28 mm. Struck. A921–184A

Munus is the right of coinage granted by the Emperor to Giovanni II in Oct. 1494. It is doubtful whether Francia, according to the tradition recorded by Vasari, engraved the dies for this coinage, as he did after 1506; but possibly the present medalet and the coins based on it (see no. 659) follow a design by him.

In S. Giacomo Maggiore, Bologna, is a relief closely resembling this portrait by one Antonio Bal . . ., which is possibly copied from an original by Francia.

Literature: Les Arts, Aug. 1908, p. 12, no. xxiii; *Corpus*, no. 606 *l*; cp. Arm. I, 104, I; Cott p. 173; Middeldorf, *Morgenroth*, no. 63.

185. *Obv.* Bust to right, with long hair. Around, IOANNES SECVNDVS BENTIVOLVS

Rev. Shield of Bentivoglio; around and across field, HANNIBALIS FI(lius) R(ei) P(ublicae) BONON(iensis) PRINCEPS

Silver, 18 mm. A922–185A

There is another specimen in silver at Florence (Supino, p. 88, no. 223); specimens in bronze in Berlin (Friedländer, p. 176, pl. xxxiv no. 2) and the Morgenroth collection.

Literature: Corpus no. 607 *c*; cp. Arm. II, 65, 21; Cott, p. 173 (as Francia ?); Middeldorf, *Morgenroth*, no. 64 (from the Oppenheimer sale, part lot 66; 'the attribution has little foundation')

BOLOGNESE SCHOOL AFTER FRANCIA

186. FRANCESCO DEGLI ALIDOSI, Cardinal of Pavia (1505), Legate of Bologna and Romagna (1508), murdered 1511.

Obv. Bust to right, in berretta and cape. Around, FR(anciscus) ALIDOXIVS CAR(dinalis) PAPIEN(sis) BON(oniae) ROMANDIOLAE Q(ue) C(ardinalis) LEGAT(us).

Rev. Jupiter, nude, with thunderbolt, in car drawn by two eagles; below, signs of Pisces and Sagittarius. Around, HIS AVIBVS CVRRVQ(ue) CITO DVCERIS AD ASTRA

59 mm. A923–186A

Cp. the relief portrait in the Louvre. Tervarent explains the reverse type as an allusion to Jupiter giving glory to those born under his ascendancy.

Literature: Corpus, no. 610; cp. Arm. III, 32, E; Cott p. 173. Tervarent, col. 71.

187. BERNARDO DE' ROSSI, Bishop of Treviso (1499), Governor of Bologna (1519–23), died 1527.

Obv. Bust to right, in berretta and cape. Around, BER(nardus) RV(beus) CO(mes) B(erceti) EP(iscopu)S TAR(visinus) LE(gatus) BO(noniae) VIC(arius) GV(bernator) ET PRAE(fectus).

Rev. A female figure holding a sun-flower in a car drawn by a dragon and an eagle; around, OB VIRTVTES IN FLAMINIAM RESTITVTAS

65 mm. A924–187A

The work of a follower of Francia, alluding to the repression by Rossi of disturbances at Ravenna ('Flaminia' means Romagna) in 1519.

Literature: Cp. Arm. II, 105, 19; III, 32, F; *Corpus*, no. 612; Cott p. 173.

MILANESE SCHOOL

Late Fifteenth Century

188. GIANGALEAZZO VISCONTI, first Duke of Milan (1354–95–1402).

Obv. Bust to right, wearing robe and chain; below, IOANNES GALEACIVS

Without reverse.

Rectangular, 157 × 122 mm. A925–188A

Possibly identical with the Bardini specimen. No other is recorded. Hill described the piece as a Milanese 'restitution' not earlier than the end of the fifteenth century. It may be noted however, that the plate of Gian Galeazzo Visconti in Paolo Giovio's history of the Visconti is closely similar to the portrait plaque. As other historical writing by Giovio inspired imaginary portrait medals (see no. 445) this piece may be early-sixteenth century.

Literature: Arm. II, 14, 19; III, 156, *b*; *Corpus*, no. 636 *b*; Cott p. 173; *Pauli Jovii Novocomensis Vitae duodecim vicecomitum Mediolani Principum*, Paris, 1549, p. 165 (portrait of Gian Galeazzo Visconti).

189. LODOVICO MARIA SFORZA (1451–1508) il Moro, seventh Duke of Milan (1494–1500).

Obv. Bust to right, in cuirass.

Without reverse.

Oval, 26 × 22 mm. A926–189A

Closely resembling the onyx cameo in Florence (no. 109), generally attributed to the Milanese gem-engraver Domenico de' Cammei. If the scale of the plate in Kris may be trusted, the piece was not produced by indirect casting from the stone.

Literature: Cott, p. 173; Kris, pl. 20, no. 85.

CARADOSSO

(b. *ca.* 1452; d. 1526/7)

Cristoforo Caradosso Foppa was employed as a goldsmith and medallist in Milan after 1475. He appears to have remained in Milan after the expulsion of Lodovico il Moro, moved to Mantua in 1505, and then to Rome, where he founded the guild of Roman goldsmiths in 1509, and died 1526/7. None of his medals are signed. For his plaquettes in the Kress collection see Pope-Hennessy, *Kress Bronzes*, nos. 47–53. For a rectangular portrait plaque of Giangiacomo Trivulzio, attributed to Caradosso, see D. W. H. Schwarz, 'Eine Bildnisplakette des Gian Giacomo Trivulzio' in *Schweizerische Landesmuseum im Zurich, Jahresberichte 66*, (1957) pp. 39–57. This piece, from the Trivulzio collection, was lot 97, pl. 11 of Münzen und Medaillen, Basel, auction XVII, 2 Dec. 1957 (The plaque is of black-patinated bell-metal; 195·1 × 151·5 mm, traces of gilding).

190. FRANCESCO I SFORZA (1401–66).

Obv. Bust to left in cuirass; on the breast, Sforza device of the hound under a tree. Around, FRANCISCVS SFORTIA VICECOMES DVX M(edio)L(an)I QVARTVS

Rev. Francesco on horseback under canopy, accompanied by soldiers, approaching a city from which issue people. Around, CLEMENTIA ET ARMIS PARTA

40 mm. A late cast. A927–190A

A companion piece to the following, and made at the same time, but commemorating a much earlier event, Francesco's entry into Milan in 1450. For the device on the breast-plate, see Enzola's medal no. 92.

Literature: Corpus, no. 653 *i*; Cp. Arm. I, 108, 5; Cott p. 173. Middeldorf, *Morgenroth*, no. 67 (*Corpus*, 653 *j*).

191. LODOVICO MARIA SFORZA (1451–1508) il Moro, seventh Duke of Milan (1494–1500).

Obv. Bust to right in armour; on breast, a female figure running, carrying a trophy. Around, LVDOVICVS MA(ria) SF(ortia) VI(ce)CO(mes) DVX BARI DVC(atus) GVBER (nator).

Rev. The Doge of Genoa (?) seated on a platform on which is engraved P(ublico) DECRETO; a procession of horsemen, headed by Lodovico (?) approaches; in background, harbour of Genoa. Around, OPTIMO CONSCILIO SINE ARMIS RESTITVTA

41 mm. A928–191A

Apparently commemorates the acquisition of Genoa by Lodovico in 1488.

Literature: Les Arts, Aug. 1908, p. 12, no. xxi; *Corpus*, no. 654 *g*; cp. Arm. I, 109, 8; Cott p. 173. Middeldorf, *Morgenroth* no. 68.

192. GIANGIACOMO TRIVULZIO, Marshal of France (1441–99–1518).

Obv. Bust to left, in plate-armour, laureate. Around, IO(annes) IACOBVS TRIVVL(tiu)S MAR(chio) VIG(evani) FRA(nciae) MARESCALVS On a square field, in corners of which shield bearing the Trivulzio arms, Sforza viper, Sforza device of three brands with buckets, and the *ruota del sole*.

Rev. 1499 and inscription recording capture of Alessandria, expulsion of Lodovico il Moro, and his capture at Novara.

Square, 46 × 46 mm. A929–192A

Attributed by Lomazzo to Caradosso.

Literature: Cp. Arm. I, 110, 11; *Corpus*, no. 655; Cott p. 173.

193. DONATO DI ANGELO BRAMANTE, architect (about 1444–1514).

Obv. Bust to front, nude, head to left. Around, BRAMANTES ASDRVVALDINVS

Rev. Architecture seated, holding compasses and square, her right foot on a weight; in background, view of St Peter's according to Bramante's design. Above, FIDELITAS LABOR

43 mm. A930–193A

Ascribed to Caradosso by Vasari, who, however, says that the medal was struck, not cast.

Literature: Les Arts, Aug. 1908, p. 12, no. xviii; *Corpus*, no. 657 *l*; cp. Arm. I, 107, 1; Cott p. 173.

194. JULIUS II, Pope, 1503–13.

Obv. Bust to right, bare-headed, in cope. Around, IVLIVS LIGVR PAPA SECVNDVS MCCCCCVI

Rev. View of St Peter's according to Bramante's design; above, TEMPLI PETRI INSTAVRACIO; below, VATICANVS M(ons).

56 mm. A931–194A

The medal is attributed to Caradosso on the authority of Vasari, and with the following medal, is to be identified with those which were buried in the foundations of the church in 1506.

Literature: Les Arts, Aug. 1908, p. 12, no. xix; *Corpus*, no. 659 *e*; cp. Arm. I, 108, 2; Cott p. 173; Middeldorf, *Morgenroth*, no. 69 (mentioning the chiaroscuro woodcut by Hans Burgkmair, of 1511, which copies this medal, and the literature on it); R. Weiss, 'The Medals of Julius II', in Warburg *Journal*, 28 (1965) pp. 163–182 (at pp. 169–172; supporting the attribution to Caradosso, giving bibliographical references for the Bramante design, and showing the imitations of the Caradosso portrait type which followed the medal).

195. Similar to the preceding, but the Pope wears skull-cap and cape with hood.

57 mm. A932–195A

Literature: Corpus, no. 660 *d*; cp. Arm. I, 108, 4; Cott p. 173 (and see preceding piece).

196. NICCOLÒ ORSINI (1442–1510), Count of Pitigliano and Nola, Captain of the Army of the Roman Church and of the Florentine Republic.

Obv. Bust to left, bald, in armour. Around, NIC(olaus) VRS(inus) PET(iliani) ET NOL(ae) COMES SANTE ROM(anae) ECCLE(sie) ARMOR(um) CAP(itaneus).

Rev. Orsini riding to right, accompanied by two halberdiers. Around, NIC(olaus) VRS(inus) PETILIANI ET NOLAE COMES REIP(ublicae) FLOR(entinae) CAP(itaneus).

41 mm. A933–196A

The titles date the medal between 1485 and 1495. No less than four other later versions were made by recasting and altering the legend of the original, to suit the various changes in Orsini's employment. The attribution of the original to Caradosso was suggested by Jean de Foville.

Literature: Corpus, no. 664 *k*; cp. Arm. II, 64, 16; Cott p. 173; Middeldorf, *Morgenroth*, no. 71.

MILANESE SCHOOL

Early Sixteenth Century

197. SIMONE TAVERNA of Milan.

Obv. Bust to right, wearing cap and coat. Around, incised, SIMON DE TABERNIS DE M(edio)L(an)O

Without reverse.

43 mm. A934–197A

Other specimens in the Milan and former W. H. Woodward collections.

Literature: Arm. II, 102, 4; *Corpus*, no. 702 *b*; Cott p. 173.

198. SCARAMUCCIA DI GIANFERMO TRIVULZIO, Bishop of Como 1508, Cardinal 1517, died 1527.

Obv. Bust to left, wearing berretta and cape. Around, SCARAMVTIA TRIVVL(tius) CAR(dinalis) COMIH IO(annis) FIRMI PRIMI F(ilius).

Rev. Prudence holding mirror and compasses, looking down at small dragon at her feet.

60 mm. A935–198A

Probably between 1518 and 1525. The error COMIH was corrected to COMEN(sis) on a later version, to which was also added the motto HAEC SOLA DOMINATVR. The workmanship appears to be Milanese. Hill argued that the female figures on the reverses of this medal, and of the medals of Pietro Piantanida (no. 423) and Jean de Lorraine (no. 424), all related to the figure of Peace on the reverse of Cellini's medal of Clement VII. Habich accepted the grouping but refused the attribution to Cellini, prefering to call the group simply Milanese. Hill noticed (*Corpus* p. 180, note to no. 705) that the bust of the Trivulzio piece was not of the same character as the rest of the group. Dworschak has attributed two of the group, the Martinioni and Piantanida medals, to Antonio Abondio.

Literature: Cp. *Corpus*, no. 703; Cott p. 174. Hill 'Notes on Italian Medals, x', in *Burl. Mag.* 18 (1910), pp. 13–21 (at p. 14); Habich, pl. lxxxiii, 3.

199. GIANGIACOMO TRIVULZIO Marshal of France (1441–99–1518).

Obv. Bust to right, laureate, wearing cuirass. Around, IO(annes) IA(cobus) TRI(vultius) MAR(chio) VIG(evani) FRAN(ciae) MARES(callus).

Rev. Bust to right, in cap and cuirass. Around, NEC CEDIT VMBRA SOLI

43 mm. A936–199A

The motto is said to have been adopted by Trivulzio when he deserted Lodovico for his enemies.

Literature: Les Arts, Aug. 1908, p. 11, no. ix; *Corpus*, no. 706 *g*; cp. Arm. II, 103, 5; Cott p. 174.

200. See Appendix.

BATTISTA (DI?) ELIA OF GENOA

Known only from the medal of Cosma Scaglia of 1480, signed by him, which the following piece closely resembles.

201. BATTISTA II DI CAMPOFREGOSO, Doge of Genoa 1478–83.

Obv. Bust to right, wearing small cap. Around, BAPT(ista) FVLGOS(ius) IANVE LIGVR(iae) Q(ue) DVX PETR(i) DV(cis) FIL(ius).

Rev. Crocodile and trochilus. Around, PECVLIARES AVDACIA ET VICTVS

42 mm. A938–201A

The bird called *trochilus* is described by Herodotus as feeding in the crocodile's mouth. The reference of the device is obscure.

Literature: Les Arts, Aug. 1908, p. 13, no. xix; *Corpus*, no. 728 *h*; cp. Arm. I, 61, 1; Cott p. 174.

MEDALLIST OF THE ROMAN EMPERORS

An unidentified medallist of the last quarter of the fifteenth century, working, to judge by his style, in North Italy, probably in Lombardy, and making medals, more or less fanciful, of Roman Emperors. The letters S C which he is fond of putting on all his works are borrowed from Roman coins (issued 'by order of the Senate'), and his inscriptions attempt in a blundering fashion to reproduce ancient models.

202. NERO.

Obv. Bust to right, laureate, wearing cuirass and mantle. Around, NERO CLAVD(ius) IMP(erator) CAES(ar) AVG(ustus) CO(n)S(ul) VII P(ater) P(atriae).

Rev. Under a palm-tree, Nero, laureate, seated to right holding a patera; before him a nude man, also laureate, standing behind a large vase. In field, S(enatus) C(onsulto) and, below, NERO AVG(ustus).

114 mm. A939–202A

Literature: Arm. I, 100, 1; *Les Arts*, Aug. 1908, p. 11, no. i; *Corpus*, no. 732 *c*; Cott p. 174.

203. HADRIAN.

Obv. Bust to right in crested helmet, cuirass, and mantle. Around, ADRIANVS AVG(ustus) CO(n)S(ul) III P(ontifex) P(ater) P(atriae) S(enatus) C(onsulto).

Rev. Hadrian, dressed as an obverse, riding to right, carrying standard; above and below, MARS VIPTOR (for VICTOR), and, in field, S(enatus) C(onsulto).

102 mm. The only known specimen. A940–203A

An example of the reverse alone, diam. 92 mm., is recorded.

Literature: Les Arts, Aug. 1908, p. 11, no. ii; *Corpus*, no. 734 *a*; Cott p. 174; Molinier, no. 14 (for the reverse alone).

204. FAUSTINA I and ANTONINUS PIUS.

Obv. Bust of Faustina to right. Around, DIVA AVGVSTA DIVAE FAVSTINA

Rev. Pius and Faustina seated facing each other, joining hands. Around, DIVA FAVSTINA DIVS ANTONINVS and, below, S(enatus) C(onsulto).

110 mm. A941–204A

Literature: Les Arts, Aug. 1908, p. 11, no. iii; cp. Arm. I, 100, 3; *Corpus*, no. 735; Cott p. 174; Antonio Morassi, 'Per la ricostruzione di Maffeo Olivieri', in *Bollettino d'Arte*, 30 (1936), pp. 237–249 (publishes the monument of Marc Antonio Martinengo in the Museo Cristiano, Brescia, in which one of the roundels, figured on p. 245, has the same composition as the medal reverse, although the handling is quite different).

205. MARCUS CROTO.

Obv. Head to right of young man; behind, MARCVS; [in front CROTO obliterated].

Rev. The same man in armour riding to left, carrying standard; below, helmet and shield; around, VICTORIAE AGVSTE and, below, S(enatus) C(onsulto).

60 mm. A942–205A

This is characterized by all the mannerisms of the 'Medallist of the Roman Emperors'. Marcus Croto has not been identified and may be a fiction of the artist, although as Middeldorf observes, the name Croto occurs in Cremona in the sixteenth century. They were painters. The Kress collection contains a second specimen of the medal on which the reverse is coarser, and the detail of the helmet crest quite different (see Appendix). The obverse legend MARCVS CRO TO appears on the specimen in the Morgenroth collection.

Literature: Cp. Arm. II, 129, 7; *Corpus*, no. 736; Cott p. 174; Middeldorf, *Morgenroth*, no. 72; d'Arco, *Arti e artefici di Mantova*, 1857, p. 92 (the name recorded as Croto, Crozio, and Croteo).

205 *bis*. See Appendix.

ROMAN SCHOOL, 1455

206. PIER BARBÒ, Cardinal of San Marco, afterwards Paul II, 1455.

Obv. Bust to left, wearing cope. Around, PETRVS BARBVS VENETVS CARDINALIS S(ancti) MARCI

Rev. Barbò shield ensigned with cardinal's hat. Around, HAS AEDES CONDIDIT ANNO CHRISTI MCCCCLV

34 mm. A944–206A

Foundation medal for the Palazzo di Venezia in Rome, 1455.

Literature: Corpus, no. 737*j*; cp. Arm. II, 31, 2; Cott p. 174; Weiss, 'Un umanista veneziano Papa Paolo II', *Civiltà Veneziana, Saggi 4*, Venice, 1958, p. 50 (The article contains the latest commentary on the Renaissance practice of foundation medals, pp. 69–81).

ANDREA GUACIALOTI
(b. 1435; d. 8 Nov. 1495)

A Florentine of Prato; became a canon of Prato, but practised as a bronze-founder (for instance, it was he who cast Bertoldo's Pazzi medal, no. 252). His medals were all made at Rome.

207. NICCOLÒ PALMIERI, Bishop of Orte (1455–1467).

Obv. Bust to left, nude. Around, NVDVS EGRES(s)VS SIC REDIBO and, incised, NICOLAVS PALMERIVS SICVLVS EP(iscopu)S ORTAN(us).

Rev. On a bracket, nude male figure standing, resting on staff and holding hour-glass; below, ANDREAS GVACIALOTVS and incised, above, CONTVBERNALIS B(enemerito) F(ecit) and, across field, VIX(it) AN(nis) LXV OBIIT A D MCCCCLXVII

63 mm. A945–207A

The third of three versions existing of this medal; the incised inscriptions (the second S in EGRESSVS and the second V in the signature are also incised) were added after the sitter's death.

Literature: Corpus, no. 744 *k*; cp. Arm. I, 49, 5; Cott p. 174; Middeldorf *Morgenroth* no. 74.

208. CALIXTUS III, Pope, 1455–8.

Obv. Bust to left, in tiara and cope. Around, CALISTVS PAPA TERTIVS

Rev. Borgia arms ensigned with tiara and crossed-keys. Around, ALFONSVS BORGIA GLORIA ISPANIE

42 mm. A946–208A

Unmistakably in the style of Guacialoti.

Literature: Cp. Arm. I, 49, 7; *Corpus*, no. 747; Cott p. 174; Middeldorf, *Morgenroth*, no. 76.

209. SIXTUS IV, Pope, 1471–84.

Obv. Bust to left, in tiara and cope. Around, SIXTVS IIII PON(tifex) MAX(imus) SACRICVLT(or).

Rev. Constancy standing to front, resting on tall staff and column; at her feet, Turkish captives, arms and banners, and galleys in harbour. Inscriptions: PARCERE SVBIECTIS ET DEBELLARE SVPERBOS SIXTE POTES; below, CONSTANTIA; engraved across field, MCCCCLXXXI

60 mm. A947–209A

Commemorates the expulsion of the Turks from Otranto in 1481, the Pope having contributed troops to the expedition. The medal is linked by its reverse type to one of Alfonso of Calabria by Guacialoti, and is certainly from his hand.

Collection: Signol (sale, Paris, 1 April 1878, lot 181).

Literature: Les Arts, Aug. 1908, p. 11, no. x; *Corpus*, no. 751 *h*; cp. Arm. I, 50, 10; Cott p. 175.

CRISTOFORO DI GEREMIA
(Active 1456–76)

Of Mantua, goldsmith, medallist, and metal-worker, came to Rome in 1456 and worked for Cardinal Scarampi, after whose death in 1465 he entered the service of the Pope; many medals of Paul II can safely be attributed to him. He died before 22 Feb. 1476. For his plaquettes see Pope-Hennessy, *Kress Bronzes*, nos. 54, 55.

210. ALFONSO V OF ARAGON, King of Naples and Sicily, born 1394, established in Naples 1442, died 1458.

Obv. Bust to right, in armour and cloak, placed over a crown. Around, ALFONSVS REX REGIBVS IMPERANS ET BELLORVM VICTOR

Rev. Alfonso seated, crowned by Mars and Bellona. Around, VICTOREM REGNI MARS ET BELLONA CORONANT and, below, CHRISTOPHORVS HIERIMIA

75 mm. A948–210A

Not much, if at all later than the death of Alfonso in 1458. The cuirass was copied by Clemente of Urbino for his medal of 1468 (see no. 100). The arrangement of crown below bust is borrowed from Pisanello (see no. 20).

Collection: His de la Salle (sale, London, Sotheby, 22 Nov. 1880, lot 22).

Literature: Les Arts, Aug. 1908, p. 11, no. xii; cp. Arm. I, 31, 1; *Corpus*, no. 754; Cott p. 175; Middeldorf, *Morgenroth*, no. 77.

211. CONSTANTINE THE GREAT.

Obv. Bust to right, wreathed with oak, wearing cuirass and mantle. Around, CAESAR IMPERATOR PONT(ifex) P P P ET SEMPER AVGVSTVS VIR

Rev. Constantine (holding winged caduceus of Peace, inscribed PAX) and the Church (holding cornucopiae) joining hands; around, CONCORDIA AVGG(ustorum) and, below, S(enatus) C(onsulto); under ground-line, CHRISTOPHORVS HIERIMIAE F(ilius).

72 mm. A949–211A

Probably cast in 1468 on the occasion of the visit of Frederick III to Rome. P P P is taken from some Roman inscription, where it means *Pater Patriae Proconsul.*

Literature: Cp. Arm. I, 31, 2; *Corpus*, no. 755; Cott, p. 175; Middeldorf, *Morgenroth*, no. 78; Pope-Hennessy, *Kress Bronzes* no. 54 (for a plaquette similar to the medal reverse).

212. LODOVICO SCARAMPI (Mezzarota), Patriarch of Aquileia (1444), died 1465 aged 63.

Obv. Head to right. Around, L(udovicus) AQVILEGIENSIVM PATRIARCA ECCLESIAM RESTITVIT

Rev. Triumphal procession before a temple. Above, ECCLESIA RESTITVTA; below, EXALTO

39 mm. A950–212A

Mezzarota, best known from Mantegna's portrait at Berlin, was the artist's patron from 1461 to 1465. The medal refers to his services in command of the Papal army. The reverse type exists as a small plaquette.

Literature: Cp. Arm. II, 37, 2; *Corpus*, no. 756; Cott p. 175. Bange no. 172 (reverse type).

213. GUILLAUME D'ESTOUTEVILLE, cardinal (1439), Archbishop of Rouen (1453), Bishop of Ostia (1461), Papal Chamberlain, 1432 until his death 1483.

Obv. Bust to right, wearing rochet. Around, G(ulielmus) DESTOVTEVILLA EPIS(copus) OSTI(ensis) CAR(dinalis) ROTHO(magensis) S(anctae) R(omanae) E(cclesiae) CAM (erarius).

Rev. Shield of arms of Estouteville, ensigned with cardinal's hat.

47 mm. A951–213A

The medal has all the marks of Cristoforo's style, in the modelling of the features and the treatment of the bust. It may date from the time of the appointment as Bishop of Ostia or a little later.

Literature: Les Arts, Aug. 1908, p. 14, no. ii; *Corpus*, no. 757 *k*; cp. Arm. II, 40, 4; Cott p. 175; Middeldorf, *Morgenroth*, no. 79; S. A. Callisen, 'A bust of a prelate in the Metropolitan Museum, New York', in *The Art Bulletin*, 18 (1936), pp. 401–406 (for a related sculptured bust attributed to Mino del Reame).

214. PAOLO DOTTI of Padua, General of Militia, 1289.

Obv. Bust to right, elderly. Around, DOTTVS PATAVVS MILITIE PREFETVS PROPTER RES BENE GESTAS

Rev. Constancy, nude, standing, resting on staff and column. Below, CONSTANTIA

61 mm. A952–214A

The identification of the person is not quite certain. Paolo I Dotti distinguished himself at Vicenza in 1289 by a feat of courage such as seems to be commemorated on the reverse. The figure was copied for other medals, by Guacialoti (no. 209), and by a Florentine medallist (no. 276).

Literature: Cp. Arm. I, 50, 11; *Corpus*, no. 758; Cott p. 175.

ROMAN SCHOOL UNDER PAUL II

215. PAUL II, Pope, 1464–71.

Obv. The Pope in public consistory. Around, +SACRVM PVBLICVM APOSTOLICVM CONCISTORIVM PAVLVS VENETV(S) P(A)P(A) II

Rev. Christ in Glory, among Saints, Sun, Moon and Stars; lower, the Doctors of the Church; and the Resurrection of the Dead; at bottom, the Virgin and the Baptist on either side of an altar. Around, IVSTVS ES DOMINE ET RECTVM IVDICIVM TVVM MISERERE NOSTRI DO(mine) MISERERE NOSTRI

79 mm. A953–215A

This piece may commemorate the consistory of Dec. 1466, at which the King of Bohemia was condemned, or that of Holy Week 1467, when the sentence was confirmed. The legend gives no clue, the piece may alternatively be a donation medal. Weiss shows that the dies were probably the work of Emiliano Orfini, mint engraver at Rome at that time. This medal is one of many casts which reproduce the original struck gold pieces. Two of these have survived; at Vienna, and in commerce, London, 1965.

Literature: Cp. Arm. II, 33, 19; III, 163 *e*; *Corpus*, no. 775; Cott p. 175; Weiss, 'Un umanista veneziano Papa Paolo II', *Civiltà Veneziana, Saggi* 4, Venice, 1958, pp. 58–9. Morrison collection, sale, London, Christie, 23 July 1965, lot 88 (second specimen of the medal in gold).

216. *Obv.* Bust to left in cope. Around, PAVLVS II VENETVS PONT(ifex) MAX(imus).

Rev. The Palazzo di Venezia. Around, HAS AEDES CONDIDIT ANNO CHRISTI MCCCCLXV

34 mm. A954–216A

A foundation medal for the Palazzo di Venezia.

Literature: Cp. *Corpus*, no. 783; Cott p. 175; Weiss (see preceding medal) p. 51.

LYSIPPUS JUNIOR

The real name of the owner of this pseudonym is unknown. He is mentioned as being a nephew of Cristoforo di Geremia, and appears to have ceased working after about 1484. He seems to have worked especially amongst his friends at the Roman Curia in the time of Pope Sixtus IV (1471–84). To the bibliography in the *Corpus*, p. 205, may be added a study of *Corpus* no. 810 by R. Weiss, 'Une médaille à demi connue de Lysippus le jeune', in *Schweizer Münzblätter*, Jahrgang 10, Heft 37 (May 1960) pp. 7–10.

217. BARTOLOMMEO PARTHENIO of Brescia, humanist.

Obv. Bust to left, in cap and gown. Around, PARTHENIVS AMICVS

Rev. A lily growing. Across field, FLORESCO CALORE PARTENII

35 mm. A late cast. A955–217A

Bartolommeo Parthenio was teaching at Rome about 1480–5. The lily, as the Virgin's flower, alludes to his name.

Literature: Arm. II, 77, 17; III, 179, H; *Corpus*, no. 802 *c*; Cott p. 175.

218. GIOVANNI FRANCESCO DE'RANGONI.

Obv. Bust to left, in cap and cuirass. Around, D(ivi or domini) IO(annis) FRANCIS(c)I D(e) RANGONIBVS P V V

Rev. Armed figure standing on a prostrate wolf or fox, resting on a spear with his right hand, which also grasps a serpent. In field, in large letters, S M; below, SECVRITAS P(o)P(uli).

37 mm. A956–218A

Possibly the Francesco Maria Rangone, a Modenese politician, who died in 1511; but if the medal is by Lysippus, as seems likely, an earlier man is probably represented. The abbreviations P V V and S M are unexplained, and obscure too is the figure on the reverse (triumphing, perhaps, over discord and faction).

Literature: Cp. Arm. II, 93, 19; *Corpus*, no. 803; Cott p. 175.

219. SIXTUS IV, Pope, 1471–84.

Obv. Bust to left, wearing tiara and cope. Around, SIXTVS IIII PONT(ifex) MAX(imus) SACRI CVLT(or).

Rev. The Pope being crowned by St Francis and St Anthony. Around, +HEC DAMVS IN TERRIS AETERNA DABVNTVR OLIMPO

41 mm. A957–219A

The obverse is close to the style of Lysippus, the reverse less so. The reference is doubtless to the actual coronation of the Pope; the saints give to him the earthly crown, the eternal one he will receive in heaven.

Literature: Cp. Arm. II, 62, 1; *Corpus*, no. 807; Cott p. 175.

220. GIOVANNI ALVISE TOSCANI (b. *ca.* 1450; d. 1478).

Obv. Bust to left, in cap and gown. Around, IOANNES ALOISIVS TVSCA(nus) AVDITOR CAM(erae).

Rev. Neptune in sea-car to front. Around, VICTA IAM NVRSIA FATIS AGITVR

40 mm. A958–220A

The meaning of the reverse, with its reference to Norcia, remains obscure. Toscani was born in Milan, and was a protégé of Francesco Sforza. He went to Rome in 1468. Under Sixtus IV he became consistorial advocate, *ca.* 1473, and in 1477 auditor general.

Literature: Cp. Arm. II, 28, 13; *Corpus*, no. 811 *i*; Cott p. 175; R. Weiss, 'Un umanista e curiale del Quattrocento-Giovanni Alvise Toscani', in *Rivista di storia della Chiesa in Italia*, 12 (1958) pp. 321–333 (for Toscani).

221. *Obv.* Bust to left, wearing round cap. Around, IOHANNES ALOISIVS TVSCANVS ADVOCATVS

Rev. In wreath, PREVENIT AETATEM INGENIVM PRECOX

73 mm. A959–221A

Literature: Cp. Arm. II, 28, II; *Corpus*, no. 812; Cott p. 175; Middeldorf, *Morgenroth* no. 82; Hess/Leu auction, Lucerne, 11 Oct. 1961, lot 991 (another specimen, ex. Kurt Simon coll).

GIOVANNI CANDIDA
(b. before 1450; d. after 1495)

The artist was born Giovanni di Salvatore Filangieri of the branch of Candida, a noble Neapolitan family. He became secretary to Charles the Bold in 1472 and spent his career as a diplomat, becoming secretary to Maximilian and Maria, 1477, settled at the court of France in 1480, and becoming a royal Councillor, 1491. Many medals have been attributed to him, besides those which bear his signature; but they show great variations of style.

MEDALS ATTRIBUTED TO CANDIDA

222. GIOVANNI CANDIDA, the medallist.

Obv. Bust to left, wearing round cap and plain robe. On left and right, IOHANNIS CANDIDA

Without reverse.

Oval, 58 × 48 mm. Four times pierced. A960–222A

Probably the work of Candida himself, although it has also been attributed to Lysippus. A beautiful and sympathetic portrait. Although the *Corpus* describes the fabric as lead it is more probably a tin or lead alloy. It is the only known specimen.

Literature: Les Arts, Aug. 1908, p. 13, no. xvi; Arm. II, 85, 9; *Corpus*, no. 823 *a* (with bibliography); Cott. p. 175 (as Candida ?); Habich, p. 83 (as Lysippus).

223. CHARLES THE BOLD, Duke of Burgundy (1433–67–77).

Obv. Head to right, laureate. Around, DVX KAROLVS BVRGVNDVS

Rev. A ram (the Fleece) couchant between two briquets inscribed VELLVS AVREVM, with a flint darting sparks on either side; above and below, IE LAI EMPRINS BIEN EN AVIENGNE; all on a field semé with sparks, in conventional wreath.

38 mm. A961–223A

According to Tourneur, who accepts Bode's attribution to Candida, this medal was made in 1474 during the siege of Neuss. The duke's motto was 'I have undertaken it, may it succeed'.

Literature: Cp. Arm. II, 40, 1; III, 167 *b*; *Corpus*, no. 828; Cott p. 176 (as Candida ?); Middeldorf, *Morgenroth*, 84 (as Candida). Tervarent, cols. 54, 55 (Briquet); 380 (Golden Fleece).

224. ANTOINE, Grand Bastard of Burgundy (1421–1504).

Obv. Bust to right, hair confined by a fillet. Around, ANTHONIVS B(astardus) DE BVRGVNDIA Moulded border.

Rev. Barbacane discharging its fiery contents; in field, NVL NE SI FROTE. All in wreath.

44 mm. A962–224A

This and the preceding belong to a small, strongly characterized group of medals made at the Burgundian Court between 1472 and 1480, and by many attributed to Candida, though they have little affinity with his signed medals. *Nul ne s'y frotte* ('Let none touch') was the device of Antoine, whose standard was yellow with a blue barbacane.

Collection: His de la Salle (sale, London, Sotheby, 22 Nov. 1880, lot 59)

Literature: Les Arts, Aug. 1908, p. 14, no. vii; cp. Arm. II, 40, 2; *Corpus*, no. 829; Cott p. 176 (as Candida ?). Tervarent, col. 43 (recording a painted portrait of Antoine, with the device).

225. MAXIMILIAN OF AUSTRIA, afterwards Emperor, and MARIA OF BURGUNDY, married 1477, died 1482.

Obv. Bust to right, with long hair, wearing wreath. Around, MAXIMILIANVS FR(ederici) CAES(aris) F(ilius) DVX AVSTR(iae) BVRGVND(iae).

Rev. Bust of Maria to right, behind two M's interlaced and crowned. Around, MARIA KAROLI F(ilia) DVX BVRGVNDIAE AVSTRIAE BRAB(antiae) C(omitissa) FLAN(driae).

48 mm. A963–225A

There exists a very large number of specimens of this charming medal, which was doubtless done for the marriage in 1477. Later, German die-engravers reproduced it in the early sixteenth century in taler form, adding the erroneous date 1479 (cp. also no. 616).

Literature: Cp. Arm. II, 80, 1; *Corpus*, no. 831; Cott p. 176 (as Candida ?); Middeldorf, *Morgenroth*, no. 85 (as Candida); L. Baldass, 'Die Bildnisse Maximilians I', in *Jahrbuch der kunsthistorischen Sammlungen in Wien*, 31 (1925) p. 249.

226. JEAN CARONDELET, President of the Parliament of Burgundy, and his wife MARGUERITE DE CHASSEY, 1479.

Obv. Bust of Carondelet to right, in cap; around, IOHANNES CARONDELETVS PRAES(es) BVRGVND(iae) and, below, 1879.

Rev. Bust of Marguerite to right, wearing pointed head-dress with veil; on right, MARGARITA DE CHASSE

46 mm. After cast. A964–226A

The obverse was made to commemorate Carondelet's nomination to the Presidency on 26 Mar. 1479. He had already been married to Marguerite for 12 or 13 years.

Literature: Cp. Arm. II, 86, 10; *Corpus*, no. 833; Cott p. 176 (as Candida ?)

227. RAIMONDO LAVAGNOLI, Commissary of Saxony in the eleventh or twelfth century.

Obv. Bust to left, in small cap. Around, RAIMVNDVS LAVAGNOLVS COMES ET COMMISSAR(ius) SAXONIE

Rev. Arms of Lavagnoli between the letters R and L. Around, TEMPORE CONRADI IMPER(antis) ANN(O) CRISTI MXLVIII

58 mm. A965–227A

The medal resembles others of Maximilian and Gruthuse which are admittedly by Candida. The portrait is doubtless imaginary, and the man has not been traced. The date ought to be either 1028 (Conrad II) or 1148 (Conrad III).

Literature: *Corpus*, no. 834; cp. Arm. II, 9, 10; Cott p. 176 (as Candida ?).

228. ROBERT BRIÇONNET, Président aux enquêtes.

Obv. Bust to right, in cap. Around, ROB(ertus) BRICONET PARLAMENTI INQVESTAR(um) PRESID(ens).

Rev. MARCET SINE ADVERSARIO VIRTVS

61 mm. Of doubtful age. A966–228A

This medal, even if it be not a contemporary casting, reproduces a medal attributed to Candida, and dating from between 1488 (when probably Briçonnet became *président aux enquêtes*) and 27 Oct. 1493 when he became Archbishop of Reims. There is another, fairly good, specimen in the Paris Cabinet, and a lead after-cast in the British Museum. The motto on the reverse was Briçonnet's device.

Literature: Corpus, no. 837 *c*; cp. Arm. II, 85, 7; Cott p. 176 (as Candida ?).

229. NICOLAS MAUGRAS, Bishop of Uzès, 1483–1503.

Obv. Bust to right, wearing rochet. Around, +NICOLAVS MALEGRASSI EP(iscopu)S VCECIENSIS High rim.

Rev. Arms of Maugras over a crozier. Around, IN VMBRA MANVS SVE PROTEXIT ME D(omi)N(u)S High rim.

84 mm. A967–229A

The attribution to Candida is far from certain, though the work is Italian and shows his influence. Maugras was Bishop of Uzès from 1483 until his death in 1503. The medal is nearer the latter date. The scallop-shells of St James which terminate the inscription on both sides are taken from the bishop's arms.

Literature: Cp. Arm. II, 86, 13; *Corpus*, no. 841; Cott p. 176 (as Candida ?); Middeldorf, *Morgenroth*, no. 86 (as Candida).

230. GIULIANO DELLA ROVERE, afterwards Julius II, and his brother CLEMENTE, Bishop of Mende (1483–1504).

Obv. Bust of Giuliano to right, wearing rochet. Around, IVLIANVS EP(iscopu)S OSTIEN(sis) CAR(dinalis) S(ancti) P(etri) AD VINCVLA

Rev. Bust of Clemente to right, wearing rochet. Around, CLEMENS DE RVVERE EP(iscopu)S MIMATEN(sis).

59 mm. A968–230A

About 1494–1499.

Literature: Corpus, no. 843 *i*; cp. Arm. II, 109, 2; Cott p. 176 (as Candida ?); R. Weiss, 'The medals of Julius II' in Warburg *Journal*, 28 (1965), pp. 163–182 (dating the della Rovere medal to 1494–1499).

SCHOOL OF CANDIDA

Early Sixteenth Century

231. THOMAS BOHIER, Général des Finances of Normandy.

Obv. Bust to right, in cap and gown. Around, THOMAS BOHIER GENERAL DE NORMANDIE; below, MCCCCCIII

Rev. Arms of Thomas Bohier, motto SIL VIENT A POINT

65 mm. Later cast. A969–231A

Thomas Bohier was appointed to the position mentioned in 1496. His motto was 's'il vient à point m'en souviendra'. No original casting of this medal seems to have survived. The original has been attributed to Candida, but was more probably the work of one of his school.

Literature: Cp. Arm. II, 142, 17; *Corpus*, no. 845; Cott p. 176 (as Candida ?); Middeldorf, *Morgenroth*, no. 87 (also later cast; as under the influence of Candida).

232. FRANÇOIS DE VALOIS, afterwards King Francis I, 1504.

Obv. Bust to right, aged ten years, in cap and robe. Around, FRANCOIS DVC DE VALOIS COMTE DANGOLESME AV X AN D(e) S(on) EA(ge).

Rev. Salamander in flames. Around, NOTRISCO AL BVONO STINGO EL REO MCCCCCIIII

65 mm. A970–232A

This is the first appearance of the salamander as the device of Francis I.

Literature: cp. Arm. II, 187, 1; *Corpus*, no. 848; Cott p. 176 (as Candida ?); Tervarent, cols. 333–4 (for the salamander device).

ROMAN SCHOOL UNDER INNOCENT VIII, ALEXANDER VI, AND JULIUS II

233. DON RODRIGO DE BIVAR Y MENDOZA (d. 1523).

Obv. Bust to right, with long hair, wearing cap and cloak. Around, MARCHIO RODERICVS DE BIVAR

Rev. Mars (MARS) and Venus (VENVS) confronted; around, QVORVM OPVS ADEST AETATIS ANO XXVI

35 mm. A971–233A

Hill dated the medal to 1497, interpreting the reverse as an allusion to Don Rodrigo's hope to marry Lucrezia Borgia. Wind however has commented that the type of the reverse is a general reference to the valour and grace of the sitter, so that the medal cannot be dated by either his earlier marriage, 1492, or to his prospective marriage. Armand believed that the medal depicted the Cid.

Literature: Corpus, no. 858 *g*; cp. Arm. III, 152, N; Cott p. 176. Wind p. 87, n. 4, fig. 58 (on reverse type).

234. MARCELLO CAPODIFERRO.

Obv. Bust to right, in cap and robe. Around, MARCELLVS DE CAPODEFERRO

Rev. Ox. Around, MERCVRIALIVM HOSPES VIRORVM

36 mm. A972–234A

Marcello Capodiferro, a Roman noble and student of history. He was one of the Conservatori in 1478. The ox is taken from his arms, the legend is adapted from Horace.

Literature: Corpus, no. 861 *e*; cp. Arm. II, 128, 5; III, 178, c; Cott p. 176.

235. BERNARDINO CARVAJAL, Cardinal of Santa Croce 1493, deposed 1511, restored 1513, died 1522.

Obv. Bust to right, in cap and cape with hood. Around, BERNARDINVS CARVAIAL CARD(inalis) S(anctae) + (Crucis).

Rev. Philosophy standing to front, wearing crown, veil, and voluminous mantle, holding MSS. and sceptre; from her breast to her feet descends a ladder, with Θ at top, P at bottom. Around, QVI ME DILVCIDANT VITAM ETERNAM HABEB(unt).

43 mm. A973–235A

The P was taken by Armand for an artist's signature. The type illustrates the vision seen by Boethius, the two letters indicating Theoretical and Practical Philosophy. The medal was probably made in Rome, about the same time as that of Don Rodrigo de Bivar (no. 233). A superior specimen is in the Victoria and Albert Museum.

Literature: Corpus, no. 862 *c*; cp. Arm. I, p. 122; Cott p. 176.

236. DOMENICO GRIMANI, Cardinal, 1493–1523.

Obv. Bust to left, sharply pointed, in vestment. Around, DOMINICVS CARDINALIS GRIMANVS

Rev. Theology (THEOLOGIA), standing before a palm-tree, takes by the hand Philosophy (PHILOSOPHIA), who is seated reading a book under a tree, and points to a radiant cloud.

53 mm. A974–236A

Often wrongly attributed to Gambello, who made and signed another medal of the same man. This was perhaps made in Rome about 1493.

Literature: Cp. Arm. I, 116, 7; II, p. 293; *Corpus*, no. 863; Middeldorf, *Morgenroth*, no. 88; Cott p. 176.

237. GUILLAUME DE POITIERS, Marquis de Cotrone (d. 1503).

Obv. Bust to left, with long hair, wearing cap and gown. Around, GVLIERMVS M(arquis) DE POITIERS Below, two left hands clasped.

Rev. Mercury, with caduceus, taking the hand of a female figure, holding cornucopiae, and probably representing the Church. Around, border of cornuacopiae from which issue flames or water.

57 mm. A975–237A

Probably made at Rome in 1489, when Guillaume de Poitiers, Marquis de Cotrone (Calabria), came as French Ambassador to the Pope. The two hands on the obverse must allude to his mission, as also the reverse. The figure of the Church resembles that on the medal of Constantine by Cristoforo di Geremia (no. 211).

Literature: Cp. Arm. II, 87, 15; *Corpus*, no. 864; Cott p. 176/7.

238. JULIUS, II, Pope, 1503–13.

Obv. Bust to right, wearing cope. Around, IVLIVS CAESAR PONT(ifex) II

Rev. Shield of Rovere ensigned with crossed-keys and tiara. Around, BENEDI(c)T(us) QVI VENIT I(n) NO(mine) D(omini).

31 mm. Struck. A976–238A

The medal was issued in Rome to commemorate the triumphal return of the Pope from Bologna in March 1507.

Literature: Cp. Arm. II, 110, 4; *Corpus*, no. 874 (where the reading should be corrected in the light of this specimen); Cott p. 177. Weiss, 'The medals of Pope Julius II (1503–1513)', in Warburg *Journal*, 28 (1965) pp. 163–182 (at p. 180).

ROMAN SCHOOL UNDER LEO X

239. LEO X, Pope, 1513–21.

Obv. Bust to left, in skull-cap and cape. Around, LEO X P(ontifex) MAX(imus). Moulded border.

Rev. Medici arms ensigned with crossed-keys and tiara. Around, GLORIA ET HONORE CORONASTI EV(m) DE(us). Moulded border.

78 mm. A977–239A

This and the following medal are the work of an artist working about 1513–15, who may be called, from the subject of his chief medals, the master of the Medici Restoration. The reverse legend is from Ps. viii. 6.

Literature: Cp. Arm. I, 159, 10; *Corpus*, no. 880; Cott p. 177.

240. GIULIANO II DE' MEDICI, Duc de Nemours (1478–1516).

Obv. Bust to left, in cap and robe. Around, IVLIANVS MEDICES L(aurentii) F(ilius) P(atricius) R(omanus). Moulded border.

Rev. Florence lying under a tree, leaning on Medici shield. Around, RECONCILIATIS CIVIBVS MAGNIFICENTIA E(t) PIETATE Moulded border.

77 mm. A978–240A

Evidently by the same hand as the medal of Leo X (no. 239). Giuliano was made a patrician of Rome on 13 Sept. 1513. The medal alludes to the entry of Giuliano into Florence in September of the preceding year.

Literature: Corpus, no. 881 *f*; cp. Arm. II, p. 94 note; Cott p. 177.

241. *Obv*. Head to left. Around, MAG(nus) IVLIANVS MEDICES

Rev. Roma seated on shields, holding Victory; below, ROMA; in field, C(onsensu) P(opuli).

34 mm. Gilt on reverse. A979–241A

This and other medals were made for distribution to the crowds at the festivities celebrating the adoption of Giuliano as citizen and baron of Rome, 1513.

Literature: Corpus, no. 889 *f*; Middeldorf, *Morgenroth*, no. 90; Cott p. 177.

ROMAN SCHOOL

About 1500

242. GIROLAMO ARSAGO, Bishop of Nice, 1511–1542.

Obv. Bust to left, wearing cape with small hood. Around, HIER(onymus) ARSAGVS EP(iscopu)S NICIEN(sis) IVLII II ALVMNVS

Rev. POST IVLII II CINERES MDXIII

45 mm. A980–242A

Literature: Arm. II, 128, 2; *Corpus*, no. 890 *b*; Cott p. 177.

243. JESUS CHRIST.

Obv. Bust to left, nimbate. Around, IHS XPC SALVATOR MVNDI

Rev. In wreath, inscription TV ES CHRISTVS FILIVS DEI VIVI QVI INHVNC MVNDVM VENISTI

90 mm. A981–243A

One of the medals, probably made in Rome or Florence, of which the earlier versions pretend to reproduce an ancient cameo with portraits of Christ and St Paul, which was sent to Innocent VIII by the Sultan about 1492. The type of the portrait is probably derived from some Flemish painting; this version of the medal may be of about 1500 or a little later. The reverse legend is from St John xi. 27.

Literature: Cp. *Corpus*, no. 901 *b*; Cott p. 177; Middeldorf, *Morgenroth*, no. 92 (with reference to a woodcut by Hans Burgkmair, after the medal): Hill, *Medallic portraits of Christ*, Oxford, 1920, pp. 20–22, fig. 10.

244. ST PAUL.

Obv. Bust to right, nimbate. Around, VAS ELECTIONIS PAVLVS APOSTOLVS

Rev. In wreath, inscription BENEDICITE IN EXCELSIS DEO DOMINO DE FONTIBVS ISRAEL IBI BENIAMIM ADOLESCENTVLVS IN MENTIS EXCESSV

88 mm. A982–244A

A companion piece to the preceding. The reverse inscription is from Ps. lxvii, 27–8. For *vas electionis* see Acts ix, 15.

Literature: Cp. Arm. II, 7, 4; *Corpus*, no. 902; Cott p. 177; Hill, *Medallic portraits of Christ*, Oxford, 1920, p. 22, fig. 11.

FLORENTINE SCHOOL

About 1464–1470

245. COSIMO DE' MEDICI, Pater Patriae (1389–1464).

Obv. Bust to left, in flat cap. Around, MAGNVS COSMVS MEDICES P P P

Rev. Florence seated, holding orb and triple olive-branch. Around, PAX LIBERTAS QVE PVBLICA and, below, FLORENTIA

75 mm. Later cast. A983–245A

A cast of this medal in gesso is let into the hand of the Botticellesque portrait of a young man in the Uffizi. It was copied from, or was imitated in, the marble relief portrait at Berlin; and it was the basis of the Bronzino portrait in the Uffizi inscribed *Cosmus Medices P P P*. It was made later than 16 Mar. 1465 when the deceased Cosimo received the title Pater Patriae; but it is copied in miniature by Antonio del Cherico in a MS. in the Laurentian Library, which, since it was done for Piero di Cosimo de' Medici, who died in 1469, is earlier than that year. P P P may be explained as *Princeps* (or *Primus*) *Pater Patriae*.

Literature: Heiss, *Florence*, i, p. 29, no. 3, pl. i, 2; *Corpus*, no. 909 *h*; cp. Arm. II, 23, 3; Middeldorf, *Morgenroth*, no. 93; Cott p. 177.

246. *Obv*. Bust to left, in flat cap (different from preceding). Around, COSMVS MEDICES DECRETO PVBLICO P(ater) P(atriae).

Rev. Similar to preceding.

78 mm. A984–246A

This medal, like the preceding, is later than 16 Mar. 1465. The work is in the neighbourhood of Niccolò Fiorentino, and is probably not by the same hand as the preceding piece. The O in PVBLICO is over an erasure, where P probably stood before.

Literature: Arm. II, 23, 2; Heiss, *Florence*, i, p. 29, no. 1, pl. i, 1; *Corpus*, no. 910 *i*; Cott p. 177.

247. *Obv.* Bust to left, in flat cap. Around, COSMVS MEDICES DECRETO PVBLICO P(ater) P(atriae).

Rev. Florence (FLORENTIA) seated, as on no. 245. Around, PAX LIBERTASQVE PVBLICA

37 mm. A985–247A

Like most of the extant specimens, this is cast; but the original was struck, and it is probable that it was the work of some later restorer of Medici portraits, which are known to have been in demand at least until the mid eighteenth century (see no. 483). The inscription is taken from one of the two larger medals of Cosimo, the bust from the other. There is a shell-cameo at Florence closely resembling this piece.

Literature: Corpus, no. 910 *bis j*; Heiss, *Florence*, i, p. 29, no. 2, pl. i, 3; cp. Arm. I, 10, 32; II, 23, 1; Cott p. 177.

BERTOLDO DI GIOVANNI
(b. *ca.* 1420; d. 1491)

Bertoldo was trained by Donatello, and appears to have worked exclusively in bronze as a medallist and maker of statuettes and reliefs. Only one medal (no. 248) is signed by him but his style is evident in a number of others. For a relief by him see Pope-Hennessy, *Kress Bronzes*, no. 45.

248. MOHAMMAD II, Sultan of Turkey (1430–51–1481).

Obv. Bust to left in turban, crescent suspended round neck. Around, MAVMHET ASIE AC TRAPESVNZIS MAGNEQVE GRETIE IMPERAT(or).

Rev. Triumphal car; Mars leads the horses; on the car, a man carrying a small figure and holding a cord which confines a group of three nude crowned women symbolizing Greece, Trebizond, and Asia (GRETIE, TRAPESVNTY, ASIE). On the side of the car, the Siege Perilous. Below, OPVS BERTOLDI FLORENTIN(i) SCVLTORIS between two reclining figures of the Sea (with trident) and the Earth (with cornucopiae).

94 mm. A986–248A

According to Jacobs the medal dates from March, April, or early May 1480. The reverse seems to allude to preparations in which Bertoldo's patron Lorenzo de' Medici was interested, for an attack on South Italy (Magna Gretie). The figure on the car represents the Sultan, bearing on his hand a small figure of *Bonus Eventus*, making a libation. The Siege Perilous was a device of Alfonso V. Babinger suggests that the Bertoldo portrait depends either on that by Costanzo da Ferrara, or on some other model which was also used by Gentile Bellini. The Bertoldo does not depend on the Bellini medal.

Literature: Les Arts, Aug. 1908, p. 8, no. vii; *Corpus*, no. 911 *i*; cp. Arm. I, 76, 1; Middeldorf, *Morgenroth* no. 94; Cott p. 177; E. Jacobs, 'Die Mehemmed-Medaille des Bertoldo', in *Jahrbuch der Preussischen Kunstsammlungen*, 48 (1927) pp. 1–17; F. Babinger, *Mehmed der Eroberer und seine Zeit*, Munich, 1953, pp. 425–6 (Bertoldo and Bellini); p. 554 (Bertoldo and Costanzo).

249. FREDERICK III, Emperor (1415–52–93).

Obv. Bust to left, in hat and furred robe. Around, FREDERICVS TERCIVS ROMANORVM IMPERATOR SEMPER AVGVSTVS

Rev. The Emperor, Pope, and Cardinals on horseback, with suite on foot, meeting on the Ponte Sant' Angelo. On the parapet, CXXII EQVITES CREAT(i) KALENDI(s) IANVARI(is) MCCCCLXIX Moulded border.

55 mm. A987–249A

Commemorating the Emperor's visit to Rome at Christmas 1468 and his creation of a number of knights on 1 Jan. 1469. The attribution to Bertoldo is due to Bode. To the specimens listed in the *Corpus* may be added one in Oxford.

Literature: Corpus, no. 912 *j*; cp. Arm. II, 39, 1; Cott p. 177.

250. ANTONIO GRATIADEI (d. 1491), Imperial envoy.

Obv. Bust to right, wearing cap and loosely rendered robe. Around, ANTONIVS GRATIA DEI CESAREVS ORATOR and, below, MORTALIVM CVRA

Rev. Triumphal car drawn by a prancing lion, ridden by a female torch-bearer, and checked by a man. In the car Mercury, on basis, blowing trumpet and surrounded by nine dancing Muses; at back, Mars (?). Above, in the air, Luna holding crescent and the Sun in his car. Below, VOLENTEM DVCVNT NOLENTEM TRAHVNT

61 mm. A988–250A

Antonio Gratiadei, Venetian friar minor, theologian, astrologer, and orator, came to Rome in Jan. 1481; on his way he stayed in Florence, when the medal was doubtless made, towards the end of 1480. The motto, from Seneca, *Ep.* 107, refers to Gratiadei's astrological studies. The resemblance to Bertoldo's work was noticed by Friedländer and the attribution definitely made by Bode. It has all the marks of his style. There is another medal of Gratiadei, quite different, by Candida.

Literature: Arm. I, 106, 2; Heiss 'Jean de Candida' in *Rev. Num.*, 8 (1890) at p. 465, no. 10; pl. xi, 3; *Corpus*, no. 913 *d*; Cott p. 177.

251. FILIPPO DE' MEDICI, Archbishop of Pisa 1462–74.

Obv. Bust to left in rochet; below, Medici shield; inscription: PHYLIPPVS DE MEDICIS ARCHIEPISCHOPVS PISANVS all in wreath made of a plant ('Solomon's seal' ?); at sides, on a ribbon, VIRTVTE SVPERA

Rev. The Last Judgement. Below, ET IN CARNE MEA VIDEBO DEVM SALVATOREM MEVM

55 mm. A989–251A

The attribution to Bertoldo, which is due to Bode *Bertoldo*, is generally accepted.

Literature: Les Arts, Aug. 1908, p. 13, no. vi; cp. Arm. I, II, 33; *Corpus*, no. 914; Cott p. 177.

252. LORENZO and GIULIANO DE' MEDICI; the Pazzi Conspiracy, 1478.

Obv. Bust of Lorenzo (LAVRENTIVS MEDICES) nearly in profile to right, placed above the Choir of the Duomo, Florence; within, priests celebrating Mass; outside, conspirators attacking Lorenzo; below the bust, SALVS PVBLICA

Rev. Bust of Giuliano (IVLIANVS MEDICES) nearly in profile to left, over the Choir of the Duomo, where Mass is being celebrated; outside it, his murder; below the bust, LVCTVS PVBLICVS

66 mm. A990–252A

Giuliano was murdered in the conspiracy of 26 Apr. 1478. This medal, which was attributed to Bertoldo by Bode for convincing reasons of style, was cast from Bertoldo's model by Andrea Guacialoti in Sept. 1478. The portraits were probably copied from paintings, perhaps by Botticelli.

Literature: Cp. Arm. I, 59, 1; *Corpus*, no. 915; Middeldorf, *Morgenroth*, no. 95; Cott p. 177.

253. LORENZO DE' MEDICI, il Magnifico (1448–1492).

Obv. Head to right; around, LAVRENTIVS MEDICES

Rev. Male figure in antique armour standing, resting on spear, sword in left hand; at his feet a figure and two river-gods, reclining with elbows on urns from which water flows. Around, OB CIVES SERVATOS and, below, AGITIS IN FATVM

33 mm. A991–253A

The resemblance in style to the Pazzi medal (no. 252) was already noted by Armand. The reverse, the exact reference of which is obscure, is inspired by a sestertius of Trajan.

Collection: His de la Salle (sale, London, Sotheby, 22 Nov. 1880, lot 130)

Literature: Cp. Arm. I, 59, 2; *Corpus*, no. 916 *i*; Cott, p. 178; Hill 'Classical influence on the Italian medal', in *Burl. Mag.*, 18 (1911) pp. 259–68 (at p. 262; pl. I, 7, medal, and 6, sestertius).

254. HERCULES and DEIANIRA.

[*Obv.* Bust to left of Francesco Diedo, wearing cap and robe with sash; around, F(ranciscus) DIEDVS LITERAR(um) ET IVSTITIE CVLTOR; below, SE(nator) VE(netus).]

Rev. Hercules, wearing lion-skin and carrying club, pursues the Centaur Nessus, who escapes to left carrying Deianira on his back; in background, on a high rock, a figure (Virtus ?) on a seat supported by a lion and an ox. Inscription: DVCE VIRTVTE and MCCCCLXXV

82 mm. Bronze gilt. After cast. A992–254A

The reverse of this piece has every mark of Bertoldo's style, and was accepted as his work by Bode *Bertoldo* p. 31 *f.* It is, however, only known in combination with an obverse which is almost certainly a good deal later (though Diedo himself died in 1483 or 1484), and has nothing to do with Bertoldo. The only other known specimen is at Turin.

Literature: Cp. Arm. II, 71, 6; *Corpus*, no. 918 *b*; Cott p. 178. *Corpus* no. 506 for the obverse).

255. (See no. 297 *a*).

NICCOLÒ DI FORZORE SPINELLI (b. 1430; d. 1514)

Called Niccolò Fiorentino. Born at Florence on 23 April 1430 and died there in April 1514. He worked in Flanders as seal-engraver in 1468; but his chief work was as medallist. He signed five medals, but an immense number of others, some of them much finer than the signed pieces, have been attributed to him on grounds of style. He is a great portraitist, but took little pains about the composition of his reverses, being frequently content to borrow motives from the antique. Next to Pisanello, however, he and his school provide the most satisfactory series of medallic portraits of Italians of the fifteenth century. See *Corpus*, pp. 243–46; Hill in Thieme-Becker 31 (1937), pp. 387–8.

256. ALFONSO I D'ESTE, afterwards Duke of Ferrara (1476–1505–34).

Obv. Bust to right, with long hair, wearing small cap. Inscription: ALFONSVS ESTENSIS

Rev. Alfonso (?) in triumphal car. Around, OPVS NICOLAI FLORENTINI MCCCCLXXXXII

71 mm. A994–256A

In 1492 the artist was paid 18 lire for composing this medal. The Marquess came to Florence on 2 April of that year on his way to Rome. The horses of the reverse are lifted directly from the Naples cameo by Athenion of Jupiter thundering against the giants.

Literature: Les Arts, Aug. 1908, p. 8, no. iv: cp. Arm. I, 84, 1; F. Malaguzzi Valeri, *La Corte di Lodovico il Moro*, vol. I

(Milan, 1913), p. 54; *Corpus*, no. 923 *f*; Cott p. 178. A. Furtwängler, *Die antiken Gemmen*, vol. I (Leipzig/Berlin, 1900) pl. lvii, 2 (for the cameo at Naples).

257. See Appendix.

ATTRIBUTED TO NICCOLÒ FIORENTINO

258. INNOCENT VIII, Pope, 1484–92.

Obv. Bust to left in cope. Around, INNOCENTII IANVENSIS VIII PONT(ifex) MAX(imus).

Rev. Justice, Peace, and Abundance. Around, IVSTITIA PAX COPIA

54 mm. A996–258A

Various attributions have been suggested for the authorship of this medal; all that can be said with certainty is that it shows strong Florentine affinities, and might have been made by Niccolò Fiorentino. Many medals of about 1480–6 in his manner represent Romans. This is a reduced version of a larger medal with the same designs. The reverse refers to the Pope's love of peace, and to the doles of corn by which he appeased the indignation roused by the severity of his police-measures.

Collection: His de la Salle (sale, London, Sotheby, 22 Nov. 1880, lot 49).

Literature: Corpus, no. 928 *f*; cp. Arm. I, 60, 5; Cott p. 178 (as Fiorentino ?); Middeldorf, *Morgenroth*, no. 98.

259. GUGLIELMO BATONATTI.

Obv. Bust to left, wearing cap. Around, GVILIELMVS BATONATTI [ET]AT(is) SVE AN(n)O 37

Rev. In a wreath, unicorn springing to left; above, a tau-cross.

38 mm. A997–259A

Other specimens in the British Museum and at Grenoble. By his dress, Batonatti is doubtless a clerk of the Roman curia; by the cross on the reverse, probably a Canon Regular of the Hospitallers of St Anthony Abbot.

Literature: Arm. II, 76, 15; *Corpus*, no. 930 *c*; Cott p. 178 (as Fiorentino ?).

260. BERNARDINO GAMBERIA, private chamberlain of Innocent VIII.

Obv. Bust to left, wearing round cap. Around, BER(nardinus) GAMB(eria) INNOCENTII VIII C(ubicularius) S(ecretus) AN(no) XXX 1485

Rev. God the Father in clouds. Below, SATIABOR CV(m) APPARVERIT

61 mm. A998–260A

Gamberia became Bishop of Cavaillon in 1501 and died in 1507. The reverse is found attached to, and seems to have been made for, a Netherlandish medal of Nicolas Perrenot; it seems to have nothing to do with Gamberia.

Literature: Cp. Arm. II, 64, 15; III, 180, *d*; *Corpus*, no. 933; Cott p. 178 (as Fiorentino ?).

261. RINALDO ORSINI, Archbishop of Florence 1474–1510.

Obv. Bust to left, wearing vestment. Around, RAYNALDVS DE VRSINIS ARCHIEPISCOPVS FLOREN(tinus).

Rev. Fortune seated, holding rudder and cornucopiae. Around, BENE FACERE ET LETARI and, below, FORT(una) RED(ux).

60 mm. A999–261A

The reverse may refer to the return of the archbishop from Rome to Florence in 1485. In style the medal falls into line with the group which it has been supposed that Niccolò Fiorentino made in Rome about that time.

Literature: Cp. Arm. I, 86, 8; *Corpus*, no. 937; Cott p. 178 (as Fiorentino ?); Münzen und Medaillen auction XVII, Basel, 2 Dec. 1957, lot 102, pl. 12 (specimen, 59 mm).

262. CHARLES VIII of France (1470–83–98).

Obv. Bust to left, wearing cap, and collar with pendant of St Michael over robe. Around, KAROLVS OCTAVVS FRANCORVM IERVSALEN ET CICILIE REX

Without reverse.

95 mm. Three piercings. A1000–262A

This is a fine enough casting, but represents only the portrait side; on the reverse should be the car of Victory led by Peace. The medal was made about 1494–5, during the expedition to Italy, when a Florentine artist, generally supposed to be Niccolò Fiorentino, produced a number of remarkable medals of Frenchmen.

Literature: Corpus, no. 945 *d*; cp. Arm, I, 89, 22; Cott p. 178 (as Fiorentino ?); Phillips, in *The Metropolitan Museum of Art Bulletin*, New York, Nov. 1950, p. 80 (specimen formerly Pierpont Morgan collection).

263. JEAN DU MAS DE L'ISLE, Councillor of Charles VIII, died 1495.

Obv. Bust to left, wearing robe. Around, IO(annes) DVMAS CHEVALIER S(eigneu)R DELISLE ET DE BANNEGON CHAMBELLAN DV ROY

Rev. Jean Du Mas, in armour, riding left, carrying bâton, on a horse wearing chanfron and bardings with arms of the sitter. Above PRESIT DECVS

88·5 mm. A1001–263A

Made in Florence, about 1494–5, like the medal of Charles VIII preceding. The sitter died at Florence in the autumn of 1495.

Literature: Corpus, no. 949; cp. Arm. I, 90, 25; Cott p. 178 (as Fiorentino ?); Middeldorf, *Morgenroth*, no. 100.

IN THE MANNER OF NICCOLÒ FIORENTINO

About 1485–1500

264. LIONORA ALTOVITI.

Obv. Bust to left, with pointed jewel on breast of dress. Around, LIONORA DE ALTOVITI

Without reverse.

70 mm. Late cast. A1002–264A

There are no early casts extant of this medal, which may have been made for the marriage in 1487 of Lionora or Dianora, daughter of Rinaldo Altoviti, to Antonio Altoviti.

Literature: Cp. Arm. II, 49, 6; *Corpus*, no. 955; Cott p. 178 (as manner of Fiorentino).

265. FRA ALBERTO BELLI (d. 1482).

Obv. Bust to left, wearing rochet, and hood over head. Around, AN IDEO TIBI BELLVS QVIA FAVSTO NOMINE VOCARIS

Rev. Faith (FIDES), holding chalice with wafer, and cross.

56 mm. A1003–265A

The inscription seems not quite certainly to identify the person with Fra Alberto Belli, canon of Ferrara, who died there in 1482. The medal, however, may have been made later, about 1497, when the Savonarola medals were popular.

Literature: Cp. Arm. I, 85, 5; *Corpus*, no. 959; Cott p. 178 (as manner of Fiorentino).

266. ANTONIO DI DANTE CASTIGLIONE.

Obv. Bust to left wearing round cap. Around, ANTONIVS FLO(rentinus) DANTIS F(ilius) DE CASTILIONIO

Without reverse.

69 mm. A1004–266A

The only known specimen.

Literature: Arm. I, 94, 6; Heiss, *Florence*, i, p. 83, pl. xi, 3; Habich, pl. xlii, 4; *Corpus*, no. 963 *a*; Cott p. 179 (as manner of Fiorentino).

267. ERCOLE I D'ESTE (1431–1505), Duke of Ferrara and Modena 1471.

Obv. Bust to left, elderly, wearing cap and armour. Around, HERCVLES DVX FERA(riae) MV(tine) ET(cetera)

Rev. Minerva (MINERVA) standing to front, resting on spear and shield.

51 mm. A1005–267A

About 1490–5. Ercole was born in 1431.

Literature: Corpus, no. 971 *b*; cp. Arm. II, 44, 3; Cott p. 179 (as manner of Fiorentino).

268. MARSILIO FICINO of Florence, humanist (1433–99).

Obv. Bust to left, wearing cap. Around, MARSILIVS FICINVS FLORENTINVS

Rev. PLATONE across field.

55 mm. A1006–268A

Shortly before 1499.

Literature: Cp. Arm. II, 49, 8; *Corpus*, no. 974; Cott p. 179 (as manner of Fiorentino); Middeldorf, *Morgenroth*, no. 101 (*Corpus*, 974 *i*).

269. PIETRO MACHIAVELLI (1460/61–1519).

Obv. Bust to left, with long hair. Around, PETRVS DE MACHIAVELIIS ZA(nobi) FI(lius)

Rev. Eagle with wings displayed standing on a stump, to which is fastened the Machiavelli shield.

73 mm. A1007–269A

About 1480–5, if, as it is said, Pietro, the son of a painter Zanobi, was born in 1460 or 1461. This is the only recorded specimen.

Literature: Les Arts, Aug. 1908, p. 11, no. vii; Arm. I, 97, 4; Heiss, *Florence*, i, p. 76, pl. ix, 1; *Corpus*, no. 982 *a*; Cott p. 179 (as manner of Fiorentino).

270. ROBERTO DI RUGGIERO DE' MACINGHI.

Obv. Bust to right, with long hair, wearing cap and gown; around, ROBERTVS MACINGIVS 1495

Rev. Nude female figure, holding a round conical shield and a peacock by its neck; above, VIGILANTIA

33 mm. The only specimen known. A1008–270A

The marks under the bust were read by Hill as being clearly a date; the last figure, 5, is made thus ç. The larger medal of this man was made in 1498.

Literature: Corpus, no. 984 *a*; Cott p. 179 (as manner of Fiorentino).

271. LORENZO DE' MEDICI, il Magnifico (1448–1492).

Obv. Bust of Lorenzo to left, with long hair, wearing robe.

Without reverse.

35 mm. A1009–271A

The other known specimen (Berlin) has the inscription MAGNVS LAVRENTIVS MEDICES This medal is the smaller of two reductions, made doubtless for popular purposes, from the large medal signed by Niccolò Fiorentino.

Literature: Les Arts, Aug. 1908, p. 13, no. xv; Arm. I, 85, 6; Heiss, *Niccolò Spinelli*, p. 21, no. 6, pl. ii, 2; *Corpus*, no. 988 *b*; Cott p. 179 (as manner of Fiorentino).

272. MARIA DE' MUCINI.

Obv. Bust to left. Around, MARIA DE MVCINY

Rev. Eagle or falcon on an armillary sphere, resting on a blazing frame-work; across the field, on a scroll, EXPECTO; below, a dog (for trustworthiness) with scroll ASSIDVVS and a lamb (for gentleness) with scroll MITIS ESTO; behind the dog, a pomegranate; field semé with plumes.

90 mm. A1010–272A

Of the two other known specimens, that at Berlin is inferior, that at Florence a modern cast. The lady is unidentified. The reverse is an allegory, of which other versions, equally obscure, are found on medals of this school; they are intended to remind us that the end of life is inevitable.

Literature: Les Arts, Aug. 1908, p. 11, no. vi. Arm. I, 97, 5. Heiss, *Florence*, i, p. 76, pl. ix, 2. Rodocanachi, *La femme italienne*, p. 40. Habich, pl. xlv, 2. *Corpus*, no. 991 *c*; Cott p. 179 (as manner of Fiorentino).

273. RUBERTO DI BERNARDO NASI.

Obv. Youthful bust to left, with long hair, wearing cap. Around, RVBERTO DI BERNARDO NASI

Rev. Virginity tying Love to a tree; between them, unicorn (for innocence) lying on the ground. Around, VIRGINITAS AMORIS FRENVM

55 mm. A1011–273A

The reverse is borrowed from the medal of Costanza Rucellai (no. 281). The date is probably about 1495, Ruberto having been born in 1479. He was prior of liberty in 1513.
Other specimens at Berlin and Paris.

Collection: Signol (sale, Paris, 1 April 1878, lot 164).

Literature: Corpus, no. 992; cp. Arm. II, 50, 11; Cott p. 179 (as manner of Fiorentino). Tervarent, cols. 19v (conquered Love); 237, ii (Unicorn).

274. See Appendix.

275. See Appendix.

276. COSTANZA BENTIVOGLIO, wife of Antonio Pico della Mirandola, married 1473, Countess of Concordia 1483.

Obv. Bust to left, wearing coif. Around, CONSTANTIA BENTIVOLA DE LA MIRAN(dula) CONCOR(diae) COMIT(issa).

Rev. Constancy standing to front, leaning on tall staff and column. Below, CONSTANTIA

59 mm. A1014–276A

The reverse is a loan from the medal of Paolo Dotti (no. 214). The medal is after 1483, when Antonio obtained the fief of Concordia.

Literature: Corpus, no. 997; cp. Arm. I, 51, 12; Cott p. 179 (as manner of Fiorentino); Wind, p. 74 *n* (reverse type a combination of the attributes of Constantia and Concordia).

277. GIOVANNI PICO DELLA MIRANDOLA, philosopher and poet (1463–94).

Obv. Bust to right, with long hair, wearing cuirass (?) with winged mask on breast. Around, IOANNES PICVS MIRANDVLENSIS

Rev. The three Graces. Around, PVLCRITVDO AMMOR VOLVPTAS

81 mm. Late cast. A1015–277A

ca. 1484–5.

Only poor casts of this version of the medal are known. While the other version (*Corpus*, no. 998 *A*) represents a portrait doctored in seventeenth-century style, though the reverse has been left alone, this version renders better the original character of the portrait, but the reverse has been retouched.

Literature: cp. Arm. I, 86, 9; cp. *Corpus*, no. 998 *B*; Cott, p. 179 (as manner of Fiorentino); Wind, pp. 49, 67 (suggesting the date for the medal, and that the reverse legend comes from Ficino, and is a reference to a trinitarian philosophy of love).

278. ANTONIO PIZZAMANI (1462–1512), Venetian scholar and protonotary apostolic.

Obv. Bust to left, with long hair, wearing cap and robe. Around, ANTONII PIZAMANI

Rev. Half-figures to front of Felicity, holding a peacock (?), Fame, helmeted, with trumpet, and Virtus, holding palm-branch. Above, FOELICITAS VIRTVS FAMA

61 mm. A1016–278A

Born in 1462, Pizzamani became Bishop of Feltre in 1504 and died in 1512. He was associated as a student in Florence with Giovanni Pico della Mirandola and Politian. The medal may be dated about 1490.
There is another specimen in Berlin.

Literature: Les Arts, Aug. 1908, p. 13, no. xvii; Arm. II, 77 19; III, 182, D; Heiss, *Florence*, i, p. 62, pl. v. 8; *Corpus*, no. 1000 *b*; Cott p. 179 (as manner of Fiorentino).

279. ANGELO POLIZIANO (1454–94) and MARIA POLIZIANA.

Obv. Bust of Politian to left, wearing cap. Around, ANGELI POLITIANI

Rev. Bust of Maria Poliziana to left, hair coiled at back of head. Around, MARIA POLITIANA

55 mm. Late cast. A1017–279A

Maria was probably the sister of the humanist, who was born in 1454 and died in 1494; the medal cannot be far from the latter date.

Literature: Cp. Arm. I, 86, 11; *Corpus*, no. 1002; Cott p. 179 (as manner of Fiorentino).

280. MARIA POLIZIANA.

Obv. Bust to left, with long hair. Around, incised, MARIA POLITIANA

Rev. Constancy standing to left, nude but for scarf, one end of which, together with an arrow (?), is held in her raised right hand; she leans on a bundle of arrows bound with a ribbon. Below, CONSTA(n)TIA

58 mm. Late cast. A1018–280A

Another specimen is in the British Museum; a third belonged to Heiss. The reverse is perhaps a complimentary borrowing from that of the medal of Costanza Bentivoglio, the image being a combination of the attributes of Constantia and Concordia.

Literature: Arm. I, 87, 13; Rodocanachi, *La femme italienne*, p. 40; *Corpus*, no. 1005 *b*; Cott p. 179 (as manner of Fiorentino); Wind, p. 74 *n* (on derivation from Costanza Bentivoglio's medal, and the meaning of the image as a martial and amiable type).

281. COSTANZA RUCELLAI.

Obv. Bust to left, hair in small coif; jewel on cord round neck. Around, COSTANTIA ORICELLARIA H(i)E(ronymi) ET FR(anciscae) FILLIA

Rev. Virginity tying Love to a tree; between them, unicorn (for Innocence) lying on the ground. Around, VIRGINITAS AMORIS FRENVM

55 mm. A1019–281A

The abbreviation HE is probably an error for HIE; Costanza would then be a daughter of Girolamo Rucellai who in 1471 married Francesca Dini. The medal, judging from the hair-dressing, seems to date from about 1485–90.

Literature: Cp. Arm. II, 50, 12; *Corpus*, no. 1011; Cott p. 180. Tervarent, cols. 19v (conquered Love); 237, ii (Unicorn).

282. GIROLAMO SAVONAROLA, Dominican preacher (1452–98).

Obv. Bust to left, in habit with hood raised. Around, HIERONYMVS SAVO(narola) FER(rariensis) VIR DOCTISS(imu)S ORDINIS PREDICHATORVM

Rev. Map of Italy, showing the chief cities (marked with their initials); above, issuing from a cloud, the hand of God threatens the land with a dagger. Around, GLADIVS DOMINI SVP(er) TERAM CITO ET VELOCITER

95 mm. A1020–282A

The only other specimen recorded was in the Cabinet of the late Dr. Hofstede de Groot. This is the best of the many medals of Savonarola, not excepting the better known one which is based on the cornelian intaglio by Giovanni delle Corniole. It probably dates from about 1497, when it is recorded that many medals of Savonarola were cast, bearing the text of his prophecy of the sword of the Lord (the French invasion).

The inscription and the reverse image derive from a dream recorded by Savonarola. Professor Middeldorf (private communication) has identified a maiolica portrait roundel of Savonarola in the Musée des Beaux-Arts, Lille (Wicar collection, diam. 7·5 cm.) as an original portrait by one of the sons of Andrea della Robbia, who became Dominicans, followers of Savonarola, and are recorded in two early sources as having made portraits of the preacher. Hill (*Corpus* p. 277) denies that the medals of Savonarola are by these two della Robbia artists, and suggests that the medals only derive from the type which they created. The Wicar roundel has not been illustrated. The portrait type differs from this medal and is closer to the portrait type of the intaglio and the paintings by Fra Bartolommeo. A photograph of the Wicar roundel is in the Warburg Institute, London. Middeldorf has also recorded that a terracotta cast of the obverse of a Savonarola medal (*Corpus* no. 1076) was formerly in the Fairfax Murray collection, and at Messrs Bruscoli, Florence.

Literature: Arm. II, 46, 17; Heiss, *Niccolò Spinelli*, p. 69 no. 3, pl. vii, 1; *Les Arts*, Aug. 1908, p. 8, no. v; *Corpus*, no. 1075 *a*; Cott p. 180 (as manner of Fiorentino); Wind p. 87, fig. 66; Fernand Beaucamp, *Le peintre lillois Jean-Baptiste Wicar*, 1762–1834, Lille, 1939, p. 591 (item 21 in an inventory, identified as Savonarola) for the maiolica roundel.

283. See Appendix.

284. OTTAVIANO SFORZA-RIARIO, Count of Forlì and Imola.

Obv. Bust to left, with long hair, wearing small cap and armour. Around, OCTAVIANVS SF(ortia) DE RIARIO FORLIVII IMOLAE Q(ue) C(omes).

Rev. OCTAVIVS RI(arius). Ottaviano with drawn sword riding to right.

75 mm. Late cast. A1022–284A

Probably made in 1498, when Ottaviano, coming to serve the Florentines in the war of Pisa, paraded at Florence with 100 men-at-arms and 50 troopers on 28 June. By the same hand as the medal of his mother, the famous Caterina (no. 283).

Literature: Arm. I, 87, 16; Heiss, *Florence*, i, p. 73, pl. viii, 3; *Corpus*, no. 1016 *d*; Cott p. 180 (as manner of Fiorentino).

285. GIOVANNI DI ANDREA DA STIA.

Obv. Bust to left, with long hair, wearing cap. Around, GIOVANNI DANDREA DA STIA

Rev. SPES Hope, with hands folded, gazing up at the Sun.

78 mm. A1023–285A

About 1485–90. The sitter, a native of Stia in the Casentino, is unidentified. There are other specimens at Berlin, Florence, and Paris.

Literature: Les Arts, Aug. 1908, p. 11, no. iv; cp. Arm. I, 95, 11; *Corpus*, no. 1017; Cott p. 180 (as manner of Fiorentino).

286. FILIPPO STROZZI, Florentine merchant-prince (1426–91).

Obv. Bust to left, wearing gown. Around, PHILIPPVS STROZA

Rev. An eagle with spread wings on a stump, to which is tied the Strozzi shield. Landscape with pine-trees in a meadow; the field semé with plumes.

98 mm. Repairs to surfaces: obv: before the profile, rev: below left wing of eagle. A1024–286A

Doubtless made for the foundation of the Strozzi Palace on 6 Aug. 1489, when it is recorded that certain medals were buried. The medal has sometimes been attributed to Benedetto da Maiano, probably for no other reason than because it resembles, as it naturally would, the sculptured bust from his hand.

A wax model closely related to the obverse portrait type and formerly in the Sambon collection, is now in the Cabinet des Médailles, Paris. An iron plaque of the portrait type, now in the Walters Art Gallery, Baltimore, is also recorded. Both wax and plaque are anepigraphic, and are perhaps related to one another, rather than to the medal portrait.

Literature: Les Arts, Aug. 1908, p. 11, no. v; cp. Arm. I, 98, 6; *Corpus*, no. 1018; Cott p. 180 (as manner of Fiorentino); Münzen und Medaillen auction XVII, Basel, 2 Dec. 1957, lot 103, pl. 14 (another specimen of the medal, d. 87·8 mm.); *Corpus* no. 1018 *bis* (wax model); Arthur Sambon collection sale catalogue, Hirsch, Munich, 9 May 1914, no. 11, pl. 1, v (wax model); J. Babelon, 'Un medaillon de cire du Cabinet des Médailles. Filippo Strozzi et Benedetto da Majano', in *Gazette des Beaux-Art* (1921) iv, pp. 203–210 (for the wax model, as by Benedetto da Maiano); *Corpus* no. 1018 *bis* (for the iron plaque); Fabriczy, p. 12 note (iron plaque); M. C. Ross, 'An iron plaque of Filippo Strozzi', in *Art in America* 31, no. 3 (1943), pp. 151–3 (figured on the cover).

287. ACHILLE TIBERTI of Cesena (d. 1501).

Obv. Bust to left, with long hair, wearing small cap and armour. Around, ACHILLES TIBERTVS CESENAS ARM(iger).

Without reverse.

73 mm. A1025–287A

Tiberti, a lieutenant of Cesare Borgia, took Forlì on 17 Dec. 1499 and was killed before Faenza on 18 Apr. 1501. This medal, which is known only in this specimen, may be dated about 1495.

Literature: Arm. II, 68, 33; *Les Arts*, Aug. 1908, p. 11, no. xi; Hill, 'Notes on Italian Medals, xxiii', in *Burl. Mag.*, 30 (1917), pp. 190–198 (at p. 191); *Corpus*, no. 1020 *a*; Cott p. 180 (as Manner of Fiorentino).

288. GIOVANNA ALBIZZI, wife of Lorenzo Tornabuoni.

Obv. Bust to right. Around, VXOR LAVRENTII DE TORNABONIS IOANNA ALBIZA

Rev. The three Graces; above, CASTITAS PVLCHRITVDO AMOR

78 mm. A1026–288A

This was doubtless made for or very soon after the marriage of Giovanna in 1486. The reverse is inspired by an antique group of the three Graces, but the precise source used by the medallist has not been identified.

Niccolò used the same reverse model for his medals of Pico della Mirandola (*ca.* 1489–94; Kress no. 277), Johann Greudner (*ca.* 1501–2; *Corpus* no. 1047) and Rafael Martin (*Corpus*, no. 1050), but with different inscriptions for those of Pico and Martin.

Panofsky interprets the type as representing the threefold aspect of Venus in terms of the trinitarian view of Love in Florentine neoplatonism. Wind, by his redating of the medal of Pico della Mirandola (no. 277), suggests that the Albizzi reverse shows a deliberate choice of type to compliment Pico.

Literature: Les Arts, Aug. 1908, p. 8, no. i; cp. Arm. I, 88, 20; *Corpus*, no. 1021; Cott p. 180 (as manner of Fiorentino); Fabriczy, pp. 124–5, pl. xxiv, 3; Panofsky, pp. 168–9, fig. 124; Wind, p. 72 (choice of type).

W. Deonna, 'Le group des trois Graces nues et sa descendance' in *Revue Archéologique*, 31 (1930) pp. 274–332 (for convenient listing of the groups in various media).

289. GIOVANNI DI FRANCESCO TORNABUONI, Florentine banker and statesman

Obv. Bust to right; around, TORNABONVS FR(ancisci) FI(lius) IOANNES

Rev. Hope praying, looking up at sun. Around, FIRMAVI Across the field, MCCCCLXXXXIII

33 mm. A1027–289A

This is a second version of the medal, the earlier bearing no date, and having been produced probably about 1480–1490. That was itself a reduction of a larger medal. This dated specimen was doubtless produced for some special occasion when medals were wanted, as for the foundation of a building. Tornabuoni was Treasurer to Pope Sixtus IV, and ambassador to Rome in 1480, 1484 and 1523.

Literature: Les Arts, Aug. 1908, p. 11, no. vii; *Corpus*, no. 1025 *e*; cp. Arm. I, 95, 13; Cott p. 180 (as manner of Fiorentino).

290. ALESSANDRO DI GINO VECCHIETTI (1472–1532).

Obv. Bust to right, in cap. Around, ALESSANDRO DI GINO VECHIETTI; below truncation, ANNI 26

Rev. Fortune with sail on dolphin passing over waves; in the water, reflection of the sun's face; on a rock an ermine holding a scroll inscribed PRIVS MORI QVA(m) TVRPARI

80 mm. A1028–290A

The sitter was born on 2 Oct. 1472, so that the medal dates from about 1498. The ermine is an emblem of purity, and the Vecchietti bore five silver ermines rampant on a blue field. The reverse of the medal forms a decorative insert on a terracotta bust medallion of Lucretia attributed to Andrea della Robbia, formerly in the Edmond Foulc collection.

Collection: His de la Salle (sale, London, Sotheby, 22 Nov. 1880, lot 71).

Literature: Les Arts, Aug. 1908, p. 11, no. xiii; Arm. I, 99, 4; *Corpus*, no. 1027 *g*; Cott p. 180 (as manner of Fiorentino). *Special Renaissance number of the Pennsylvania Museum Bulletin*, 25, no. 132 (Feb. 1930) p. 10 (for the della Robbia medallion). Tervarent, col. 145, v (Fortune and dolphin).

291. UNKNOWN MAN.

Obv. Between the letters N A, bust to left of young man wearing richly decorated cuirass, with winged mask on breast.

Without reverse.

Lead, 78 mm. A1029–291A

All other known specimens seem to be over-chased, and the date of this lead seems doubtful. They represent, however, more or less distantly, a Florentine original of the late fifteenth century: a portrait, whether of Giuliano de' Medici idealized (in which case the letters in the field have to be explained away as representing a motto), or some person such as Niccolò or Nerio Acciaiuoli, it seems idle in the circumstances to discuss.

Literature: Cp. Arm. II, 49, 5; III, 173, *c*; *Corpus*, no. 1030; Cott p. 180 (as manner of Fiorentino).

LATER MEDALS IN THE MANNER OF NICCOLÒ FIORENTINO

292. IPPOLITO D'ESTE, born 1479, cardinal 1493, died 1520.

Obv. Bust to left, wearing cap and plain dress. Around, HIPPOLYTVS ESTENSIS

Without reverse.

45 mm. A1030–292A

Other specimens at Naples and Vienna. Probably made at Florence by an artist in the circle of Niccolò Fiorentino. Ippolito d'Este, son of Ercole I d'Este, was hurrying to Rome on the death of Pope Alexander VI, 1503, when he was delayed by breaking a leg. The medal may date from that time.

Literature: Corpus, no. 1045 *c*; cp. Arm. III, 169, G; Cott p. 180 (as manner of Fiorentino).

293. See Appendix.

294. GIANOZZO DI BERNARDO SALVIATI (b. 1462).

Obv. Bust to right, with long hair, wearing small cap. Around, GANOZO DI BERNARDO DI MARCHO DI MESERE FORESE SALVIATI

Rev. Fortune, with sail, on a dolphin proceeding over the waves; in the water, radiant reflection of the sun. On the right, ARIDEAT VSQVE

89 mm. A1032–294A

The only recorded specimen. Gianozzo was born at Florence on 11 Feb. 1462. The medal is rather after than before 1500, judging by the apparent age of the sitter. He was prior of liberty in 1515.

Literature: Arm. I, 99, 3; Heiss, *Florence*, i, p. 89, pl. xiii, 5; *Corpus*, no. 1065 *a*; Cott p. 181 (as manner of Fiorentino). Tervarent, col. 145, v (Fortune and dolphin).

295. MICHELANGELO DI GUGLIELMINO TANAGLIA (1437–1512).

Obv. Bust to left, aged. Around, MICHELANGELVS D(omi)NI G(ulielmini) DE TANAGLI

Rev. Half-figure of a youthful pilgrim, wearing peaked cap and an animal's skin; carries staff and scroll inscribed BONA FORTVNA

46 mm. A1033–295A

Michelangelo Tanaglia was a Florentine official, and author of an Italian poem *De Agricultura* dedicated to the Duke of Calabria. Tanaglia's interest in gems and medals is attested by a letter from him to Piero de' Medici, 1492, and by a letter from Michelangelo Buonarroti to his brother of 1510. There are other specimens of the medal at Arezzo, Berlin, and Florence. The plaquette-like reverse of the medal seems ill adapted to the obverse.

Literature: Arm. II, 51, 15; Heiss, *Florence*, i, p. 151, pl. xx, 3; *Corpus*, no. 1066 *d*; Cott p. 181 (as manner of Fiorentino). Michelangelo Tanaglia, *De Agricultura* (edition of A. Roncaglia and Tammaro de Marinis), Bologna, 1953, p. xi (for the letter from Tanaglia); Giovanni Poggi, Paola

Barocchi, R. Ristori (editors) *Il Carteggio di Michelangelo*, Florence, vol. I, 1965, p. 111 (for the letter with mention of Tanaglia).

296. LORENZO DI GIOVANNI TORNABUONI (1466–1497).

Obv. Bust to left, with long hair. Around, LAVRENTIVS TORNABONVS IO(annis) FI(lius).

Rev. Mercury walking three-quarters to right, armed with sword, carrying caduceus.

78 mm. A1034–296A

One of three recorded specimens. Lorenzo was the husband of Giovanna Albizzi (no. 288) and was executed on 17 Aug. 1497 for intriguing with Piero de' Medici for the restoration of that dynasty. Hill interpreted the reverse type, which is an improved version of that on a medal of Turriano of 1498 (*Corpus*, no. 1089), as referring to the fate of Lorenzo, and suggested that the medal and its companion piece of Lorenzo's sister Lodovica (*Corpus*, no. 1069) were made after the restoration of the Medici. Wind comments that the sword-bearing Mercury was a renaissance commonplace.

Literature: Les Arts, Aug. 1908, p. 8, no. iii; *Corpus*, no. 1068 *a*; cp. Arm. I, 88, 19; Cott p. 181 (as manner of of Fiorentino); Wind, p. 74, n. 1 (on the reverse type).

297. See Appendix.

FLORENTINE SCHOOL

Late Fifteenth Century

297*a*. MATHIAS CORVINUS, King of Hungary (1458–90).

Obv. Bust to right, laureate. Around, MATHIAS REX HVNGARIAE BOHEMIAE DALMAT(iae).

Rev. Cavalry battle between Hungarians and Turks; in foreground, a statue on a column. Below, MARTI FAVTORI

52 mm. A993–255A

The attribution of this medal to Bertoldo, by Bode, has not been accepted. Hill shows that the obverse type is probably contemporary with the king, but believed the facture to be much later, as a 'restitution'. Hill also denied the reverse to Bertoldo, Habich accepting it. Middeldorf (private communication) doubts the Florentine origin for the medal, and even doubts that the reverse is of Italian origin. A nineteenth century reproduction of the medal is recorded by Balogh.

Literature: Cp. Arm. II, 82, 9; *Corpus*, no. 920 *g*; Middeldorf, *Morgenroth*, no. 96 (*Corpus* 920 *h*); Cott p. 178. For the iconography of Mathias Corvinus see Jolán Balogh, 'Mátyás Király Ikonografiája' in *Mátyás Király Emlékkönyu*, Budapest, 1940, pp. 437–548 (where this medal is p. 463, fig. 12/129, and the nineteenth century reproduction, p. 531, fig. 12 *b*).

FLORENTINE SCHOOL

Late Fifteenth Century

PORTRAITS OF FAMOUS MEN

298. ARISTOTLE.

Obv. Bust to right, with long hair and beard, wearing cap. Around, ΑΡΙΣΤΟΤΕΛΗΣ

Without reverse.

85 mm. A1036–298A

Probably Florentine work of about 1500. The type reproduces an image, known also in reliefs and engravings, which was regarded in the late fifteenth and sixteenth century as a portrait of Aristotle. A relief of Aristotle is in the Kress collection. The medal is the best of the known examples, the others being at Bologna, Milan, and Venice (Museo Correr).

Literature: Corpus, no. 1090 *d*; Cott p. 181; Pope-Hennessy, *Kress Bronzes*, no. 373 (with references for the typology of Aristotle portraits).

299. DANTE ALIGHIERI, Florentine poet (1265–1321).

Obv. Bust to left, in laureate cap with falling point and stringed ear-flaps. Around, DANTHES FLORENTINVS

Rev. Dante standing before the Mountain of Purgatory.

In moulded frame, making 68 mm. A1037–299A

The reverse is based on the painting made in 1465 by Domenico di Michelino, in the Duomo at Florence. The medal itself dates from the end of the fifteenth century.

Literature: Cp. Arm. II, 11, 1; *Corpus*, no. 1092; Cott p. 181.

300. GIOVANNI BOCCACCIO, Florentine writer (1313–75).

Obv. Bust to left, head and neck swathed in cloth, and laureate. Around, IOH(ann)ES BOCATIVS FLORE(ntinus).

Rev. Wisdom gazing at a serpent which she holds up.

56 mm. Late cast. A1038–300A

The original was evidently a rough piece of work, a pendant to the Petrarch following. It probably dated from about 1500.

Literature: Cp. Arm. II, 12, 8; *Corpus*, no. 1093; Cott p. 181.

301. FRANCESCO PETRARCA of Arezzo, poet (1304–74).

Obv. Bust of Petrarca to right, laureate, head and neck swathed in cloth. Around, FRANCISCVS PETRARCA FLORENTINVS

Rev. Female figure (Poetry) walking in a wood, plucking laurels.

55 mm. Late cast. A1039–301A

Companion piece to the preceding. The portrait may have been copied from an earlier miniature.

Literature: Cp. Arm. II, 12, 4; *Corpus*, no. 1094; Cott p. 181.

302. GIANFRANCESCO PALLAVICINI.

Obv. Bust to left, in flat cap. Around, IO(annes) FRANCISCVS MARCHIO PALLAVICINVS CO(mes).

Without reverse.

Lead, 51 mm. A1040–302A

The only other recorded specimen, at Berlin, has a reverse of Pallas (an allusion to the name), holding a halberd. Armand (whom the *Corpus* quotes, by a misprint, as giving the diameter of 57 mm.) identifies the man, perhaps rightly, as the son of Orlando, Marchese di Zibello, who died in 1497, and was a partisan of Lodovico Sforza.

Literature: Corpus, no. 1135 *b*; cp. Arm. III, 175, C; Cott p. 181.

UNATTRIBUTED MEDALS

Before about 1530

303. LAURA DE NOVES (1307/8–1348), friend of Petrarch.

Obv. Bust to waist of a girl to left, with long hair, her right hand on her heart, her left hand holding a book; above, and below, incised, DIVA LAVRA (PA)RIXIENSIS; in two upper corners, fleurs-de-lis incised; pedimental top containing a mask.

Without reverse.

Lead, rectangular, 133 (including triangular pediment) × 81 mm. A1041–303A

A pendant to a portrait of Petrarch (*Corpus* no. 1136 *a*, bronze specimen in the Victoria and Albert Museum, London). Cott notes that although Hill reconstructed the inscription as (B)RIXIENSIS and identified the sitter as Laura of Brescia (d. 1469), W. Suida observed in commerce another cast of the plaquette with the inscription PARIXIENSIS intact, together with the companion plaquette of Petrarch.

Literature: Arm. II, 161, 15; III, 154, G; Heiss, *Florence*, i, p. 137, pl. xvii, 6; *Corpus*, no. 1137 *a*. Cott p. 181.

304. A CARRARA?

Obv. Bust of boy to left, with long hair, wearing flat cap and coat. Around, incised, DE CAR

Rev. The heraldic *carro*, incised.

32 mm. A1042–304A

This little medal must date from about 1500; but at that time the original Carraresi were extinct. The incised inscriptions and the *carro* may be incorrect; and it is to be observed that the portrait resembles the young Francesco, son of Giangaleazzo Sforza, as represented in the drawing in the Uffizi attributed to Leonardo da Vinci.
The only specimen known. Grotemeyer has published another of these sixteenth-century Carrara restitutions, of Francesco I or Francesco II.

Collection: possibly F. Spitzer (sale, Paris, April-June 1893, I, lot 1347).

Literature: Les Arts, Aug. 1908, p. 13, no. xxi; *Corpus*, no. 1156 *a*; Cott p. 181; P. Grotemeyer, 'Seltene italienische Medaillen in der Münchner Münzsammlung', in *Mitteilungen der Bayerischen Numismatischen Gesellschaft*, 53 (1935) pp. 138–144 (at pp. 140–3, pl. xxi, 4).

305. BALDASSARRE DI CRISTOFORO CASTIGLIONE, author of the 'Courtier' (1478–1529).

Obv. Bust to right; around, BALTHASAR CASTILION(eus) CR(istophori) F(ilius).

Rev. Aurora stepping from her car; on either side a Psyche with butterfly wings restrains a horse; the car rises above the edge of the Globe, on which part of the Mediterranean is shown. Above, TENEBRARVM ET LVCIS

37 mm. axis ↓ A1043–305A

Aurora symbolizes Castiglione's culture. There was a tradition that this medal was made by Raphael; the reverse may go back to some design of his, which has been adapted to the round. Castiglione was born 6 Dec. 1478, and must be about 40 years old here. The authorship of the medal, which lacks character, is quite uncertain. Habich gives the medal as either Mantuan, by a follower of Cristoforo di Geremia and Melioli, or Roman, by a follower of Cristoforo. There is an anonymous restitution of the medal (with reverse, the sea), and another restitution by Mercandetti.

Literature: Cp. Arm. II, 100, 10; Habich, pl. lxvii, 3; *Corpus*, no. 1158; Cott p. 181.

306. LOUIS XII, King of France (1462–98–1515).

Obv. Bust to left, in flat cap with spiked crown, and armour. Around, LVDOVICVS D(ei) G(ratia) REX FRANCORVM

Rev. A woman seated, head on hand; towards her runs a semi-nude woman pursued by a veiled woman with dagger; followed by Mars on horseback, holding torch and whip and accompanied by three hunting-leopards. Above, in clouds, thunder-bearing Jupiter. Below, MDI3 nearly obliterated. Above, Jupiter holding thunderbolt.

71 mm. A1044–306A

The medal, of Italian work, probably commemorates the disasters to the French arms in 1513. The mourning figure is Italy; the *furia francese*, pursuing a victim, is herself pursued by Mars.

Literature: Les Arts, Aug. 1908, p. 14, no. v; *Corpus*, no. 1167 *g*; cp. Arm. II, 139, 1; Cott p. 182; Middeldorf, *Morgenroth*, no. 114 (*Corpus*, 1167 *h*; dated on rev., 1513).

307. *Obv.* Bust to left, wearing cap and robe.

Rev. LVD(ovicus) XII incised.

35 mm. A1045–307A

Another specimen at Milan (Brera collection in the Castello).

Literature: Arm. II, 140, 7; *Les Arts*, Aug. 1908, p. 14, no. xi; *Corpus*, no. 1168 *b*; Cott p. 182.

308. FRANCIS I, King of France (1494–1515–47).

Obv. Bust to left, beardless, in helmet decorated with crown and crest of salamander in flames (?). Around, FRANCIS(cus) R(e)X FRANCOR(um) P(ri)MVS DOMITOR ELVETIOR(um).

Rev. Trophy of arms. Around, DEO FAVENTE ET IMPERATORIS VIRTVTE

51 mm. A1046–308A

Perhaps made at Milan. From the same hand as a medal of Battista da Vercelli (*Corpus*, 1192). The title given to Francis dates the medal in or after 1515.

Literature: Cp. Arm. II, 188, 6; *Corpus*, no. 1168 *bis*; Cott p. 182.

309. BERNARDINO FRANCESCONI of Siena.

Obv. Bust to left, in cap and gown. Around, +BERNARDINVS FRANCISCONVS SENE(n)SIS

Rev. Arms of Francesconi. Around, +A(nno) D(omini) MDXX BER(nardinus) FRAN(cisconus) FVNDAVIT HANC DOMVM

45 mm. A1047–309A

The medal may have been made at Siena, where the Palazzo Francesconi was founded on 5 May 1520, for which occasion this medal was intended.

Literature: Cp. Arm. II, 98, 21; *Corpus*, no. 1170; Cott p. 182.

310. MATTIA and LUDOVICO UGONI.

Obv. Bust of Mattia to left in berretta and cape; around, MATHIAS VGO EP(iscopu)S PHAMAVG(ustanus). Below, branch of laurel.

Rev. Bust of Ludovico to left, wearing armour, hair in net-cap; around, LVDOVICVS VGONIVS; below, two branches.

58 mm. The only specimen known. A1048–310A

Mattia was Bishop of Famagusta from 1504 to 1530. Ludovico is not known.

Literature: Arm. II, 104, 16; *Corpus*, no. 1190 *a*; Cott p. 182.

311. UNKNOWN MAN, about 1500.

Obv. Bust to right, beardless, in large cap with circular medallion.

Without reverse.

44 mm. The only specimen known. A1049–311A

Literature: Corpus, no. 1194 *a*; Cott p. 182.

312. CASTRUCCIO CASTRACANE DEGLI ANTELMINELLI of Lucca (1281–1328).

Obv. Bust to left, wearing cap with drapery, doublet and cloak. Around, CASTR(uccius) ANT(elminellus) LVCEN(sis).

Without reverse.

28 mm. A1050–312A

Probably not earlier than Machiavelli's biography, which was published in 1532. Compare the portrait in the Museum Jovianum by Paolo Giovio (*Elogia Vir. Ill.*, 1596, p. 38).

Literature: Cp. Arm. III, 153, C; *Corpus*, no. 1253; Cott p. 182.

313. Omitted.

II

ITALIAN MEDALS FROM THE TIME OF BENVENUTO CELLINI ONWARDS

The materials in Hill's *Corpus* end at about 1530, and there is no reference work but Armand for the remaining sixteenth-century Italian medals. The medals in this part, including some later pieces, are arranged under schools in the following way: Florentine, Roman, Paduan, Venetian, Milanese and Emilian. Then come non-localised medals, unattributed medals, and fictitious portraits. A concordance to Armand will be found at pages 273–276.

FRANCESCO DA SANGALLO
(b. 1494; d. 1576)

Florentine sculptor and medallist.

See U. Middeldorf, in Thieme-Becker, 29 (1935) pp. 404–406 (with bibliography for the medals, criticisms of and additions to the attributions in Armand); U. Middeldorf, 'Portraits by Francesco da Sangallo', in *Art Quarterly*, I (1938), pp. 109–138 (at p. 138, catalogue of the medals); Habich, p. 75, pl. lvi, 1–4; Forrer, 5, 324–331; Pope-Hennessy, *Italian High Renaissance and Baroque Sculpture*, London, 1963, Catalogue vol. pp. 56–7 (biography and critical bibliography).

314. GIOVANNI DE' MEDICI DELLE BANDE NERE, born 1498, died 1526, a celebrated condottiere, and father of Cosimo I.

Obv. Bust to right, in cuirass. Around, IOANNES MEDICES DVX FORTISS(imus) MDXXII Incised on truncation, FRANC(iscus) SANGALLIVS FACIEB(at).

Rev. Winged thunderbolt. Around, NIHIL HOC FORTIVS

92 mm. A1051–314A

Made long after Giovanni's death, perhaps about 1570, which is the date of the medal by Sangallo of Alessandro and Cosimo de' Medici in the same style.

Literature: G. Clausse, *Les Sangallo*, 3 vols., Paris, 1900–2, iii, p 217; cp. Arm. I, 157, 2; Friedländer, *Ital. Schaumünzen* p. 169, no. 1, pl. xxxiii; Habich pl. lvi, 4; Cott p. 182. Bottari-Ticozzi, I, p. 228, letter from Vincenzo Borghini to Federigo di Lamberto, 1565 (an attack on the notion that Giovanni used the *impresa* of a winged thunderbolt). For the marble bust by Francesco da Sangallo of Giovanni delle Bande Nere see Pope-Hennessy (cited above) Text vol. pp. 93–4, fig. 119.

DOMENICO DE' VETRI
(b. after 1480; d. 1547)

Domenico di Polo di Angelo de' Vetri was court medallist to Alessandro I and Cosimo I de' Medici. He was taught gem-engraving in the shop of Giovanni delle Corniole and Pier Maria da Pescia. His medals were struck from steel dies.

See G. F. Hill, in Thieme-Becker 9 (1913) p. 408; H. de la Tour, 'Domenico di Polo, médailleur et graveur sur pierres fines du duc Alexandre de Médicis', in *Procès-verbaux et Mémoires, Congrès international de Numismatique*, Paris, 1900, pp. 382–399, pls. xxxii, xxxiii (the article made the proper distinction between de' Vetri and Francesco dal Prato, distributing between them the medals grouped by Armand under the artist *médailleur au signe de Mars*. The plates include the gem of Alessandro de' Medici by de' Vetri); Habich, p. 118, pl. lxxxii, 1–4; Forrer, 4, pp. 639–641 (gem wrongly labelled); Supino, nos. 248–264.

315. COSIMO I DE' MEDICI, first Grand Duke; born 1519, Duke of Florence 1537, Grand Duke of Tuscany 1569, died 1574.

Obv. Bust to right, in cuirass. Around, COSMVS MED(ices) II REIP(ublicae) FLOR(entinae) DVX

Rev. Capricorn; above, eight stars. Around, ANIMI CONSCIENTIA ET FIDVCIA FATI

35 mm. Struck. A1052–315A

Vasari (ed. Milanesi, v, p. 384) says that this medal was made by Domenico di Polo in 1537; but Cosimo, who was then only 18 years old, has here a distinct beard. The capricorn was Cosimo's device, and appears as an adjunct symbol, for instance, to the figure of Cosimo as Apollo in the sculptured group by Domenico Poggini, 1559.

Literature: Cp. Arm. I, 144, 2; III, 58, *b*; Cott p. 182; Alvarez-Ossorio, p. 188, no. 123; U. Middeldorf and F. Kriegbaum, 'Forgotten sculpture by Domenico Poggini', in *Burl. Mag.*, 53 (1928), pp. 9–17 (for the sculptured group in the Boboli gardens). For the capricorn device and Cosimo I see Tervarent, col. 60.

316. ALESSANDRO DE' MEDICI (first Duke of Florence, 1510–23–37) and COSIMO I DE' MEDICI (see no. 315).

Obv. Head of Alessandro to right. Around, ALEXANDER MED(ices) FLORENTIAE DVX P(rimus).

Rev. Head of Cosimo to left, beardless. Around, COSMVS MED(ices) FLORENTIAE DVX II

34 mm. A1053–316A

The original was struck from dies; there are specimens in silver in the British Museum and at Vienna. Attributions vary between Cellini, Domenico di Polo, Francesco dal Prato, and Domenico Poggini, of whom the second seems to have most claim.

Literature: Arm. I, 150, 19; III, 59, *e*; Heiss, *Florence*, ii, p. 9, no. 6, pl. i, 7; Cott p. 182 (as Domenico ?).

FRANCESCO DAL PRATO
(b. 1512; d. 1562)

Francesco Ortensi di Girolamo dal Prato, Florentine medallist, goldsmith and painter, the son of Girolamo d'Andrea who was also a goldsmith and medallist by whom no medals are now known. Many of the medals by Francesco were once attributed to Domenico di Vetri (Domenico di Polo).

See P. Grotemeyer, in Thieme-Becker, 27 (1933) p. 351; H. de la Tour, 'Domenico di Polo, médailleur et graveur sur pierre fines du duc Alexandre de Médicis', in *Procès-verbaux et Mémoires, Congrès international de Numismatique*, Paris, 1900, pp. 382–399, pls. xxxii, xxxiii (the article which made the distinction between the medals of de' Vetri and Francesco dal Prato); Habich, p. 118, pl. lxxx, 1, 2; Forrer, 4, pp. 331–332; Supino, no. 265.

317. ALESSANDRO DE' MEDICI, first Duke of Florence (see no. 316).

Obv. Bust to right, draped. Around, ALEXANDER MED(ices) DVX FLORENTIAE I

Rev. Peace, holding olive-branch, seated to right; with a torch she fires a pile of arms. Around, FVNDATOR QVIETIS MDXXXIIII Below, sign of Mars.

43 mm. A1054–317A

Literature: Cp. Arm. I, 151, 4; Heiss, *Florence*, ii, p. 9, no. 3, pl. i, 4; H. de la Tour (cited above), pl. xxxiii, 3 (showing that the piece was not by Domenico di Polo, but by Francesco dal Prato); Cott p. 182. Hill, B.M.G., p. 37 ('the sign of Mars . . . is merely the sign of the celestial power chosen by the Duke as his protector'). Tervarent, col. 382, iv.

CESARE DA BAGNO
(b. 1530; d. 1564)

A competent modeller, whose best work is a portrait medal of Cosimo I de' Medici. See Thieme-Becker, 2, pp. 360–1; Forrer, 1, pp. 113–4. Max Rosenheim, 'Medal of Cosimo I, Duke of Florence, by Cesare da Bagno', in *Num. Chron.*, 10 (1910), pp. 412–3; and Rosenheim collection (sale, London, Sotheby, 30 April 1923, lot 105) for the medal of Cosimo I in lead.

318. ALFONSO II D'AVALOS (1502–46), Marquess of Vasto.

Obv. Bust to left, in cuirass, with scarf. Around, ALF(onsus) DAV(a)L(os) MAR(chio) GV(asti) CAP(itaneus) G(eneralis) CAR(oli) V IMP(eratoris).

Without reverse.

Lead, 66 mm. Four times pierced. A1055–318A

Usually has, as reverse, a portrait of Fernando Francesco II, with artist's signature.

Literature; Cp. Arm. I, 174, 1; Forrer, 1, p. 113 (engraving of the complete medal); Alvarez-Ossorio, p. 99, no. 178; Cott p. 182.

PASTORINO DE' PASTORINI
(b. 1508; d. 1592)

Pastorino, born near Siena, was a glass-painter when young, but achieved considerable repute by modelling portraits in wax, and casting them, usually in lead. He was active in Parma, Ferrara, Novellara, Bologna, and Florence, and appears to have produced his medals between 1540 and 1586. His work in Ferrara included die engraving and portraiture between 1554 and 1559. He settled finally in Florence in 1576. More than two hundred medals are signed by or attributed to Pastorino. The earlier medals, comparatively seldom signed and less often dated, are small (as no. 320) and were mostly made from about 1540 to 1554; the later medals have a border of large pearls on a raised band. Pastorino was a popular, skilful, but rather superficial artist.

See G. F. Hill in Thieme-Becker, 26 (1932), p. 289; Habich, pp. 122–3, pl. lxxxiv and lxxxv (twenty-two pieces illustrated including the Titian and Ariosto portraits)

Fabriczy, pp. 145–150, pls. xxx, xxxi; Forrer, 4, pp. 408–422 (useful listing of works); Hill, N.I.A., adds seventeen pieces to the lists in Armand; Müller, *Nachtrag*, no. 2, attributes one piece to Pastorino. Illustrations of medals by Pastorino are still to be sought in Heiss, *Florence* ii; in Habich (as cited above); in Keary, B.M.G. (first ed. 1881) pl. vii; (second ed. 1893) pl. vi; in the B.F.A.C. exhibition catalogue, 1905 (pl. xlv); and in four articles by Hill, *Some medals by Pastorino da Siena*, in *Burl. Mag.*, 9 (1906) pp. 408–412; *Some Italian medals in the British Museum*, in *Burl Mag.*, 10 (1907) pp. 384–7 (at p. 387); 'Some lead Italian medals', in *Archiv für Medaillen- und Plakettenkunde*, 5 (1925/6) pp. 20–25 (at pp. 23–4, pl. iii); 'Edward Courtenay', in *Num. Chron.*, 5 (1925), pp. 265–7.

319. BEATRICE DA SIENA, unidentified.

Obv. Bust to right; around, BEATRICE DE SENA; incised on truncation, P

Rev. A wheat-sheaf; around, EXINANITVS REPLEO

43 mm. A1056–319A

Another specimen at Vienna, and a late cast in the British Museum.

Literature: Arm. I, 189, 6; Heiss, *Florence*, ii, p. 100, no. 7, pl. vii, 16; Cott p. 182.

320. COSTANZA BUTI, unidentified.

Obv. Bust to right. Around, COSTANTIA DE BVTI

Without reverse.

35 mm. A late cast, finely chased. A1057–320A

Unsigned, but entirely in Pastorino's style. There is an old lead cast in the British Museum.

Literature: Arm. I, 190, 14; Heiss, *Florence*, ii, p. 106, pl. viii, 10; Cott p. 183.

321. CAMILLO CASTIGLIONE (1517–98), son of Baldassarre.

Obv. Bust to right, in cuirass. Around, CAMILLVS DE CASTILIONO BAL(dassaris) F(ilius). Incised on truncation, 1561 P

Without reverse.

68 mm. A1058–321A

Literature: Arm. I, 191, 17; Heiss, *Florence*, ii, p. 108, pl. viii, 12; Cott p. 183.

322. CORNELIA SICILIANA, unidentified.

Obv. Bust to right, draped, wearing flat cap. Around, CORNELIA SICILIANA

Rev. Truth seated, unveiling herself. Around, INTER ONNES (sic) VERITAS

34 mm. A later cast. A1059–322A

This medal is unsigned, but markedly in the style of Pastorino. He seldom attempts a reverse for his medals.

Literature: Cp. Arm. I, 192, 24; Hill, 'Notes on Italian medals, xxvii', in *Burl. Mag.*, 42 (1923), p. 44; Cott p. 183.

323. ERCOLE II D'ESTE, fourth Duke of Ferrara (1508–34–59).

Obv. Bust to left, in cuirass and mantle. Around, HERCVLES II FERRARIAE DVX IIII

Without reverse.

39 mm. A1060–323A

Another specimen is at Vienna. This portrait is also found attached to the portrait of Francesco d'Este (no. 324).

Literature: Arm. II, 295, 35 *bis*; Cott, p. 183. Supino, nos. 332 and 333 (for other Este medals by Pastorino, of Cardinal Ippolito, 1509–1572, and Alfonso II, 1533–1597, fifth Duke of Ferrara).

324. FRANCESCO D'ESTE, son of Alfonso I, Marquess of Massa (1516–78).

Obv. Bust to right, in cuirass. Around, FRANC(iscus) ESTEN(sis) MARCH(io) MASSAE; incised on truncation, 1554 P

Without reverse.

40 mm. A1061–324A

Often found combined with portraits of other Estensi by the same hand (no. 323).

Literature: Cp. Arm. I, 193, 30; Cott p. 183.

325. LUCREZIA DE' MEDICI, daughter of Cosimo I, first wife of Alfonso II d'Este, born 1545, married 1558, died 1561.

Obv. Bust to left, with jewelled band on head. Around, LVCRETIA MED(ices) FERR(ariae) PRINC(eps) A(nno) A(etatis) XIII Incised on truncation, 1558 and, on shoulder, P

Without reverse.

66 mm. Bronze gilt. A1062–325A

Literature: Rodocanachi, *La femme italienne*, p. 40; cp. Arm. I, 195, 40; Cott p. 183.

326. ELEONORA D'AUSTRIA, Duchess of Mantua, wife of Guglielmo I Gonzaga, born 1534, married 1561, died 1594.

Obv. Bust to left, wearing flat cap, dress with high collar and small ruff. Around, LEONORA DVCISSA MANTVAE Incised on truncation, P 1561

Without reverse.

69 mm. A1063–326A

The sale of the D. J. Levy collection, lot 127 (London, Sotheby, 30 Nov. 1964) contained a pink wax portrait of this Duchess of Mantua, by or after Pastorino, dated 1561. It was formerly in the Walcher von Moltheim collection.

Literature: Cp. Arm. I, 199, 64; Cott p. 183.

327. ISABELLA TROTTI NEGRISOLI.

Obv. Bust to right, dress with collar open in front. Around, YSSAB(ella) TROT(ti) NEGRISOLI A(nno) E(tatis) XXXIII Incised on truncation of arm, 1550

Without reverse.

56 mm. A1064–327A

There is no trace of the usual signature P, but the style is unmistakable. On a specimen at Vienna the date seems to be 1556. The lady belonged to the Trotti of Ferrara.

Literature: Arm. I, 209, 129; Cott p. 183.

328. ISABELLA MANFRO DE' PEPOLI.

Obv. Bust to right, wearing long veil; dress with puffed sleeves. Around, ISABELLA MANFRO DE PEPOLI 1571 Incised on truncation of arm, P

Without reverse.

65 mm. Cast hollow. A1065–328A

The Pepoli, into whose family this lady married, were a Bolognese family.

Literature: Cp. Arm. I, 204, 94; Cott p. 183; Habich, pl. lxxxiv, 5.

329. LODOVICA FELICINA ROSSI.

Obv. Bust to right, hair bound with strings of pearls. Around, LVDOVICA FELICINA RVBEA Incised on truncation, 1557 P

Without reverse.

63 mm. Cast hollow. A1066–329A

The sitter belonged to the Felicini of Bologna.

Collection: Joseph Fau (sale, Paris, 3 March 1884, lot 461).

Literature: Cp. Arm. I, 205, 102; Cott p. 183; Supino, no. 347; Habich, pl. lxxxv, 4.

330. GIROLAMA SACRATA of Ferrara.

Obv. Bust to right, wearing dress with net chemisette and puffed sleeves. Around, HIERONIMA SACRATA MDLV Incised on truncation of arm, P

Without reverse.

69 mm. Cast hollow. A1067–330A

Literature: Rodocanachi, *La femme italienne*, p. 220; cp. Arm. I, 206, 108; Cott p. 183; Habich, pl. lxxxv, no. 2; Bange, no. 236, pl. 28 (a cut-out profile portrait of this medal; dating confused with the medal of 1560, below).

331. GIROLAMA SACRATA of Ferrara.

Obv. Bust three-quarters to right, wearing dress with standing collar. Around, HIERONIMA SACRATA 1560 Incised on truncation, P

Without reverse.

62 mm. A1068–331A

Literature: Cp. Arm. I, 206, 109; Cott p. 183.

332. GIROLAMA, daughter of Galeazzo Farnese, wife of Alfonso SAN VITALE, widowed 1560.

Obv. Bust to right, hair passing through veil and hanging down back. Around, HIERONIMA FARNESIA D(e) S(an) VITALI Incised on truncation of arm, P 1556

Without reverse.

64 mm. Cast hollow. A1069–332A

Literature: Rodocanachi, *La femme italienne*, p. 40; cp. Arm. I, 206, 113; Cott p. 183; Habich, pl. lxxxv, 8.

333. GINEVRA TROTTI.

Obv. Bust to right, hair bound with strings of pearls. Around, GINEVERA TROTTI A(nno) A(etatis) XXIII Incised on truncation, 1586P

Without reverse.

58 mm. Late cast. A1070–333A

The date is possible, for Pastorino lived until 1592; but it has hitherto been read 1556 (which is probable in the light of no. 327). His latest date on a medal, otherwise, is 1579.

Literature: Cp. Arm. I, 209, 128; Heiss, *Florence*, ii, p. 167, pl. xvi, 2; Cott p. 183.

334. NICOLOSA, daughter of Francesco Bacci of Arezzo; wife of Giorgio VASARI the painter; married 1548.

Obv. Bust to left, hair braided. Around, NICOLOSA BACCI DE VASARI Incised on truncation, P 1555
Incised on truncation, P 1555

Without reverse. Cast solid.

58 mm. Not an early cast. A1071–334A

Literature: Cp. Arm. I, 209, 130; Heiss, *Florence*, ii, p. 167, pl. xvi, 4; Cott p. 183.

335. FRANCESCO (or Franceschino) VISDOMINI of Ferrara, humanist and hebraist (1509–73).

Obv. Bust to right, in habit with hood. Around, FRANC(iscus) VISDOMINVS FERRARIEN(sis). Incised on truncation, 1564 P

Rev. A right hand, issuing from a cloud, holding a flaming sword. Around, VOX DOMINI IN VIRTVTE

67 mm. A1072–335A

Visdomini was a very learned man, called the 'Demosthenes of his times'. The motto of the reverse was used by his family. A very fine thin casting, so that, besides the usual piercing, a hole has broken through the field.

Literature: Cp. Arm. I, 210, 133 (signature not recorded); Heiss, *Florence*, ii, p. 169, pl. xvi, 8; Cott p. 183.

336. UNIDENTIFIED MAN.
Obv. Bust to left, with slight beard, in cuirass. On truncation, incised P 1557

Without reverse.

Bust only, cut out, height 37 mm. Cast hollow and gilt. A1073–336A

Literature: Cott p. 183.

337. UNKNOWN LADY.
Obv. Bust to right, hair braided and pearled, chain round neck, low dress.

Without reverse.

30 mm. Gilt. A1074–337A

The other known specimens show a raised pearled border.

Literature: Cp. Arm. I, 211, 144 (Piot specimen); Heiss, *Florence*, ii, p. 170, pl. xvii, 7 (Paris specimen); Habich, pl. lxxxv, 9; Cott p. 183.

GIAMPAOLO POGGINI
(b. 1518; d. 1582)

Giampaolo was the elder brother of Domenico. He worked with his brother for the court of Cosimo I de' Medici, in Brussels, 1555–1559 at the behest of Philip II of Spain, and from 1559 in Spain, where his works included eighteen medals of Philip II and his family.
See P. Grotemeyer, in Thieme-Becker, 27 (1933) p. 188; Habich, p. 118, pl. lxxx, nos. 3–7 (series for Philip II); Forrer, 4, pp. 632–5; 8, p. 141; G. Kubler, 'A medal by G. P. Poggini depicting Peru and predicting Australia', in *Mitteilungen des Kunsthistorischen Institutes in Florenz*, 11 (1964), pp. 149–152.

338. See Appendix.

338*a*. ALESSANDRO FARNESE, third Duke of Parma and Piacenza (1545–86–92).
Obv. Bust to left, young, wearing cuirass and mantle. Around, ALEXANDER FARNESIVS P(armae) P(lacentiae) PRINC(eps) AN(no) XIII NAT(us).

Without reverse.

37 mm. A1228–490A

Also found with a reverse (HVIVS AVRA MDLXXII) in the Victoria and Albert Museum (Salting). But, as Armand remarks, this date is 14 years later than the obverse, for Alessandro was born in 1545; and the date is absent from the British Museum specimen. P. H. C. Allen suggested that this medal is by G. P. Poggini.

Literature: Cp. Arm. II, 265, 12; Cott p. 184 (as G. Poggini ?); Grotemeyer, in Thieme-Becker, 27 (1933), p. 188 (gives the medal to Giampaolo, but also cites it as by Domenico in that entry); A. Caro, *Lettere Familiari* (ed. Greco), Florence, 3 vols., 1957–61, nos. 490, 680 (letters giving a number of Farnese and other imprese).

DOMENICO POGGINI
(b. 1520; d. 1590)

Domenico was the younger brother of Giampaolo and the son of a gem-cutter, Michele. He was a craftsman of very accomplished academic style, both as sculptor in bronze and as medallist. He was also known as a die-cutter, goldsmith, and poet. His medals date between 1552 and 1590. He produced a large group of struck medals for the Medici, besides some cast medals.
See P. Grotemeyer, Thieme-Becker, 27 (1933), pp. 187–188; P. Grotemeyer, 'Domenico Poggini als Münzstempelschneider', in *Numismatik*, I, 1932, pp. 42–44; Habich, p. 118, pl. lxxxi; Forrer, 4, pp. 628–632.

339. LODOVICO ARIOSTO, the poet, born at Reggio d'Emilia 1474, died 1533.
Obv. Bust to right, in gown with slashed sleeves. Around, LVDOVICVS ARIOSTVS On truncation, incised, DOM(inicus) POG(ginus) F(ecit).

Without reverse.

51 mm. Cast hollow (Incuse of the obverse). A1076–339A

The reverse belonging to this medal shows a right hand with shears cutting off a serpent's tongue, and the motto PRO BONO MALVM

Literature: Cp. Arm. I, 254, 2; Habich, pl. lxxxi, 5; Cott p. 184.

340. ALFONSO II D'ESTE, fifth Duke of Ferrara (1533–59–97) and his wife LUCREZIA DE' MEDICI (see no. 325).
Obv. Bust to right of Alfonso, in cuirass and cloak. Around, ALPHON(sus) ESTEN(sis) FERRAR(iae) PRINCEPS

Rev. Bust to right of Lucrezia. Around, LVCRETIA MED(ices) ESTEN(sis) FERR(ariae) PRINCEPS

47 mm. Late cast. A1077–340A

Literature: Cp. Arm. I, 260, 36; Cott p. 184.

341. COSIMO DE' MEDICI (1519–74), Duke of Florence 1537, Grand Duke of Tuscany 1569.
Obv. Bust to right, in cuirass and mantle. Around, COSMVS MED(ices) FLOREN(tiae) ET SENAR(um) DVX II; below, 1561

Rev. View of the Uffizi, with the Palazzo Vecchio in the background; in front, Equity with scales and cornucopiae.

Around, PVBLICAE COMMODITATI

41 mm. Struck. A1078–341A

The building of the Uffizi was ordered by decree in 1560.

Literature: Cp. Arm. I, 256, 13; Heiss, *Florence*, ii, p. 52, no. 5, pl. iv, 6; Cott p. 184; Alvarez-Ossorio, p. 189, no. 254.

342. ELEONORA DE TOLEDO, first wife (1539) of Cosimo I de' Medici; died 1562.

Obv. Bust to left, back hair in net, dress open in front over stiff bodice and lace chemisette. Around, ELEONORA FLORENTIAE DVCISSA

Rev. A pea-hen standing to front, with wings spread sheltering six young ones. Around, CVM PVDORE LAETA FOECVNDITAS

43 mm. A1079–342A

The medal has been ascribed by Milanesi (*apud* Armand) to Domenico Poggini, which may be right, if he made the medal of Sibilla Lippi, of which the reverse is similar (Arm. III, 123, G). Armand himself prefers Domenico di Polo, and dates the medal about 1540, when Eleonora was still young. The *impresa* of the reverse was designed by Giovio (*Lettere*, ed. Domenichi, 1561, f. 56 *b*, 9 Aug. 1551).

Literature: Cp. Arm. II, 199, 20; III, 249, *c*; Cott p. 184; Middeldorf, *Morgenroth*, no. 139 (as D. Poggini); Alvarez-Ossorio, p. 230, no. 256 (as D. Poggini).

343. GIULIO NOBILI, Florentine Senator (1537–1612).

Obv. Bust to right, in doublet and cloak. Around, IVLIVS NOBILIVS P(atricius?) FLOR(entinus) and, below, 1570

Rev. Nude female figure standing to front, holding scales; a swan at her side. Around, HVIVS BENIGNITATE NOBILIS ET CLARVS

42 mm. A1080–343A

The attribution to Poggini on grounds of style seems sound.

Collection: S. Addington (sale, London, Sotheby, 19 May 1886, lot 38).

Literature: Arm. III, 123, F; Cott p. 184.

344. CAMILLA PERETTI, sister of Sixtus V, died 1591.

Obv. Bust to right, in veil. Around, CAMILLA PERETTA SYXTI V P(ontificis) M(aximi) SOROR Incised on truncation, D P

Rev. Façade of S. Lucia at Grottamare. Around, SANTA LVCIA AN(no) D(omini) M D LXXXX; incised on a panel under the pediment, CAMILLA PERETTA

47 mm. A1081–344A

Camilla married Giambattista Mignucci, who died in 1566 or earlier. The medal commemorates the foundation of the collegiate church at Grottamare on the Adriatic coast near Montalto.

Literature: Cp. Arm. I, 258, 27; Heiss, *Florence*, ii, p. 64, no. 10; Supino, no. 465; Berlin, Simon collection, no. 344; Litta, *Peretti*, no. 5 (specimen in Milan); Alvarez-Ossorio, p. 205, no. 265 (245 in text); Cott p. 184.

345. NICCOLÒ TODINI of Ancona, Captain of Castel Sant' Angelo, 1585–91.

Obv. Bust to right, in cuirass and ruff. Around, NICOL(aus) TODIN(us) ANC(onitanus) ARCIS S(ancti) ANG(eli) PREFECTVS Incised on truncation, D P

Rev. View of the Castel Sant' Angelo.

44 mm. A1082–345A

Literature: Cp. Arm. I, 259, 28; E. Rodocanachi, *Le Château Saint-Ange*, Paris, 1909, p. 180 and pl. 34; Cott p. 184; Alvarez-Ossorio, p. 229, no. 266.

346. BENEDETTO VARCHI, Florentine historian and man of letters (1502–65).

Obv. Bust to right, in doublet and cloak. Around, B(enedetto) VARCHI Incised on truncation, D P

Rev. A man lying at the foot of a laurel-tree; around, COSI QVAGGIV SI GODE

51 mm. Late cast. A1083–346A

Probably the medal mentioned by Annibal Caro in a letter of 20 April 1561, to Leonardo Salviati, when it was doubtless new.

Literature: Cp. Arm. I, 259, 30; Cott p. 184; Supino no. 467 (artist's initials not mentioned); Alvarez-Ossorio, p. 235, no. 267; A. Caro, *Lettere Familiari* (ed. Greco), Florence, 3 vols., 1957–61, no. 796.

R C

A medallist influenced by Domenico Poggini; Milanesi guessed that the initials are for Regolo Coccapani of Carpi, a jeweller who worked at Florence, or Raffaello Casellesi, a jeweller of Florence.

347. CAMILLA ALBIZZI, 1556.

Obv. Bust to right. Around, CAMILLA ALBITIA FLOS VIRG(inum) AETAT(is) SVAE

Rev. Apollo pursuing Daphne, whose hands sprout into laurel. Around, FORTVNA NO[N] MVTAT GENVS and, below, 1556 R C

45 mm. Late cast. A1084–347A

Literature: Cp. Arm. I, p. 187; Heiss, *Florence*, ii, p. 19, pl. i, 13; Cott p. 184.

PIER PAOLO GALEOTTI
(b. 1520; d. 1584)

Galeotti was called Romano from his birth-place, and signs his medals P.P.R. He was brought by Cellini from Rome to Florence, and was his pupil in goldsmithery and medal making. He accompanied Cellini to Ferrara and to Paris. From 1552 Galeotti, having settled in Florence, 1550, worked mainly as a medallist, and in 1555 Varchi commented on Galeotti as an equal of Domenico Poggini (*Sonetti*, ed. 1555, I. 252), especially for his Medici portraits. He appears to have worked briefly as a die-cutter at the papal mint in 1575, substituting for Lodovico Leoni (Martinori, fasc. xi, p. 67). The evidence of his medals also suggests that Galeotti had employment at, or at least commissions from, Milan, Genoa, and Turin. The earliest of his eight dated medals is of Cardinal Madruzzo, 1552, and he produced some seventy other medals, besides a series of twelve on the works of Cosimo I.

As Habich observes, Galeotti seems to have had a liking for pictorial reverses, using idyllic landscape, delicate figure composition, and swirling water, in a skilful manner. Galeotti is well represented in the Kress collection. See Forrer, 2, pp. 190–4; 7, pp. 336–7 (remains the most convenient account, with longest list of works); Thieme-Becker, 13, pp. 91–92; Habich, p. 136, pl. xcviii, nos. 1–9; Supino, nos. 383 ff (for medals of Cosimo I).

347*a*. BARBARA BORROMEO, wife of Camillo Gonzaga, married 1555, died 1572.

Obv. Bust to right in thin dress, cloak knotted on shoulder. Around, BARBARA GONZ(aga) BORR(omea) COM(itissa) NOVELL(arae) ANN(orum) XVII

Rev. Two summits of Pindus, on each a flaming vase; on left, Pegasus flying. Above, NON VLLI OBNOXIA VENTO

49 mm. A1225–487A

Most descriptions of this piece give NOXIA. It partakes of the style of Domenico Poggini and Galeotti, the reverse probably indicating the latter artist.

Literature: Cp. Arm. II, 202, 4; III, 250, *a*; Cott p. 194 (as Italian, 16th century).

347*b*. ALESSANDRO CAIMO, jurist of Milan.

Obv. Bust to left, in doublet. Around, ALEXAND(er) CAYMVS P(etri) PAVLI F(ilius) MEDIOL(anensis) I(uris) V(triusque) D(octor) ET BON(arum) ART(ium) AMATOR MDLVI

Rev. Boat on the sea; in the bows, Fortune, nude, holding up sail; in stern, helmeted woman, with spear, seated steering. Around, OPTANDA NAVIGATIO.

46 mm. A1226–488A

Galeotti has been suggested as the artist of this medal. The specimen in the Oppenheimer sale, lot 127 was so described.

Literature: Cp. Arm. II, 203, 2; Cott. p 185. Habich, pl. xcviii, 7, rev. (cp. the handling of the waves on a signed medal of Carpentier).

348. ANTONIO CALMONE, Secretary of Philip II.

Obv. Bust to right, in doublet. Around, ANTONIVS CALMONE AET(atis) AN(no) 34; in left PPR

Rev. A flowering shrub growing up through thorns. Above, DIFFICVLTAS INITII FERENDA

43 mm. A1085–348A

Another medal of Calmone by the same hand mentions his office and is dated in 1570.

Literature: Cp. Arm. I, 228, 3; Habich, pl. xcviii, 3; Cott p. 184.

349. BIANCA PANSANA CARCANIA.

Obv. Bust to left, dress with high collar and puffed sleeves. Around, BLANCA PANSANA CARCANIA and, in right corner, PPR

Rev. An island in a stormy sea, where people are drowning; on the island a circular wall enclosing a high rock, at foot of which a kneeling figure. Around, TE SINE NON POSSVM AD TE

55 mm. A1086–349A

Literature: Les Arts, Aug. 1908, p. 12, no. xv; Rodocanachi, *La femme italienne*, p. 220; cp. Arm. I, 233, 31; Cott p. 184. Löbbecke, lot 82, pl. vii (uniface lead specimen, 56 mm., bought by Vogel, not in his sale of 4 Nov. 1924).

350. GIROLAMO FIGINO, Milanese painter (second half sixteenth century).

Obv. Bust to left, loosely draped. Around, HIERONIMVS FIGINVS MDLXII

Rev. Minerva, armed, standing to front; at her feet, instruments of music and sculpture. Around, OMNIS IN HOC SVM

37 mm. A1087–350A

Reasonably attributed to Galeotti, who made a medal of Figino's master, Lomazzo. The latter in a poem celebrates Figino's talents as a painter, musician, and singer. Other specimens in the British Museum and formerly T. W. Greene collection.

Literature: Arm. II, 232, 14; III, 251, D; cp. Hill P.M.I.A.. p. 63, no. 4; Cott p. 184.

351. FRANCO LERCARI.

Obv. Bust to left, in doublet. Around, FRANCVS LERCARIVS R(egius ?) CONS(iliarius) and PPR

Rev. Female figure walking to left, carrying cornucopiae;

on left, a tree; landscape background and starry sky. Above, HVNC REGVNT OMNIAQ(ue) DOMANT

56 mm. A1088–351A

Other specimens in the Paris Cabinet des Médailles; Oppenheimer collection, sale lot 125 (in gilt bronze, ex. T. W. Greene collection).

Literature: Cp. Arm. I, 230, 13; Cott p. 184.

352. CRISTOFORO MADRUZZO, b. 1512, Cardinal, Prince Bishop of Trent 1539, of Brixen 1542, died 1587.

Obv. Bust to left, loosely draped. Around, CRISTOPHORVS MADR(utius) CAR(dinalis) EP(iscopu)S PRIN(ceps) Q(ue) TRIDENTINVS; below, PPR 1552 (?)

Rev. Female figure on a pedestal beside a river pointing to the sun, which is reflected in its waters.

35 mm. A1089–352A

According to Rizzini the landscape shows the Adige separating Trento from Dos Trento. The date on the obverse could be read 1556 (Bergmann), 1552 (Armand and the Kress specimen), or 1561 (Mazzuchelli).

Literature: Cp. Arm. I, 231, 20; II, p. 297; Cott p. 184; Rizzini, no. 319; J. Bergmann, *Medaillen auf... Männer des Oesterr. Kaiserstaates*, Vienna, 1858, I, pl. iii, 9, 10; *Museum Mazzuchellianum* I p. 376, pl. lxxxiii, vi.

353. *Obv.* Bust to left, loosely draped. Around, CHRISTOPHOR(us) MADRVCIVS CAR(dinalis) AC PRIN(ceps) TRIDENTI(nus) BRIXIN(ensis) Q(ue) EP(iscopu)S and, behind bust, PETRVS PAVLVS ROM(anus).

Rev. A harbour, containing ships, closed by a chain; without, Neptune reclining on back of a dolphin.

44 mm. A1090–353A

The reverse was suggested by the harbour of Ostia on sestertii of Nero. Armand reads BRIXIAE on obverse, and P.P.RO on reverse.

Literature: Cp. Arm. I, 231, 17; Keary, B.M.G., no. 175; Cott p. 184.

354. TOMMASO MARINI of Genoa, Duke of Terranuova.

Obv. Bust to right, in doublet and furred gown. Around, THOMAS MARINVS DVX TERRAENOVAE Incised on truncation, P P R

Rev. Sun shining on sea. Above, NVNQVAM SICCABITVR ESTV

52 mm. A1091–354A

Literature: Cp. Arm. I, 232, 25; Cott p. 185; Alvarez-Ossorio, p. 183, no. 245 (who also reproduces, no. 246, another medal of the sitter, unattributed); Löbbecke, lot 83.

355. JACOPO DE' MEDICI (1497–1555), Marquess of Marignan, and general of Charles V.

Obv. Bust to right, in cuirass and cloak. Around, IA(cobus) MED(ices) MARCH(io) MELEG(nani) ET CAES(aris) CAP(itaneus) G(e)N(er)ALIS ZC (etc.) and, in left corner, P P R

Without reverse.

56 mm. A1092–355A

Sometimes found as a hybrid with an alien reverse belonging to a medal of Marcantonio Magno, legend QVO ME FATA VOCANT.

Literature: Cp. Arm. I, 232, 26; Cott p. 185; Habich, pl. xcvii, no. 4 (for the Magno medal, Arm. III, 273, J., as in the style of Leoni); Alvarez-Ossorio, p. 197, no. 240 (Jacopo de' Medici medal with alien reverse); C. C. Vermeule, 'An imperial medallion of Leone Leoni and Giovanni Bologna's statue of the flying Mercury', in *The Numismatic Circular* (London), Nov. 1952, at col. 510, note 10 (observing that the reverse type may be based on a trial piece by Leone Leoni for a medal of Maximilian II).

356. CASSANDRA MARINONI, wife of Deifobo II Melilupi, killed in 1575.

Obv. Bust to right, rich dress, light veil behind. Around, CASSANDRA MARIN(oni) LVP(i) MARCH(ionissa) SO(raniae) and, in left corner, P P R

Rev. Circular temple; in background, city. Above, FORMAE PVDICITIAE Q(ue) S(acrum).

57 mm. A1093–356A

Literature: Les Arts, Aug. 1908, p. 12, no. xvii; Rodocanachi, *La femme italienne*, p. 220; cp. Arm. I, 232, 27; Cott p. 185.

357. GIAMPAOLO MELILUPI, son of Deifobo II and the preceding Cassandra.

Obv. Bust to left, as a boy, in cuirass. Around, IO(annes) PA(ulus) LVP(us) II MAR(chionis) SO(raniae) FIL(ius) AETATIS ANNORVM VI and, in inner arc behind, P P R

Rev. A child addressing a warrior (Deifobo II), who stands holding up a bâton; both in armour; arms at feet of Deifobo. Above, TE SEQVAR

50 mm. A1094–357A

Literature: Cp. Arm. I, 233, 28; Cott p. 185; Rizzini, 326.

358. ELISABETTA SCOTTI, wife of Giov. Alvise Gonfalonieri.

Obv. Bust to right, veiled. Incised across field, F A

Rev. Type obliterated; around, [IO(annes)] ALVISIVS CONFALONER[IVS]

40 mm. Late cast, tooled. A1095–358A

This is an interesting case of the alteration of a medal. It has been made from a specimen of the medal Arm. I, 229, 8, which bore both portraits. A wax positive was made;

the lady's name was erased; the man's portrait was pressed out with the fingers, whose prints are still visible, but his name is still in great part legible. A bronze casting having been made from this positive, the letters F A were incised on it.

Literature: Cott p. 185; Hill, 'Eight Italian Medals', in *Burl. Mag.*, 14 (1908–9), p. 216, pl. ii, 4 (where Hill published the medal of the husband, Arm. II, 229, 22, in which the obverse legend had faulted in such a way that the model for the medal can be seen to have been prepared by impressing the profile and the legend from separate parts).

359. CHIARA TAVERNA.

Obv. Bust to left, veil at back of head, rich dress. Around, CLARA TOL(entina) TABERNA VX(or) SVP(remi) CANCELL(arii) and, below truncation of arm, P P R

Rev. On clouds over landscape, Cybele, holding caduceus, in car drawn to right by two lions. Above, FERTILITAS IN PACE ET QVIETE

62 mm. A1096–359A

Chiara, of the family of the Counts of Tolentino, married Francesco Taverna (no. 360).

Literature: Arm. I, 235, 39; III, 113, *f*; Cott p. 185; H. G. Gutekunst sale (Hirsch, Munich, 7 Nov. 1910, lot 63; second specimen). Tervarent, col. 85 (the Car of Cybele).

360. FRANCESCO TAVERNA, Milanese jurisconsult, Count of Landriano (1488–1560).

Obv. Bust to right in gown. Around, FRA(nciscus) TABERNA CO(mes) LANDR(iani) MAGN(us) CANC(ellarius) STA(tus) MEDIO(lanensis) AN(no) LXVI and, in right corner, P P R

Rev. In landscape with trees, temple, etc., hound seated, looking up at constellation of the Goat. Above, IN CONSTANTIA ET FIDE FELICITAS

65 mm. A1097–360A

Literature: Cp. Arm. I, 235, 38; Hill, B.M.G., p. 39, fig. 46; Cott p. 185.

360*a*. GIANFRANCESCO TRIVULZIO (1504–73) Marquess of Vigevano, Count of Mesocco (1518–49), Rheinwald, and Stoss.

Obv. Bust to right, in armour and cloak; around, IO(annes) FRAN(ciscus) TRI(vultius) MAR(chio) VIG(evani) CO(mes) MVSO(chi) AC VAL(lis) REN ET STOSA(e) D(ominus). On the truncation, AET(atis) 39

Rev. Fortune on a dolphin, blown on by winds, passing over the waves, which are full of swimmers and drowning people. Above, FVI SVM ET ERO

60 mm. A1243–505A

The medal has been attributed to Galeotti, the age of the sitter dates the medal to about 1548, before the artist was re-settled in Florence.

Literature: Cp. Arm. II, 302, 13 *bis*; Cott p. 185 (Romano ?); Habich, p. 135, pl. xcvi, 5 (as unknown Milanese master); Keary, B.M.G., no. 169 (as Galeotti); Hill, B.M.G., p. 39, no. 109 (as hardly in style of Galeotti); Alvarez-Ossorio, p. 232, no. 447. Tervarent, col. 145, v (Fortune and dolphin).

GASPARO ROMANELLI

(Active 1560–1609)

Gasparo Romanelli of Aquila was active in Florence as medallist and goldsmith from about 1560, and is recorded as delivering a monstrance for the church of S. Maria di Collemaggio in Aquila in 1609. He is known from a letter of A. F. Doni to have made a medal of that writer; other medals, some signed G.R.F., are attributed to him with some probability. See G. Ceci, in Thieme-Becker, 28 (1934) p. 544; G. Pansa, 'Masello Cinelli di Sulmona e Gaspare Romanelli dell' Aquila', in *Rivista Abruzzese di Scienze, Lettere, ed Arti*, 22 (1907) pp. 236–244 (at pp. 241–4); Heiss, *Florence* ii, pp. 22–6; Forrer 5, p. 199 (including descriptions of the five medals of Vettori attributed to Romanelli).

361. PIETRO VETTORI the Younger, Florentine scholar, 1499–1585.

Obv. Bust to left, wearing gown. Around, P(etrus) VICTORIVS AET(atis) SVAE AN(no) LXXIX

Rev. An olive-branch. Around, LABOR OMNIA

45 mm. A1098–361A

Literature: Cp. Arm. II, 259, 10; Heiss, *Florence*, ii, p. 25, no. 2, pl. ii, 3; Cott p. 185; Alvarez-Ossorio, p. 237, no. 450.

362. *Obv.* Bust to left, in fur-trimmed gown. Around, PETRVS VICTORIVS AET(atis) SVAE AN(no) LXXX. Below bust, an olive spray.

Rev. Minerva holding olive-branch and spear. Around, INVENTRIX OLEAE ET ALTRIX INGENIOR(um).

38 mm. Struck. A1099–362A

Vettori wrote on the cultivation of the olive. This medal dates from 1574. Only one of the five medals of the sitter is signed by Romanelli, and dated 1580. They are reproduced in Bandini's life of Vettori of 1758 (title page and facing p. civ) and in Heiss.

Literature: Cp. Arm. II, 260, 12; Heiss, *Florence*, ii, p. 26, no. 4, pl. ii, 4; Supino, no. 506; Cott p. 185.

GASPARE MOLA

(b. *ca.* 1580; d. 1640)

Mola was born at Coldrè, near Como. His name also appears as Gasparo Molo. He began his career as a goldsmith in Milan, and worked in Florence, from *ca.* 1608, as a die-cutter. He remained there two years, and subsequently worked for the mints of Modena and Guastalla, 1613–14. He settled in Rome, and was appointed papal mint master in 1625 in succession to J. A. Moro. Mola was also a skilled armourer, as is testified by the helm and shield by him now preserved in the Bargello, and once ascribed to Cellini. Mola contributed reliefs to the scheme for the decoration of the doors of the Cathedral at Pisa. See Thieme-Becker, 25 (1931) pp. 27–8; Forrer, 4, pp. 111–7; 8, p. 68 (useful for the listing of works); A. Bertolotti, 'Giacomo Antonio Moro, Gaspare Mola e Gasparo Morone-Mola incisori nella zecca di Roma', in *Archivio Storico Lombardo* 4 (1877) pp. 295–335 (including documents: the first article to distinguish between the work of the three artists); Martinori, *Annali*, III, fasc. 14 pp. 56, 86 (biography), pp. 70–78 (medals by Mola).

Documents on Mola at Mantua form an appendix to A. Magnaguti, *Le Medaglie mantovane*, Mantua, 1921, pp. 165–8. Documents concerning Mola and the Florentine court are quoted in A. Magnaguti, *Ex Nummis Historia, IX, Le medaglie dei Gonzaga,* Rome, 1965, pp. 51–3; a small group of the Florentine medals is listed in Supino, *Il medagliere Mediceo*, Florence, 1899, nos. 595–607 (with references and corrections to the illustrations in Heiss, *Florence et les Florentins*, vol. II). The exquisite models in wax for coinage, some by Mola and some by Mazzafirri, illustrated in B.F.A.C. exhibition catalogue, London, 1912, pl. lxvii, are also published by Hill, 'Notes on Italian medals, xxvi', in *Burl. Mag.*, 31 (1917), pp. 211–7, plate facing p. 212. These waxes are now in the British Museum. Forrer, 4, p. 116, mentions two medals of private persons by Mola. That of Cassiano dal Pozzo is mentioned in a letter to him from Jacopo Ligozzi, 21 Dec. 1632 (Bottari-Ticozzi, I, p. 357).

For Mola as a relief artist, see Pope-Hennessy, *Italian High Renaissance and Baroque Sculpture*, 1963, Catalogue vol. pp. 89, 90.

363. VINCENZO GONZAGA, fourth Duke of Mantua (1562–87–1612).

Obv. Bust to right, in cuirass with scarf. Around, VINCENTIVS GONZAGA. Below, GASP(ar) MOLO F(ecit).

Rev. St George and the Dragon. Around, D(ei) G(ratia) DVX MANT(uae) IIII ET MONT(is) F(errati) II ET C and, below, PROTEC(tor) NOSTER ASPICE

43 mm. A1100–363A

There are other specimens in the British Museum (struck), in the Magnaguti collection (in silver and in bronze), and at Copenhagen (cast).

Literature: Cott p. 185; Magnaguti, nos. 57, 58, pl. xii; Keary, *Guide*, no. 215 (for British Museum specimen).

364. (See 484*c*).

ROMAN SCHOOL, XVI CENTURY

GIOVANNI BERNARDI DA CASTELBOLOGNESE

(b. 1496; d. 1553)

Bernardi worked at the papal mint in Rome between 1534–8 and 1541–5, but had a much greater reputation as a crystal engraver. For biography, see Thieme-Becker, 3, pp. 435–6; for his engraved crystals see E. Kris, *Meister und Meisterwerke der Steinschneidekunst*, Vienna, 1929. For plaquettes after his engraved crystals see Pope-Hennessy, *Kress Bronzes*, nos. 29–43.

365. CLEMENT VII, Pope (1523–34).

Obv. Bust to right, bearded, in cope. Around, CLEM(ens) VII PONT(ifex) MAX(imus).

Rev. Joseph revealing himself to his brethren; above, EGO SVM IOSEPH FRATER VESTER

33 mm. Restrike, from cracked dies. A1102–365A

One of the modern restrikes issued by the Vatican mint.

The original was, according to Vasari, engraved by Giovanni Bernardi. It cannot, as Thurston has suggested (*Holy Year of Jubilee*, London, 1900, p. 52) have been connected with the Jubilee of 1525, for Clement is bearded.

Literature: Cp. Arm. I, 138, 4; Habich, pl. lxxvii, 5; Cott p. 186 (as perhaps by Bernardi). For the restriking of papal medals in the nineteenth century see F. Mazio, *Serie dei coni di medaglie pontificie . . . esistenti nella pontificia zecca di Roma,* Rome, 1824 (where this medal is no. 47).

ALESSANDRO CESATI

(Active 1538–1564)

Alessandro Cesati called il Greco or Grechetto, son of an Italian father and a Cypriote mother. He worked in Rome from 1538, first in the service of Cardinal Alessandro Farnese, then from 1540 for some twenty years as Master of the Papal Mint; in 1561 he went to serve the Duke of Savoy, but left for Cyprus in 1564. His work represents the highwater mark of academic finish in Rome.

See Forrer, 1, pp. 389–392; 7, pp. 173–4; Hill, in Thieme-Becker, 6, pp. 313–4; Habich, pp. 116–7, pl. lxxvii, nos. 6–10; Martinori, *Annali*, fasc. 9, pp. 40, 42–4 and fasc. 10, pp. 22–30 (for critical lists of papal medals).

366. PAUL III, Pope (1534–49).

Obv. Bust to right, in cope. Around, PAVLVS III PONT(ifex) MAX(imus) AN(no) XI

Rev. Ganymede watering the Farnese lilies, resting his left hand on shoulder of the eagle. Above, ΦΕΡΝΗ ΖΗΝΟΣ and, below, ΕΥΡΑΙΝΕΙ

40 mm. Struck. A1103–366A

Φερνὴ Ζηνός (dowry of Zeus), a pun on the name Farnese, and *εὖ ῥαίνει* (he waters well) refer to the grant by Paul to his son Pierluigi of the Duchies of Parma and Piacenza in 1545. The medal has nothing to do with the Jubilee as Thurston (*Holy Year of Jubilee*, London, 1900, p. 52) supposes; but the medal was reissued again in 1550 with modifications alluding to that event.

Literature: Cp. Arm. I, 172, 5; Cott p. 186.

367. EMANUELE FILIBERTO, tenth Duke of Savoy (1528–53–80), and MARGUERITE DE FRANCE (married 1559, died 1574).

Obv. Bust of the Duke to right, wearing cuirass and mantle. Around, EMANVEL PHILIBERTVS III D(ux) SABAVDIAE X On the shoulder, A F

Rev. Bust of the Duchess to left, in rich dress, with light veil. Around, MARGARITA FRA(n)C(isci) REG(is) F(ilia) D(ucissa) SABAVDIAE On truncation of arm, A F

41 mm. Struck. Once gilt. A1104–367A

Armand misread the signature on this specimen A P. If not A(lexander) F(ecit) it is A(λέξανδρος) E(ποίει), for Cesati sometimes signs in Greek.

Literature: Arm. I, 173, 13; III, 77, *b*; Cott p. 186.

368. DIDO, Queen of Carthage.

Obv. Bust to right, wreathed, hair in coils and falling on neck, drapery fastened on right shoulder. Around, in Greek, ΔΙΔΩ ΒΑΣΙΛΙΣΣΑ

Rev. View of Carthage, with galleys lying in harbour before it; above, on left, ΚΑΡΧΗΔΩΝ

45 mm. A1105–368A

All of the known specimens seem to be cast, but the original was die-struck. The British Museum specimen reads *ΔΙΔΩΝ*; on most others for the N is substituted a leaf.

Literature: Cp. Hill, 'Classical influence on the Italian medal', in *Burl. Mag.*, 18 (1911), p. 267, pl. ii, 8. Cott, p. 186.

369. PRIAM, King of Troy.

Obv. Bust to right, diademed; around, ΠΡΙΑΜΟΣ ΒΑΣΙΛΕΥΣ

Rev. View of Troy, with galleys in harbour before it; on wall of citadel, ΙΛΙΟΝ; above, ΤΡΟΙΑ

39 mm. A1106–369A

The original was struck from dies; all of the published specimens, however, appear to be casts.

Collection: His de la Salle (sale, London, Sotheby, 22 Nov. 1880, lot 164).

Literature: Cp. F. Parkes Weber, 'Attribution of medals of Priam, Augustus, and Alexander the Great to a medallist of Pope Paul III, possibly, Alessandro Cesati', in *Num. Chron.*, 17 (1897), pp. 314–7. Hill, 'Classical influence on the Italian medal', in *Burl. Mag.*, 18 (1911), p. 267, pl. ii, 5; Cott p. 186.

GIOVANNI ANTONIO DE' ROSSI (b. 1517; d. after 1575)

The artist was born in Milan, was working in Venice in 1543, and went to Rome in 1546, where he signed medals of Marcellus II and of Paul IV, 1556, 1557. After a period at the court in Florence he returned to Rome as an engraver with Cesati, whom he succeeded in 1561. During his Roman periods he also produced medals of Pius IV (seven dies), Pius V (nine dies), and Gregory XIII (three dies). In 1562 he cut a celebrated cameo of Cosimo I de' Medici and his family, and he also cut a cameo of Pius V. See Thieme-Becker, 29 (1935) p. 60; Habich, p. 11, fig. 44, p. 117, pl. lxxix, 5, 6, 8; Forrer, 5, pp. 216–9 (reproducing the medal of Henry II of France, 1558); 8, p. 175; Supino, nos. 418–432.

369*a*. JULIUS III, Pope (1550–5).

Obv. Bust to left, in cope. Around, [D](ivus) IVLIVS III PONT(ifex) O[P]T(imus) MAX(imus) AN(no) V

Without reverse.

Lead, 80 mm. A1120–383A

This lead apparently derives from an unsigned model by de' Rossi for a medal of Julius III of 1555. The attribution is clear from comparison with the following medal. The Berlin specimen (Simon no. 329) shows the reverse of Atlas, with inscription NON IMPAR ONERI FORTITVDO.

Literature: Arm. II, 215, 8; Martinori, *Annali*, fasc. 10, p. 28 (obverse legend restored, after Armand, as OPT); Cott p. 187 (as Italian).

370. MARCELLUS II, Pope (1555).

Obv. MARCELLVS II PONT(ifex) MAX(imus). Bust to left, in cope. Below, IO(annes) ANT(onius) RVB(eus) MEDIOL(anensis).

Rev. The Church seated reading the Gospels, holding a rudder as symbol of the Papal power ruling the world.

76 mm. A1107–370A

Literature: Cp. Arm. I, 244, 5 (reverse figure as Prudence); *Tresor, méd. papes*, pl. x, 3; F. Bonanni, *Numismata Pontificum Romanorum*, Rome, 1699, I, p. 260 (for the interpretation of the reverse); Martinori, *Annali*, fasc. 10, p. 47; Cott p. 186.

370*a*. PIUS IV, Pope (1559–65).

Obv. Bust to left, wearing cope with reclining figure of St John the Evangelist on orphrey, head of Christ on morse; around, PIVS IIII PONT(ifex) OPT(imus) MAX(imus) AN(no) I

Without reverse.

67 mm. A1121–384A

Another specimen in the British Museum.

Literature: Cp. Arm. II, 216, 15; *Tresor, méd. papes*, pl. xi, 6; Martinori, *Annali*, fasc. 10, p. 78 (as probably by de Rossi); Cott p. 187 (as Italian).

371. VINCENZO BOVIO of Bologna.

Obv. Bust to left, with long beard, in gown. Around, VINC(entius) BOVIVS BONONIEN(sis) PROTHONOT(arius) APOST(olicus).

Rev. Religion standing to front, holding cross, and looking up at the sun's rays; behind her, an ox (for Bovio); on the ground to right, a yoke, to which she points. Around, ANTIDOTVM VITAE

72 mm. Gilt. A1108–371A

The same reverse is found attached to a portrait of Paul IV signed by Rossi. Bovio in 1550 was *primicerius* of the cathedral of Bologna.

Literature: Cp. Arm. I, 247, 26; Cott p. 186; Arm. I, 244, 7, and *Tresor, méd. papes*, pl. xi, 1 (for the medal of Paul IV).

GIAN FEDERIGO BONZAGNI (d. after 1586)

Bonzagni was born in Parma, son of Gian Francesco. He was active as sculptor, goldsmith, medallist and die-engraver, and is documented in Rome from 1554 as an assistant to his brother Gian Giacomo and to Alessandro Cesati. His medals are dated between 1547–1575, and number more than fifty. See S. Lottici, in Thieme-Becker, 4, p. 329; for descriptions of medals, Armand and for papal medals, Martinori, *Annali*, fasc. 9, pp. 26, 40, 42, 43, 45; fasc. 10, pp. 23, 58–61, 75–9, 82; fasc. 11, pp. 22, 24, 26, 76–9, 86; fasc. 12, p. 39.

372. PIUS IV, Pope (1559–65).

Obv. Bust to right, in cope. Around, PIVS IIII PON(tifex) MAX(imus) O(ptimus) P(rinceps).

Rev. The Porta Pia. Above, PORTA PIA, below, ROMA

31 mm. Struck. A1109–372A

Literature: Cp. Arm. II, 217, 18; III, 105, 1; Cott, p. 186.

373. PIUS V, Pope (1566–72).

Obv. Bust to left, in skull-cap and cape with hood. Around, PIVS V PONT(ifex) OPT(imus) MAX(imus) ANNO VI and, below, F(edericus) P(armensis).

Rev. The Battle of Lepanto. On a galley, an angel with cross and chalice; God hurling lightning from above. Above, DEXTERA TVA DOM(ine) PERCVSSIT INIMICVM 1571

37 mm. Silver, struck. A1110–373A

Literature: Cp. Arm. I, 226, 33; Cott p. 186.

374. IPPOLITO II D'ESTE, son of Alfonso I, born 1509, cardinal 1538, died 1572.

Obv. Bust to left, in cape with hood. Around, HIPPOLYTVS ESTEN(sis) S(acrae) R(omanae) E(cclesiae) PRESB(yter) CARD(inalis) FERRAR(iensis). Below, FED(ericus) PARM (ensis).

Without reverse.

46 mm. Cast hollow (Incuse of the obverse). A1111–374A

Other specimens show a reverse with Abraham receiving the three angels and the legend NE TRANSEAS SERVVM TVVM

Literature: Cp. Arm. I, 222, 4; Habich, pl. lxxviii, 2; Cott p. 186; Alvarez-Ossorio, p. 143, no. 216.

375. PIERLUIGI FARNESE, first Duke of Parma and Piacenza (1503–45–7).

Obv. Bust to right, in cuirass and mantle. Around, P(etrus) LOYSIVS F(arnesius) PARM(ae) ET PLAC(entiae) DVX I Below, I(oannes) F(edericus) PARM(ensis).

Rev. Bird's-eye view of the citadel of Parma, with gate opening on a stream. Around, AD CIVITAT(is) DITIONISQ(ue) TVTEL(am) MVNIM(entum) EXTRVCTVM

40 mm. Struck. A1112–375A

Many specimens are known.

Literature: Cp. Arm. I, 222, 6 (the signature incomplete); Cott p. 186; Litta, *Farnese*, ii, 1. (Two varieties are published; Alvarez-Ossorio, p. 147, no. 220. Hill, N.I.A., no. 103).

FEDERIGO COC...

This artist may be Coccola, Cocciola or de Cocchis. Forrer (I, p. 445) describes three medals of Pope Clement XIII besides these two pieces in the Kress collection as bearing the signature F.CO or F.C. Martinori, *Annali*, vol. 2, fasc. 10, pp. 68, 86, mentions a Federigo Cicciolo who engraved seals in 1560 and 1564, and ascribes the three papal medals to one Federigo de Cocchis who is recorded as a member of the College of Goldsmiths (fasc. xi p. 85). These three names could well represent the same artist.

376. JEAN PARISOT DE LA VALLETTE, Grand Master of Malta (1557–68).

Obv. Bust to right, in armour and mantle, with cross of Malta on breast; around, F(rater) IO(annes) VALLETA M(agnus) M(agister) HOSP(italis) HIER(usalem); below, F(edericus) CO

Rev. David striking off the head of Goliath; Philistines fleeing; above, VNVS X MILLIA Below the head of Goliath, letters I O B stamped.

50 mm. A1113–376A

This refers to the defence of Malta in 1565.

Literature: Cp. Arm. I, 262, 4; Cott p. 186; Alvarez-Ossorio, p. 233, no. 312; E. H. Furse, *Mémoires numismatique de l'Ordre Souverain de Saint Jean de Jérusalem*, Rome, 1889, p. 323.

377. PROSPERO PUBLICOLA SANTACROCE, Roman, born 1514, cardinal 1565, died 1589.

Obv. Bust to right, wearing cape with hood. Around, PROSPER SANCTACRVCIVS S(anctae) R(omanae) E(cclesiae) CARD(inalis). On truncation, FED(ericus) COC.

Rev. Bird's-eye view of a building with garden in front. Above, GEROCOMIO; below, 1579

54 mm. A1114–377A

For the villa at Gericomio, built by Cardinal Santacroce in 1579 as the place of his retirement, on the road between S. Gregorio da Sassola and Tivoli, see R. A. Lanciani, *Wanderings in the Campagna*, Boston-New York, 1909, p. 118.

Literature: Cp. Arm. I, 263, 5; Cott p. 186; Alvarez-Ossorio, p. 222, no. 315.

LORENZO FRAGNI
(b. 1548; d. 1618)

Fragni was born in Parma, and was called to Rome by his uncle and master, Gian Federigo Bonzagni, with whom he worked in the papal mint from 1572 until 1586. He produced medals of Gregory XIII and of Sixtus V. See Thieme-Becker, 12, pp. 274–5; Forrer, 2, pp. 133–5 (fuller list of Fragni's productions); Habich, p. 117, pl. lxxviii, nos. 5–7.

378. SIXTUS V, Pope (1585–90).

Obv. Bust to right, wearing skull-cap and cape with hood; around, SIXTVS V PONT(ifex) OPT(imus) MAX(imus).

Below, L(aurentius) PAR(mensis).

Rev. Securitas seated to right, holding fleur-de-lis sceptre, her head resting on her right hand; beside her, flaming altar; around, SECVRITAS POPVLI ROMANI and, below, ALMA ROMA

37 mm. Struck. A1115–378A

One of the hybrids common in the Papal series; for the reverse is from a die made for Paul III (hence the fleur-de-lis), probably by Cesati.

Literature: Cp. Arm. I, 282, 27; Cott p. 186.

GIOVANNI PALADINO
(Active to *ca.* 1572)

Paladino was a Roman medallist and author of a series of medals of the Popes from Martin V (1417–1431) to Pius V (1566–1572). He is believed to have been active during the reigns of Pius V and his predecessor, his portraits being based on earlier medals. This medal series was extended by Giambattista Pozzi, a Milanese artist of the later sixteenth century to include all of the Popes from St Peter to Alexander V (1409–1410), the portraits being entirely imaginary.

See Grotemeyer, in Thieme-Becker, 26 (1932), p. 154; Forrer, 4, pp. 366–7 (useful summary listing of the medals); Supino, nos. 533–564 (no illustrations); Martinori, *Annali*, fasc. 11, pp. 26, 27, 69 (citing only two pieces. No documents on the career). For Pozzi's series of medals see Forrer, 4, pp. 680–1.

379. LEO X, Pope (1513–21).

Obv. Bust to right, in cope. Around, LEO X PONTIFEX MAX(imus).

Rev. Liberality emptying money from a horn; around her, mitre, cardinal's hat, crown, books, instruments of music, etc. Above, LIBERALITAS PONTIFICIA

33 mm. Restrike. A1116–379A

One of the modern restrikes issued by the Vatican mint. The original dies are attributed to Paladino.

Literature: Cp. Arm. III, 144, M; Supino, no. 560 (40 mm); Cott p. 186. For the restriking of papal medals in the nineteenth century see F. Mazio, *Serie dei coni di medaglie pontificie . . . esistenti nella pontificia zecca di Roma*, Rome, 1824.

UNATTRIBUTED PAPAL MEDALS

380. CLEMENT VII, Pope (1523–34).

Obv. Bust to right, bearded, in cope. Around, CLEMENS VII PONTIFEX MAX(imus).

Without reverse.

68 mm. A1117–380A

The attribution to Sangallo, which has been suggested, is unsatisfactory. The Morgenroth catalogue mentions that the medal resembles that by Francesco dal Prato (Habich, pl. lxxx, 1), and also that Alfonso Lombardi made a portrait of the Pope (perhaps a medal; cf. *Corpus*, p. 157).

Literature: Arm. II, 166, 4; Middeldorf, *Morgenroth*, no. 142; Cott p. 186.

381. PAUL III, Pope (1534–49).

Obv. Bust to right, in cope. Around, PAVLVS III PONT(ifex) MAX(imus).

Rev. Fight between a griffin and a serpent. All in wreath.

62 mm. A1118–381A

The griffin is supposed to represent the Perugians, who had revolted on account of the salt-tax and were subdued by the Pope in 1540. Hill's MSS note that the medal has been attributed to Belli, G. G. Bonzagni, and Cesati. No satisfactory attribution to any medallist has been made.

Literature: Cp. Arm. II, 166, 6; Keary, B.M.G., 319 (as Valerio Belli?); Cott p. 187.

382. *Obv.* Bust to right, in cope decorated with fleurs-de-lis.

Without reverse.

Height 84 mm., cast hollow, without background.

A1119–382A

A variant on which the cope is decorated with six chalices is in the Kestner Museum, Hanover.

Literature: Les Arts, Aug. 1908, p. 12, no. xi; Cott p. 187.

383. (See 369*a*).

384. (See 370*a*).

SCHOOL OF PADUA

FOLLOWER OF RICCIO

385. ANDREA BRIOSCO (*ca.* 1470/5–1532), called Riccio, celebrated Paduan bronze sculptor.

Obv. Bust to left, lightly draped. Around, ANDREAS CRISPVS PATAVINVS AEREVM D(ivi) ANT(onii) CANDELABRVM F(ecit).

Rev. A broken laurel tree with withered top; a leafy branch springing from the trunk lower down; above, a star. Inscription: OBSTANTE GENIO

52 mm. A1122–385A

This medal is by many supposed to be the work of the artist himself, but the ruined tree, from which a fresh branch springs, seems to allude to his death in 1532, the branch representing his school. The inscription on the obverse describes him as maker of the famous candlestick in the Santo at Padua.

Literature: Les Arts, Aug. 1908, p. 12, no. xxii; cp. Arm. I, 120, 1; *Corpus*, p. 140; Cott p. 187. Pope-Hennessy, *Kress Bronzes*, nos. 203–231 (for plaquettes by Riccio). Tervarent, col. 232, ii.

VALERIO BELLI

(b. *ca.* 1468; d. 1546)

Valerio Belli was born at Vicenza, and worked in Rome as a celebrated crystal and gem engraver. He left Rome in the fifteen-twenties, and moved to Venice, and to Vicenza. His reputation as a crystal engraver rivalled that of Giovanni Bernardi. Belli made a few medals, and a series of some fifty so-called coins of ancient worthies which were struck from dies, but which are mostly known in the form of casts, like no. 387. For his career see Thieme-Becker, 3, pp. 249–250; Forrer, 1, pp. 158–160; F. Barbieri in *Dizionario Biografico* degli Italiani, 7, Rome, 1965, pp. 682–4. J. Babelon, 'Une Médaille de la reine Artémise par Valerio Belli', in *Berliner Münzblätter*, 52 (1932) pp. 399–403. For his engraved work see E. Kris, *Meister und Meisterwerke der Steinschneidekunst*, Vienna, 1929. There is a lead reproduction of the self portrait medal by Valerio Belli in the collection, for which see no. 385*a* in the Appendix. The plaquettes by Belli in the Kress collection are Pope-Hennessy, *Kress Bronzes*, nos. 4–25.

385*a*. See Appendix.

386. PIETRO BEMBO (1470–1547) promoted Cardinal, 1538.

Obv. Head to left. On left, PETRI BEMBI

Rev. Bembo, reclining under trees beside a stream, holding a branch.

34 mm. Struck. A1123–386A

Perhaps the piece of which Belli is recorded as having made dies in 1532.

Literature: Cp. Arm. I, 136, 4; Habich, pl. lxxvi, 6; A. von Sallet, 'Zwei italienische Medaillen', in *Zeitschrift für Numismatik,* 10 (1883), pp. 194–6 (for the reverse as seated Bembo, wrongly dated to 1520); Bottari-Ticozzi, I, pp. 528–9 (for letters from Bembo to Belli, of 28 Feb. and 12 March 1532); Alvarez-Ossorio, p. 107, no. 116; Cott p. 187.

387. HELEN OF TROY.

Obv. Bust to right; around, ΕΛΕΝΗ ΒΑΣΙΛΙΣΣΑ

Rev. Concord seated, holding cornucopiae; on left, ΟΜΟΝΟΙΑ ΕΛΛΗΝΩΝ

29 mm. A1124–387A

Other specimens in the British Museum (cast, without rev.), at Vienna, and formerly in the Rosenheim collection (struck).

Literature: Cott p. 187; Habich, pl. lxxvi, nos. 1–4, 7, 9 (for the coins of ancient worthies).

GIOVANNI DAL CAVINO
(b. 1500; d. 1570)

Cavino of Padua was the most famous of all imitators of ancient Roman coins, and the name Paduans came to be applied to most sixteenth century imitations of Roman sestertii and medallions. A large number of dies, mainly by Cavino, are preserved in the Paris Cabinet des Médailles. They were bought from the conte Giovanni de Lazzara of Padua by Th. Lecomte and bequeathed by him to the Abbey of Ste. Geneviève, Paris, in 1670 (Forrer, I, p. 366). They were published by Claude du Molinet, *Le Cabinet de la Bibliothèque de Sainte Geneviève*, Paris, 1692 (pp. 92–118, pls. 23–27, mainly imitations of Roman coins). Present opinion seems to be that the Cavino versions of Roman coins were produced with the intent to deceive the collector, and were recognised as such during the sixteenth century. Both the imitation coins and the portrait medals are well represented in the Kress collection.

Besides the accounts given by Forrer, I, pp. 366–373 (useful listing of the works) and G. F. Hill, Thieme-Becker, 6, pp. 236–7, may be noted Richard Hoe Lawrence, *Medals by Giovanni Cavino the Paduan*, New York (privately printed), 1883 (for the list of 113 pieces); G. F. Hill, 'Classical influence on the Italian medal' in *Burl. Mag.*, 18 (1911), pp. 259–268; M. Bernhart, 'Paduaner' in *Blätter für Munzfreunde*, 1912, cols. 5054–5060, pl. 200; G. Habich, *Medaillen der italienischen Renaissance* (1924), pp. 110–111; G. Kisch, 'Numismatisches "Kunstfälschertum" im Urteil der Zeitgenossen', in *Schweizerische Numismatische Rundschau*, 36 (1954), pp. 31–4; R. H. Chowen, 'Paduan forgeries of Roman coins', in *Renaissance Papers* (University of S. Carolina) 3 (1956), pp. 50–65; J. R. Jones, 'Cavino's imitations of Roman coins', in *The Numismatic Circular* (London), 72, no. 11 (Nov. 1965) pp. 232–3 (for Cavino's reputation and early literary references); F. Cessi, 'Pezzi editi e inediti di Giovanni da Cavino al Museo Bottacin di Padova', in *Padova*, 11, (1965) nos. 1, pp. 22–9; 2, pp. 13–8; 3, pp. 26–32. For Cavino's contemporary reputation the publication of his epitaph may be noted, by J. D. Köhler, in *Historische Münzbelustigung*, vol. 18 (Nuremberg, 1746) pp. 102–4.

388. ALFONSO II D'AVALOS (1502–1546) Marquess of Vasto.

Obv. Bust to right in cuirass. Around, ALFON(sus) AVOL(us) MAR(chio) GVAS(ti) CAP(itaneus) GEN(eralis) CAR(oli) V IMP(eratoris).

Rev. Palm-tree; on left, a man in cloak with hands behind his back, and a pile of arms; on right, a woman (Africa) seated on a cuirass, mourning, beside a ship's prow. Around, AFRICA CAPTA and, below, C C

37 mm. Cast. (The original was struck.) A1125–388A

The reverse is borrowed from one of Cavino's imitations of a 'Judaea Capta' sestertius of Vespasian. C C may be for *Carolo Caesari* or *Concessu Caesaris* (since *Senatus Consulto* would be out of place).

Literature: Cp. Arm. II, 163, I; III, 78, A; Cott p. 187; Alvarez-Ossorio, p. 99, no. 183.

389. ALESSANDRO BASSIANO, Paduan scholar, and the MEDALLIST.

Obv. Busts of Bassiano with short beard and Cavino with long beard to right, jugate, draped in antique fashion. Around, ALEXAND(er) BASSIANVS ET IOHAN(nes) CAVINEVS PATAVINI

Rev. Genius, sacrificing. Around, GENIO BENEVOLENTIAE DVLCIS (from same die as no. 392).

36 mm. Struck. A1126–389A

This reverse was made for Cavino's medal of Giannantonio Dolce (no. 392). His dies, as will be seen, are often found wrongly combined.

Bassiano advised the medallist in his restitutions of the antique.

Literature: Arm. I, 180, 10; cp. Hill, P.M.I.A., p. 51, no. 28, pl. xxiii; Cott p. 187. For Bassiano See E. Zorzi, 'Un antiquario padovano del sec. xvi—Alessandro Maggi da Bassano', in *Bollettino del Museo Civico di Padova*, 51 (1962), pp, 41–98.

390. GIAMPIETRO MANTOVA BENAVIDES, Paduan physician, died 1520.

Obv. Bust to left in robe. Around, IO(annes) PET(rus) MAN(tua) BONAVI(tus) MEDICVS PATER

Rev. Façade of temple; within, statue of goddess holding cornucopiae; around, AETERNITAS MANT(uana).

36 mm. Struck. A1127–290A

Other specimens at Brescia and Vienna. This medal was probably made some time after the death of Benavides to the order of his son, Marco Mantova Benavides.

Literature: Cp. Arm. I, 179, 4; Cott p. 187; J. D. Köhler, 'Eine Medaille auf drey berühmte Paduaner, den Jureconsultum Marcum Mantuam Bonavitum, den Antiquarium Alexandrum Bassianum, und den Medailleur Johannem Gavineum von A. 1570', in *Historische Münzbelustigung*, 18 (Nuremberg, 1746) pp. 97–104. Hill, N.I.A., no. 26 (for a medal of the son).

391. GIROLAMO CORNARO.

Obv. Bust to right with long beard, in robe. Around, HIER(onymus) CORNELIVS

Rev. Cornaro seated on platform, distributing alms. Around, PAVPERTATIS PATAVINAE TVTOR; below, MD XXXX; on platform, DEO OPT(imo) FAV(ente).

37 mm. Struck. A1128–391A

Literature: Cp. Arm. I, 180, 12; Cott p. 187; Alvarez-Ossorio, p. 130, no. 185.

392. GIOVANNI ANTONIO VINCENZO DOLCE, Paduan jurist, born 1482, canon of Padua 1516, died 1554 (?).

Obv. Bust to left with long beard, in robe. Around, IO(annes) AN(tonius) VIN(centius) DVLCIVS IVR(is) CON(sultus) CAN(onicus) PATAVIN(us) AETA(tis) LVII and, below, 1539

Rev. Genius, holding dolphin in left hand, sacrificing with patera in right hand over flaming altar. Around, GENIO BENEVOLENTIAE DVLCIS

37 mm. Struck. A1129–392A

Literature: Arm. I, 181, 14; Cott p. 187; Hill, N.I.A., no. 76 (for a variant).

393. GIOVANNI MELS, jurist, born at Udine, died 1559.

Obv. Bust to right, in cloak. Around, IOANNES MELSIVS IVR(is) C(onsultus).

Rev. Mels as Genius sacrificing with patera on altar; holds cornucopiae in left hand. Around, GENIO MELSI

38 mm. Struck. A1130–393A

Literature: Cp. Arm. I, 182, 20; Cott p. 187.

394. BALDUINO DEL MONTE, brother of Pope Julius III. Count of Montesansavino 1550, died 1556.

Obv. Bust to left, in doublet and fur-trimmed robe. Around, BALDVINVS DE MONTE COMES

Rev. Combat between two horsemen. Around, MAGIS VICI SED TIBI

42 mm. Struck. A1131–394A

The reverse, which is too large for the obverse, really belongs to a medal of Antinous by Cavino.

Literature: Cp. Arm. I, 182, 22; Cott p. 187; Alvarez-Ossorio, p. 199, no. 191.

395. GIROLAMO (d. 1558), Count of Panico, and POMPEO LUDOVISI (d. 1565).

Obv. Busts of the two to left, jugate. Around, HIERONYMVS PANICVS PAT(avinus) POMPEIVS LODOVISIVS BON(oniensis).

Rev. Genius sacrificing, as on no. 392 (from same die).

37 mm. Struck. A1132–395A

The reverse, as already observed, belongs to the medal of Dolce (no. 392). Girolamo, Count of Panico, Paduan poet and musician, died blind in 1558. Pompeo Ludovisi of Bologna received the title of Count from Paul III; he died in 1565. His son was Gregory XV.

Collection: His de la Salle (sale, London, Sotheby, 22 Nov. 1880, lot 158).

Literature: Cp. Arm. I, 183, 25; Cott p. 187; Hill, 'Notes on Italian Medals XIII. Some Florentine medals', in *Burl. Mag.*, 22 (1912), p. 131–8 (at p. 137, pl. II, F., variant reverses of the medal).

396. FRANCESCO QUIRINI, Venetian patrician, poet, and soldier.

Obv. Bust to right, draped. Around, FRANC(iscus) QVIRINVS

Rev. Wolf and Twins. Above, PERPETVA SOBOLES

37 mm. Struck. A1133–396A

The dies of both sides are preserved in Paris. Francesco Quirini was writing in 1544.

Literature: Cp. Arm. I, 184, 30; Cott, p. 188; Alvarez-Ossorio, p. 212, no. 193; Rosenheim sale lot 140 (specimen with substituted inscription ALEXANDER MEDICES). Rizzini 282 (for a medal of Girolamo Quirini attributed to Cavino).

397. LUCA SALVIONI, Paduan jurist.

Obv. Bust to right, in robe. Around, SALVIONVS IVR(is) CON(sultus).

Rev. Ceres holding book and cornucopiae; at her feet, a boar's head. Around, LEGIFERAE CERERI

38 mm. Struck. A1134–397A

The inscription on the obverse, which should read LVCAS SALVIO NVS. PAT(avinus) IVR(is) CON(sultus), has been partly erased. Other specimens are in the British Museum, at Brescia, at Madrid. The dies of both obverse and reverse are preserved in Paris.

Literature: Cp. Arm. I, 184, 31; Cott p. 188; Rizzini no. 278; Alvarez-Ossorio, p. 221, no. 187 (with reverse M. M. Benavides).

398. COSIMO SCAPTI.

Obv. Head to right. Around, COSMVS SCAPTIVS

Rev. Salus seated to left, before a statuette of Bacchus placed on a column under a vine; she gives drink from a patera to a serpent, which rears itself from the ground over a branch of the vine. Around, P(ontifex) M(aximus) TR(ibunicia) P(otestate) X IMP(erator) VI CO(n)S(ul) III P(ater) P(atriae) and, below, SALVS

38 mm. Struck. A1135–398A

Another specimen is in the British Museum. The reverse is from the die of one of Cavino's imitation sestertii (no. 409).

Literature: Cp. Arm. I, 184, 33; Cott p. 188.

399. HOMER.

Obv. Bust to right, bearded, in cloak. Around, ΟΜΗΡΟϹ

Rev. Armed male figure standing, eagle at his feet, between (on left) seated woman with cornucopiae and (on right) seated man with globe and spear, approached by Victory; below, two reclining river-deities, one with a dragon, the other with another monster.

35 mm. Struck. A1136–399A

The die of the obverse is in the collection of Paduan dies at Paris. A cast specimen was in the Lanna collection (lot 347). Sabatier, *Médailles contorniates*, Paris, 1860, pl. xii, 6, illustrates a specimen instead of the original contorniate from which it was derived.

Literature: Cott p. 188.

400. IMITATION OF SYRACUSAN MEDALLION.

Obv. Four-horse chariot on pedestal; above, Victory flying to crown the charioteer; below, two shields, cuirass, and helmet.

Rev. Head of Arethusa to left, wreathed with reeds; around, four dolphins; behind neck, a scallop-shell; above, ΣΥΡΑΚΟΣΙΩΝ

38 mm. Struck. A1137–400A

A fairly close copy of the silver medallion or piece of ten drachms, in the style of Euainetos, issued by Syracuse at the end of the fifth century B.C. (Hill, *Coins of Ancient Sicily*, 1903, frontispiece.) The chief variation is in the exergue of the obverse, where there should be a cuirass, one shield, two greaves, and a helmet, not to mention the word ΑΘΛΑ, which, however, is rarely legible on originals. The detail is, in general, too scholarly to be by any of the usual imitators, such as Belli and Cesati, and the work not dry enough for Cavino. But a die closely resembling the obverse is preserved among the Paduan dies at Paris.

Literature: Cott p. 188; Hill, P.M.I.A., p. 49 (notes that the reverse is known also as reverse of Valerio Bellis self-portrait medal).

401. AGRIPPINA Senior, daughter of Marcus Agrippa, wife of Germanicus. Died A.D. 33.

Obv. Bust to right, hair in club behind, tresses falling down neck. Around, AGRIPPINA M(arci) F(ilia) GERMANICI CAESARIS

Rev. Funeral car drawn by two mules. Above, S(enatus) P(opulus) Q(ue) R(omanus) and MEMORIAE AGRIPPINAE

35 mm. Struck. 'Sestertius.' A1138–401A

The obverse die corresponds to the coin of Agrippina restored by Titus or Nerva (Cohen, *Monnaies frappées sous l'Empire romain* (Paris 1880–92), 2nd ed., i, p. 231, nos. 4, 5). The obverse die preserved at Paris corresponds, on the other hand, to an earlier coin struck under Caligula (Cohen, no. 1). The reverse of this specimen is from the existing die at Paris.

Literature: Cp. Lawrence, no. 8; Cott p. 188.

402. ANTONIA, daughter of M. Antony. Died A.D. 37.

Obv. Bust to right; around, ANTONIA AVGVSTA

Rev. Claudius, with toga drawn over head, holding simpulum; around, TI(berius) CLAVDIVS CAESAR AVG(ustus) P(ontifex) M(aximus) TR(ibunicia) P(otestate) IMP(erator), S(enatus) C(onsulto)

31 mm. Struck. 'Dupondius.' A1139–402A

The obverse die is preserved at Paris. The original is a dupondius of Claudius, H. Mattingly, *Coins of the Roman Empire in the British Museum* vol. I (London 1923), p. 188, 166, pl. 35, 8. Lawrence wrongly says that on the genuine coin the figure represents Antonia as Vestal, while on the Paduan the figure 'is bearded and resembles Claudius'.

Literature: Cp. Lawrence, no. 6; Cott p. 188.

403. NERO, Emperor, A.D. 54–68.

Obv. Head of Nero to right, laureate, beard closely cropped. Around, NERO CLAVD(ius) CAESAR AVG(ustus) GER(manicus) P(ontifex) M(aximus) TR(ibunicia) P(otestate) IMP(erator) P(ater) P(atriae).

Rev. Ceres seated, holding torch and ears of corn; facing her, Annona standing, holding cornucopiae; between them, modius on a cippus; in background, galley. Around, ANNONA AVGVSTI CERES and, below, S(enatus) C(onsulto).

35 mm. Struck. 'Sestertius.' A1140–403A

The dies for this are not preserved. The original was a sestertius of Nero, similar to the coin cited in H. Mattingly, *Coins of the Roman Empire in the British Museum*, vol. I (London 1923) pl. 45, 19.

Literature: Cp. Lawrence, no. 16; Cott p. 188.

404. SABINA, wife of Hadrian, died A.D. 136.

Obv. Bust to right, wearing stephane; hair elaborately coiled on back of head. Around, SABINA AVGVSTA HADRIANI AVG(usti) PI(i).

Rev. Ceres seated to left on modius, holding three ears of corn and a lighted torch. Below, S(enatus) C(onsulto).

34 mm. Struck. 'Sestertius.' A1141–404A

The dies for this are not extant, and Cavino's authorship may be doubted. It is copied from a sestertius, Cohen, 2nd ed., ii, p. 253, no. 69; H. Mattingly, *Coins of the Roman Empire in the British Museum* Vol. III (London, 1936), p. 537, 1879, pl. 99, 2.

Literature: Cott p. 188.

405, 405 *bis*. ANTINOUS, the favourite of Hadrian. Died A.D. 130.

Obv. Bust of Antinous to right, drapery fastened on right shoulder. Around, ΟCΤΙΛΙΟC ΜΑΡΚЄΛΛΟC Ο ΙЄΡЄVCΤΟΥ ΑΝΤΙΝΟΟΥ ('Hostilius Marcellus, priest of Antinous').

Rev. Mercury taming Pegasus. Around, ΑΝЄΘΗΚЄ ΤΟΙC ΑΧΑΙΟΙC ('dedicated [this coin] to the Achaeans').

Two examples, (405) 41 mm. struck, and (405 *bis*) 38 mm. cast. A1466–726A: A1142–405A

The former is struck in two metals, brass centre and copper outer ring. The reverse comes from the existing die; that of the obverse differs slightly from the existing one.

Literature: Cott p. 188 (both specimens); cp. Lawrence, no. 51; G. Blum, 'Numismatique d'Antinoos' in *Journal Internat. d'Archéologie Numismatique* (Athens), xvi (1914), p. 36, no. A.

406. ANTONINUS PIUS, Emperor, A.D. 138–161.

Obv. Bust to right, laureate, in paludamentum and cuirass. Around, ANTONINVS AVG(ustus) PIVS P(ater) P(atriae) TR(ibunicia) P(otestate) XVI

Rev. Roma, helmeted, seated to left on a cuirass, her right foot on a helmet; the Emperor approaches, holding a sceptre in his left hand, and offering her with his right a fleur-de-lis; behind, a Victory approaches to crown her, carrying a palm-branch; below, CO(n)S(ul) III

37 mm. Struck. 'Medallion.' A1143–406A

The obverse is struck from the die preserved at Paris, and the reverse (which really belongs to a medallion of Verus, no. 408) from a die which seems to be by another hand.

Literature: Cp. Lawrence, no. 55; Cott p. 188.

407. FAUSTINA Junior, wife of Marcus Aurelius, died A.D. 176.

Obv. Bust to right, hair confined by fillet and in chignon. Around, FAVSTINA AVG(usta) ANTONINI AVG(usti) PII FIL(ia).

Rev. Sacrifice by the Empress and five women and a child before a circular temple containing a statue of Mars (?). Below, S(enatus) C(onsulto).

35 mm. Struck. 'Sestertius.' A1144–407A

From the existing dies. No original Roman model exists; the older writers took the Paduan for an original.

Literature: Cp. Lawrence, no. 59; Cott p. 188.

408. LUCIUS VERUS, Emperor, A.D. 161–9.

Obv. Bust of Verus to right, laureate, in cuirass and paludamentum. Around, L(ucius) VERVS AVG(ustus) ARM(eniacus) PARTH(icus) MAX(imus) TR(ibunicia) P(otestate) VIIII

Rev. All as on the medallion of Antoninus Pius (no. 406).

38 mm. Medallion, struck in two metals, the centre brass, the outer ring copper. A1145–408A

The obverse die is slightly different from that preserved at Paris; the reverse die, as already observed, seems to be by some quite different engraver. It is copied from an actual medallion of Verus (Cohen, 2nd ed., iii, p. 178, no. 66; Gnecchi, *Medaglioni Romani* (Milan, 1912), ii, pl. 72, no. 7).

Literature: Cp. Lawrence, no. 62; Cott p. 188.

409. COMMODUS, Emperor, A.D. 177–192.

Obv. Bust to right, laureate, in cuirass and paludamentum. Around, M(arcus) COMMODVS ANTONINVS AVG(ustus) PIVS BRIT(annicus).

Rev. Salus feeding serpent; design and inscriptions all as on medal of Cosimo Scapti (above, no. 398).

42 mm. Struck. 'Medallion.' A1146–409A

From the existing dies. An imitation, with varied legend, of a sestertius. See Cohen, *Monnaies frappées sous l'Empire romain,* 2nd ed., iii, p. 319, note 1; Mattingly, *Coins of the Roman Empire in the British Museum*, iv. p. 799, 556, pl. 106, 1.

Literature: Cp. Lawrence, no. 64; Cott p. 189.

410. SEPTIMIUS SEVERUS, Emperor, A.D. 193–211.

Obv. Bust to right, laureate, in cuirass and paludamentum. Around, L(ucius) SEPTIMIVS SEVERVS PERTINAX AVG(ustus) IMP(erator) VII

Rev. Mars resting on spear and shield; cuirass on ground behind him; around, DIVI M(arci) PII F(ilius) P(ontifex) M(aximus) TR(ibunicia) P(otestate) IIII CO(n)S(ul) II P(ater) P(atriae).

39 mm. Struck. 'Medallion.' A1147–410A

From the existing dies. Copied from a medallion, Cohen, iv, p. 18, no. 132; Gnecchi, iii, pl. 93, no. 5; J. M. C. Toynbee, *Roman Medallions* (American Numismatic Society, *Numismatic Studies* no. 5, 1944) p. 161, pl. xliii, 7. Severus assumed the style of son of Marcus Aurelius, hence *Divi Marci Pii filius.*

Literature: Cp. Lawrence, no. 69; Cott p. 189.

MONOGRAMMIST H B

A classicizing, possibly Paduan, engraver of about 1525–50.

411. *Obv.* Head of Hercules to right, lion-skin round neck.

Rev. Hercules in cuirass, lion-skin over arm, standing leaning on spear; a messenger brings him the shirt of Nessus. Below, monogram of H B and a bird.

40 mm. A1148–411A

The head of Hercules is probably taken from an ancient gem. A specimen struck in silver is in the Kunsthalle at Hamburg. The British Museum has a variant, on oval flan, with subject reverse and legend GENIO SALVTIS. There is a specimen similar to the Kress piece in Oxford.

Literature: Cp. Habich, p. 111, pl. lxxvi, 15; M. Bernhart, 'Paduaner', in *Blätter für Münzfreunde*, June 1912, no. 6, pl. 200, fig. 4 (illustrating a struck specimen); Claude du Molinet, *Le Cabinet de la Bibliothèque de Sainte Geneviève*, Paris, 1692, p. 112, no. xl (doubting that the initials stand for Ercole Bassiano); Molinier, I, no. 48 (as after an engraving by Hans Sebald Beham, and not to be associated with Cavino); Löbbecke, 1908, lot 116 (as Ercole Bassiano); Bange, no. 120, pl. 22; Cott p. 189.

GIOVANNI MARIA MOSCA
(Active 1515–1553)

Mosca was a Paduan, active as portrait sculptor and medallist in his native town and in Venice, 1515–1529/30. He migrated to Poland, 1530, where in 1532 he cast four medals of Sigismund I, his queen, son, and daughter.
See Hill, 'Some Italian medals of the sixteenth century' in Habich Festschrift, p. 10; Thieme-Becker, 25 (1931), pp. 174–6; Cracow exhibition catalogue, 1964, *L'Art à Cracovie entre 1350 et 1550*, nos. 259–261 (three medals by Mosca with full bibliographical references for the artist's career and work in Poland).

412. SIGISMUND AUGUSTUS, King of Poland, born 1520, associated to the crown 1530, died 1572.

Obv. Bust to left, in very high relief, wearing broad hat with plume, robe and chain. Around, D(ivus) SIGISMV(n)DVS II REX POLONIE A(nn)O REGNI N(ost)RI III AETATIS XIII ANNO D(omini) MDXXXII

Rev. Lion to left. Around, PARCERE SVBIECTIS ET DEBELLARE SVPERBOS and IVSTVS SICVT LEO; below, IOHANNES MARIA PATAVINVS F(ecit).

66 mm. Later cast. A1149–412A

An original lead specimen of the medal was in the auction catalogue no. 1678, Rudolph Lepke, Berlin, 22–23 April 1913, lot 316, pl. iii. The motto is from Virgil, *Aen.* vi. 853.

Literature: Cp. Arm. I, 140, 3; Cott p. 189; Cracow exhibition catalogue (cited above) no. 261 (Later cast in chased silver, 66·3 mm).

ANDREA SPINELLI
(b. 1508; d. 1572)

Spinelli was born in Parma, and died in Venice. He was a pupil of Gian Francesco Bonzagni, and was principally active in Venice, where he was appointed assistant engraver in 1535, chief engraver 1540. He held the office until he was replaced by his son Marcantonio in 1572.
See N. Pelicelli, in Thieme-Becker, 31 (1937), p. 385; Habich, p. 120, pl. lxxvi, 16, 17.

413. ANDREA GRITTI, Doge of Venice, 1523–38.

Obv. Bust to left in ducal cap and robe; around, ANDREAS GRITI DVX VENETIAR(um) MDXXIII

Rev. Church of S. Francesco della Vigna. Below, AN(dreas) SP(inelli) F(ecit). Around, DIVI FRANCISCI MDXXXIIII

36 mm. A1150–413A

Literature: Cp. Arm. I, 155, 4; Heiss, *Venise*, p. 134, no. 1, pl. ix, 1; Alvarez-Ossorio, p. 171, no. 144; Cott p. 189.

414. ANTONIO MULA, Duke of Crete 1536, member of the Council of Ten for the third time and Councillor for the fourth time 1538.

Obv. Bust to left in robes. Around, ANT(onius) MVLA DVX CRETAE X VIR III CONS(iliarius) IIII

Rev. Mula and another man, in robes, joining hands. Below, AND(reas) SPIN(elli) F(ecit). Around, CONCORDIA FRATRVM 1538

40 mm. Struck. A1151–414A

Literature: Cp. Arm. I, 154, 1; Heiss, *Venise*, p. 135, pl. ix, 3; Habich, pl. lxxvi, 17; Alvarez-Ossorio, p. 201, no. 142 (no. 143 on plate); Cott p. 189.

415. GIROLAMO ZANE, Venetian Senator.

Obv. Bust to left, in robe. Around, HYERO(nymus) ZANE SENAT(or) OPT(imus).

Rev. St Jerome in landscape; below, AND(reas) SPINELI F(ecit) 1540

40 mm. Struck. Gilt. A1152–415A

On a specimen formerly in the Rosenheim collection the date was altered by engraving to 1543.

Literature: Cp. Arm. I, 156, 9; Heiss, *Venise*, p. 137, pl. ix, 5; Hill, 'Eight Italian medals', in *Burl. Mag.*, 14 (1909), pp. 210–217, at p. 210.

416. VENICE 1539.

Obv. The Doge Pietro Lando and senators kneeling before Christ, who stands, holding banner and blessing them; above, SENATVS VENETVS; below, 1539; around, CONCORDIA PARVAE RES CRESCVNT

Rev. Venice, crowned, seated on lion, holding cornucopiae and scales; on left, galley at sea, on right, arms; below, AND(reas) SPINELLI F(ecit); around, ADRIACI REGINA MARIS

40 mm. Struck. A1153–416A

Literature: Cp. Arm. I, 155, 6; Cott p. 189.

416*a*. ETERNITY and FAME 1541.

Obv. Eternity, veiled, standing to front, holding a globe on which is the Phoenix on its pyre. Around, SEMPITERNITAS

Rev. Fame, winged, seated on a celestial globe, blowing two trumpets. Above, 1541; below, IMOR(ta)L(i)TAS

36 mm. Struck. A1256–517A

Another specimen is at Vienna. The form of the 5 in the date (a reversed 3) is found at Venice on Andrea Spinelli's medals. This may be by him.

Literature: Cott p. 189 (as Spinelli ?).

I. A. V. F.

417. PIETRO LAURO, Modenese poet and scholar.

Obv. Bust to right, wearing gown. Around, P LVCET ALMA VIRTVS RAMIS VIRENS SEMPER C V 47 On the truncation, I. A. V. F.

Rev. Within a wreath, CEDA(n)TVR A MORTE INIQVE LACESSENTES LINGVE VIPERIBVS SIMILES V 1555

57 mm. A1154–417A

A puzzling medal, doubtless made at Venice, where Lauro lived nearly all his life. The inscriptions are acrostics, yielding P LAVRVS C V and CAMILLVS V. But since the signature is I. A. V. F. the artist cannot be Camillus V(enetus), even if the identification of this man with the Venetian sculptor Camillo Bossetti were possible, as is suggested in the *Mus. Mazzuchellianum*. The same work suggests that C V is for *clarissimus vir*.

Literature: Cp. Arm. I, p. 185; *Museum Mazzuchellianum* I, lxiv. 1; Hill, 'Notes on Italian medals, xxiii,' in *Burl. Mag.*, 30 (1917), pp. 190–8 (at p. 192); Cott p. 189.

JACOPO TATTI, called SANSOVINO (b. 1486; d. 1570)

Jacopo Tatti was a pupil of the Florentine sculptor Andrea Sansovino, and adopted his name. Tatti worked in Florence and Rome as architect and sculptor, went to Venice in 1527, on his way to France, and was persuaded to remain, working both as architect and sculptor.

See Weihrauch in Thieme-Becker, 32 (1938), pp. 465–70; Habich, p. 129, pl. lxxxvi, 5, 6; R. Gallo, 'Contributi su Jacopo Sansovino', in *Saggi e Memorie di Storia dell'Arte* Venice, I (1957), pp. 81–105 (at pp. 101–4, for Sansovino and the Rangone monument); Pope-Hennessy, *Italian High Renaissance and Baroque Sculpture*, 1963, Catalogue vol. p. 51 (for biography and critical bibliography).

417*a*. TOMMASO RANGONE of Ravenna (1493–1577).

Obv. Bust to right, in robe. Around, THOMAS PHILOLOGVS RAVENNAS

Rev. A female figure placing a wreath on an ox's horns; in the clouds, God the Father. Around, VIRTVTE PARTA DEO ET LABORE

54 mm. A1238–500A

Tommaso Rangone, known as Philologus, was born Gianozzi, and took his new surname after serving under the Conte Guido Rangoni. Tommaso studied at Padua, becoming in 1518 a professor in Philosophy, and later in Astronomy. He moved to Venice, as a doctor. He restored the church of San Giuliano, employing Sansovino and Alessandro Vittoria. This and the following medal were tentatively ascribed to Sansovino by Habich. Professor Middeldorf (private communication) and Mr John Pope-Hennessy have both pointed out that the monumental seated figure of Rangone is by Sansovino, and that R. Gallo (cited above) misinterprets the documents which he publishes. Cessi gives this medal and the following piece to Vittoria, but the handling of the bust and lettering would argue against Vittoria, and leave Sansovino as more probably the artist, especially as he was responsible for the monumental representation of Rangone.

Literature: Cp. Arm. II, 196, 18; Habich, p. 129, pl. lxxxvi, 5; Alvarez-Ossorio, p. 214, no. 415; Cessi, *Alessandro Vittoria, medaglista* (1525–1608), Trento, 1960, pp. 72–4, pl. 14 (as Vittoria); Cott pp. 189–190 (as Sansovino ?). Pope-Hennessy (cited above) Catalogue vol. p. 109, note to pl. 116 (on the Rangone monument).

417*b*. *Obv*. Bust to right, bearded, in gown. Around, THOMAS PHILOLOGVS RAVENNAS

Rev. Jupiter in the guise of an eagle bringing the infant Hercules to Juno, who lies recumbent and sleeping within the Milky Way, below, lilies growing and three birds. Around, A IOVE ET SORORE GENITA

39 mm. A1240–502A

The reverse illustrates the legendary creation of the Milky Way. Jupiter wished to give his son Hercules the immortality due to the son of a god, and so carried the child to the sleeping Juno to be fed. The milk falling in the heavens created the Milky Way, and falling on earth, created lilies. The choice of this type has been seen as a reference to Rangone's own adoption, and as the forerunner of the painting of the same subject by Tintoretto, a friend of Rangone.

Literature: Cp. Arm. II, 196, 20; Habich, p. 129, pl. lxxxvi, 6 (as Sansovino ?); Fabriczy, p. 81 (as Vittoria); Francesco Cessi, *Alessandro Vittoria, medaglista* (1525–1608), Trento, 1960, pp. 76–7, pl. 15 (as Vittoria, *ca.* 1560 ?); Cott, p. 190 (as Sansovino ?). E. Mandowsky, '"The origin of the Milky Way" in the National Gallery', in *Burl. Mag.*, 72 (1938), pp. 88, 89, 93 (where the connection between Rangone and Tintoretto was first suggested); Cecil Gould, *National*

Gallery Catalogues. The sixteenth-century Venetian School, London, 1959, pp. 89–91, no. 1313 (for the painting by Tintoretto, dated to shortly before 1578). Tervarent, col. 4 i. For another portrait medal of Rangone, see no. 420*a*.

DANESE CATTANEO
(b. *ca.* 1509; d. 1573)

Habich has collected under this name a number of medals, formerly attributed to the 'Venetian Medallist of 1550'. The sculptor Danese Cattaneo was a pupil of Sansovino, and a number of the medals of this group are of people who are known to have been in touch with him. For the medals see Habich, pp. 127–8, pl. lxxxix; for sculpture, Pope-Hennessy, *Italian High Renaissance and Baroque Sculpture*, 1963, Catalogue vol. pp. 109–111.

418. (See 419*a*).

419. ELISABETTA QUIRINI, daughter of the Venetian Francesco Quirini; married Lorenzo Massolo, widowed 1556.

Obv. Bust to left, hair braided; around, ELISABETTAE QVIRINAE

Rev. The three Graces.

41 mm. A1156–419A

Elisabetta Quirini is the subject of the painting in the Louvre (S. de Ricci, *Description*, i, 1913, no. 1201) described as of the School of Paolo Caliari, and formerly attributed to Tintoretto. This is proved by an engraving in the Berlin Cabinet by Joseph Canale after a painting attributed to Titian, whose friend she was. The Louvre painting probably goes back to the original by Titian, which was painted in 1544. She was living in 1556, when her husband Lorenzo Massolo died.

Literature: Cp. Arm. I, 121, 4; III, 49, *a*; Habich, pl. lxxxix, 4; Cott p. 189.

AFTER DANESE CATTANEO

419*a*. GIOVANNI DE' MEDICI DELLE BANDE NERE (1498–1526) father of Cosimo I.

Obv. Bust to left, in doublet and cloak. Around, GIOVANNI DE MEDICI

Rev. Thunderbolt issuing from a cloud. Around, FOLGORE DI GVERRA

57 mm. A1155–418A

Cattaneo made a medal immediately after the death of Giovanni (Habich, pl. lxxxix, 5) of which replicas were made in 1546. Pietro Aretino mentions the medal in a letter to Cosimo I of April 1546.

Literature: Cp. Arm. II, 95, 8; Habich, p. 127; Middeldorf, *Morgenroth*, no. 122 (as after Cattaneo); Cott p. 189 (as Cattaneo); *Lettere sull'Arte di Pietro Aretino* (ed. Pertile and Camesasca), Milan, 1957–60, vol. 2, pp. 164–6, no. cccil.

ALESSANDRO VITTORIA
(b. 1525; d. 1608)

Alessandro Vittoria came to Venice from Trento, in 1543, and became a pupil of Jacopo Sansovino, with whom he worked for nine years. Vittoria produced a group of medals in which the handling of the bust and the style of lettering are characteristic and distinctive. The medals include a portrait of Pietro Aretino. On Vittoria as a medallist see Francesco Cessi, *Alessandro Vittoria, medaglista* (1525–1608), Trento, 1960 (in the series *Collana di Artisti Trentini*), with bibliography. Middeldorf, *Morgenroth*, no. 125 (medal of Antonio Bossi; with discussion and literature); Habich, p. 128, pl. xc, 1–7. The work by Proske (cited under Leone Leoni) includes the medal of Daniele de Hanna (Cessi, p. 81, 3, plate 19) as by Leoni. The reverse type appears in the decorations of the bronze figure of Philip II amongst other reverse types by Leoni. The medal of Daniele still seems more in the style of Vittoria than that of Leone Leoni. For Vittoria as a sculptor see Pope-Hennessy, *Italian High Renaissance and Baroque Sculpture*, London, 1963, Text vol. pp. 81–3; Catalogue vol. p. 114 (biography and critical bibliography).

420. GASPARE BORGIA, Bishop of Segorbe 1530, died 1556.

Obv. Bust to right, in gown. Around, GASPARIS A BORGIA EPI(scopus) SEGOBRICEN(sis).

Without reverse.

52 mm. A1157–420A

The attribution of this piece to Vittoria begins with Rizzini. It is denied by Cessi on the grounds that Borgia was bishop of Seville from 1632, a confusion based on misreading the latinised name of Segorbe. Although there is no documentary support for the attribution to Vittoria the handling of the bust and the clumsy form of the lettering can be paralleled from his medals (cp. bust of Pietro Aretino, lettering of the proof medal of Caterina Chieregata; Cessi pls. 7, 5*b*). Borgia attended the Council of Trent, 1551–2, the medal may date from that time.

Literature: Arm. II, 185, 2; Cott p. 189; Rizzini, no. 215; Cessi, p. 41; Konrad Eubel, *Hierarchia catholica medii et recentioris aevi*, Padua 1910, vol. 3, p. 315 (for Borgia's career).

420*a*. TOMMASO RANGONE of Ravenna (1493–1577).

Obv. Bust to left. Around, THOMAS RANGONVS RAVEN(nas).

Rev. Apollo seated, the sun above him, places a wreath on the head of a lion. Around, LEO IMPERAT SOL ET APOLLO

18 mm. A1239–501A

Rangone was born Tommaso Giannozzi, and took his new name from Conte Guido Rangoni under whom he had served in a military expedition. Tommaso studied at Padua, becoming in 1518 a professor in Philosophy, and later in Astronomy. He moved to Venice, and practised as a doctor. He restored the church of San Giuliano, employing Sansovino and Alessandro Vittoria. Only two other specimens are recorded, Paris, Cabinet des Médailles (Armand-Valton collection) and Venice, Museo Correr.

Literature: Cp. Arm. III, 246, E; Cott p. 190 (as Sansovino ?); Cessi, p. 80, pl. 18 (Venice specimen, as Vittoria). For two other portrait medals of Rangone, see nos. 417*a*, 417*b*.

421. CATERINA SANDELLA, wife of Pietro Aretino.

Obv. Bust to left, loosely draped; around, CATERINA SANDELLA; below, A V

Without reverse.

56 mm. A1158–421A

Probably made about the time of the marriage in 1548. The signed medals by Vittoria seem all to date early in his career. The medal is not mentioned in the letters of Aretino.

Literature: Cp. Arm. I, 160, 4; II, 298, 4; Habich, pl. xc, 6; Cessi, p. 71, pl. 13 *b*; Cott p. 189. *Lettere sull'Arte di Pietro Aretino* (ed. Pertile and Camesasca), Milan, 1957–60, vol. 3, i, p. 229.

MILANESE SCHOOL

This school produced about the middle of the sixteenth century an interesting group of medals marking the transition between Benvenuto Cellini and the later masters more definitely associated with Milan, such as Leone Leoni.

422. (See 484*b*).

423. PIETRO PIANTANIDA of Milan.

Obv. Bust to right, in cuirass and cloak. Around, CAP(itaneus) PET(rus) PLANTANIDA AET(atis) AN(no) XXXVI

Rev. Faith, holding chalice in left hand, pointing with right to heaven. Around, DVM SPIRITVS HOS REGET ARTVS

50 mm. A1160–423A

A wax model from the Whitcombe Greene collection, now in the British Museum, of a medal of Sigismund III of Poland bears the same reverse type and legend. The Piantanida medal is ascribed to a follower of Abondio by Habich (in 1932), and given to Abondio by Dworschak. See also the note to no. 484*b*.

Literature: Cp. Arm. II, 179, 9; III, 223 D; Cott p. 190; Habich, p. 121, pl. lxxxiii, 4; Hill, 'Notes on Italian medals, X', in *Burl. Mag.*, 18 (1910) pp. 13–21 (at p. 19, pl. ii. B); Regling, in *Amtliche Berichte aus den Königlichen Kunstsammlungen*, 41 (1920), p. 93; Habich, in 'Staatliche Münzsammlung Erwerbungsbericht' in *Münchner Jahrbuch der Bildenden Kunst*, N.F. 9 (1932), p. 61, pl. II, 4 (as unknown ? Milanese follower of Abondio); Dworschak, *Antonio Abondio, medaglista e ceroplasta* (1538–1591), (in the series *Collana di Artisti Trentini*), Trento, 1958, p. 50. Hill, 'Notes on Italian Medals, XVI', in *Burl. Mag.*, 24 (1914), pp. 211–7 (at p. 211, pl. F: model for the medal of Sigismund III).

424. JEAN DE LORRAINE, born 1498, cardinal 1518, died 1550.

Obv. Bust to right in berretta and gown. Around, IO(annes) CAR(dinalis) LOTHORINGIAE

Rev. Prudence, holding mirror in left hand, compasses in right, advancing to right, a dragon at her feet. Around, SIC ITV[R] AD ASTRA

51 mm. A1161–424A

Literature: Cp. Arm. I, 149, 17; Cott p. 190; Habich, p. 121, pl. lxxxiii, 2; Hill, 'Notes on Italian medals, X', in *Burl. Mag.*, 18 (1910), pp. 13–21 (at p. 14, pl. i, B); Regling, in *Amtliche Berichte aus den Königlichen Kunstsammlungen*, 41 (1920) pp. 93–4; Alvarez-Ossorio, p. 178, no. 133.

425. GIANFRANCESCO MARTINIONI, Milanese physician.

Obv. Bust to right, with pointed beard, wearing doublet and gown; around, IO(annes) FRANC(iscus) MARTINIO MEDIOLAN(ensis) MEDICVS; on truncation of arm, ANN(o) 27

Rev. Bust of Hippocrates (?) to left, with long beard, wearing tall round hat surrounded with circlet inscribed ΦΙΛΕΛΛΗΝ; around, ΕΛΛΑΔΟΣ ΣΩΘΕΙΣΗΣ ΔΩΡΟΝ 'the gift of the Hellas which he saved'.

48 mm. A1162–425A

In the *Museum Mazzuchellianum* the head on the reverse is called Hippocrates (whose Aphorisms were printed by Martinioni in 1552). Rudolphi-Duisberg identifies the head as Aristotle. With the medal of Piantanida (no. 423) this piece is ascribed by Dworschak to Abondio.

Literature: Cp. Arm. II, 160, 11 (age wrongly recorded as 37); Cott p. 190; Habich, pl. lxxxiii, 5; T. W. Greene, 'Notes on some Italian medals', in *Num. Chron.*, 13 (1913) p. 418; *C. A. Rudolphi recentioris aevi numismata virorum de rebus medicis et physicis... edidit... Carol. Ludov. de Duisburg,* Dantzig, 1862, p. 9, no. xx; *Museum Mazzuchellianum,* I, p. 261, pl. lviii, I; F. Dworschak, *Antonio Abondio, medaglista e ceroplasta* (1538–1591), (in the series *Collana di Artisti Trentini*), Trento, 1958, p. 50.

LEONE LEONI
(b. 1509; d. 1590)

Leoni was born near Como, the son of an Aretine, and died in Milan. He was both a sculptor and medallist. For the greater part of his career he was officially Master of the mint in Milan, 1542–1545 and 1550–1559. His employment by the emperor however took him to Brussels, to Augsburg, and in 1559 to Spain. He was also employed as engraver at the papal mint, 1537–1540, causing the imprisonment of Cellini in 1538, and being himself sent to the galleys in 1540 for a murderous assault on a colleague. Andrea Doria procured his release. His visits to both the Low Countries and to Spain greatly influenced the development of the medal in those centres.

See E. Plon, *Les Maitres italiens au service de la Maison d'Autriche. Leone Leoni et Pompeo Leoni,* Paris, 1887; Habich, pp. 130–134; F. Schottmüller and G. F. Hill, in Thieme-Becker, xxiii (1929) pp. 84–7 (with a special but selective bibliography for medals), to which may be added: F. Kenner, 'Leone Leoni's Medaillen für den kaiserlichen Hof', in *Jahrbuch der kunsthistorischen Sammlungen in Wien,* xiii (1892) pp. 55–93; B. G. Proske, 'Leone Leoni's medallic types as decoration', in *Notes Hispanic* (Hispanic Society of America) vol. 3, 1943, pp. 48–57 (important for documenting, by association with details on the bronze figure of Philip II, five of Leoni's medal reverses); C. C. Vermeule, 'An imperial medallion of Leone Leoni and Giovanni Bologna's statue of the flying Mercury' in *The Numismatic Circular* (London) Nov. 1952, cols. 505–9; C. C. Vermeule, 'A study for a portrait medallion by Leone Leoni and a note on the media employed by Renaissance and later medallists', in *The Numismatic Circular,* Nov. 1955, cols. 467–9; P. Valton, 'Médaille de Danaé par Leone Leoni', in *Rev. Num.,* 9 (1905) pp. 496–8; Hill, 'Notes on Italian medals, VII', in *Burl. Mag.,* 15 (1909) pp. 94–8 (at pp. 97–8, medal of Charles V).

426. CHARLES V, Emperor (born 1500, King of Spain 1516, Emperor 1519–56, died 1558).

Obv. Bust to right, laureate, in cuirass with Fleece and scarf. Around, IMP(erator) CAES(ar) CAROLVS V AVG(ustus).

Rev. Jupiter thundering against the Giants. Around, DISCITE IVSTITIAM MONITI

72 mm. Late cast. A1163–426A

The reverse refers to the victory of Mühlberg, 1547.

Literature: Cp. Arm. I, 162, 1; III, 64, *a*; Plon, p. 260, pl. xxxi, 1, 2; Cott p. 190. C. C. Vermeule, 'A study for a portrait medallion by Leone Leoni and a note on the media employed by renaissance and later medallists', in *The Numismatic Circular,* Nov. 1955, cols. 467–9 (republication of the wax model for the obverse of this medal).

427. (See no. 484*a*).

428. BACCIO BANDINELLI, Florentine sculptor (1493–1560).

Obv. Bust to right; around, BACIVS BAN(dinellus) SCVLP(tor) FLO(rentinus).

Rev. Within a laurel-wreath, CHANDOR ILLESIS

39 mm. A1165–428A

The original was struck, and showed on the truncation of the arm LEO, which is not apparent on this specimen.

Literature: Cp. Arm. I, 163, 4; III, 66, *g*; Plon, pl. xxxiii, 3; Hill, P.M.I.A., p. 55, no. 32, pl. 15; Cott p. 190; Habich pl. xcii, 7.

429. MICHELANGELO BUONARROTI, Florentine artist (1475–1564).

Obv. Bust to right, in loose cloak. Around, MICHAELANGELVS BONARROTVS FLOR(entinus) AET(atis) S(uae) ANN(o) 88 On truncation, LEO

Rev. A blind man with staff and water-flask, led by a dog. Around, DOCEBO INIQVOS V(ias) T(uas) ET IMPII AD TE CONVER(tentur).

59 mm. A later casting. A1166–429A

Modelled at Rome, prepared in Milan, and sent to Michelangelo in two silver and two bronze specimens, 14 March 1561. There was evidently an earlier version in which the cord by which the dog is held by the man was tightly stretched, not loose as on extant specimens. According to Vasari the reverse subject was suggested by Michelangelo himself. The reverse legend is from Psalm LI, 13. In March 1561 when the medal was dispatched, Michelangelo would have been 86 not 87 as the inscription on the medal records. The latest discussion of the medal is that provided in the notes to Barocchi's edition of Vasari's life of Michelangelo.

A wax portrait medallion (not a model for the medal) was presented by C. D. E. Fortnum to the British Museum in 1893, for which no early provenance is recorded either in the MS catalogue of the Fortnum collection, Ashmolean Museum, Oxford, or in Fortnum's publication of the piece.

Literature: Cp. Arm. I, 163, 6; III, 66, *i*; Plon, p. 270–2, pl. xxxiii, 1 and 2 (medal); pp. 164–5, 178 (letters concerning the medal); Hill, P.M.I.A., p. 60, no. 40; Habich, pl. xcii, 2; Cott p. 190; E. Steinmann, *Die Porträtdarstellung des Michelangelo,* 1913, pls. 49–53; Giorgio Vasari, *La Vita di Michelangelo* (ed. P. Barocchi) Milan/Naples 1962, vol. I, p. 109, vol. 4, pp. 1735–1738; C. D. E. Fortnum, 'On the original portrait of Michel Angelo by Leone Leoni', in *Archaeological Journal*, vol. xxxii, 1875, pp. 1–15 (for wax portrait); Lomazzo, *Trattato dell'Arte della Pittura* (Rome, 1844 edition) vol. 1, p. 314 (variant version of the medal reverse).

430. ANDREA DORIA, the Genoese admiral (1468–1560), and the ARTIST.

Obv. Bust of Doria to right, in cuirass and cloak; behind shoulder, trident; around, ANDREAS DORIA P(ater) P(atriae).

Rev. Bust of Leoni to right; behind, a galley and a fetter-lock; below, anchor at end of chain attached to the galley. All in a circle of fetters.

43 mm. A1167–430A

Most, if not all, extant specimens are cast, but the original would seem to have been from dies. The medal was made in 1541 at Genoa, and commemorates the release of Leone Leoni, at the instance of Doria, from the galleys to which he had been condemned by the Pope in 1540 for a murderous assault on a fellow craftsman, Pellegrino di Leuti.

Literature: Cp. Arm. I, 164, 8; III, 68, *k*; Plon, p. 256, and pl. xxix, 1; Hill, P.M.I.A., p. 53, no. 30, pl. 15; Habich, pl. xcii, 1; Cott p. 190; Supino, 292 (in silver and bronze); Alvarez-Ossorio, p. 133, no. 170. P. Grotemeyer, 'Eine Medaille des Andrea Doria von Christoph Weiditz,' in Contennial Publication of the American Numismatic Society (edited by H. Ingholt) New York, 1958, pp. 317–327 (This is a re-publication and re-attribution to Weiditz, of the portrait piece published by Bernhart, *Nachträge* p. 74, then known only in a lead copy. A specimen, circular and in silver, d. 84·9 mm., was lot 104, Münzen und Medaillen auction XVII, Basel, 2 December 1957, plate 13. The obverse is a bust left, the reverse standing figure of Doria as Neptune, flanked by the crouching figures of Liberty and Peace.) A plaquette of Doria by Leoni in the Kress collection is Pope-Hennessy, *Kress Bronzes.* no. 75. A companion plaquette of Doria's adopted son Giannettino by Leoni is published by Hill, 'Andrea and Giannettino Doria', in *Pantheon* 4 (1929) pp. 500–1. For a medal of Giannettino by Leoni, see Plon, pp. 39, 257.

431. ANDREA DORIA.

Obv. Same as preceding.

Rev. Starboard view of a galley at sea; standard with double-headed eagle on poop; small boat containing two rowers coming away; a fisherman angling from a rock in the foreground.

42 mm. A1168–431A

Literature: Cp. Arm. I, 164, 9; III, 68, *l*; Plon, pl. xxix, 2; Cott p. 190; Habich pl. xci, 1.

432. IPPOLITA DI FERDINANDO GONZAGA (1535–63).

Obv. Bust to left, in loose-fitting dress with scarf. Around, HIPPOLYTA GONZAGA FERDINANDI FIL(ia) AN(no) XVI and, in inner arc, ΛΕΩΝ ΑΡΗΤΙΝΟΣ

Without reverse.

Lead, 69 mm. Cast hollow. A1169–432A

The reverse belonging to this represents Ippolita as the huntress Diana, with motto PAR VBIQ(ue) POTESTAS The young lady married (1) 1548 Fabrizio Colonna (died 1551), (2) 1554 Antonio Carafa. The portrait type was copied by da Trezzo in his medal of the same sitter dated to the next year (no. 438). There is also an earlier medal (dated AN.XV) and unattributed, in the Kress collection (see Appendix, 433).

Literature: Cp. Arm. I, 163, 7; III, 66, *j*; Plon, pl. xxxii, 7 and 8; Habich, pl. xcii, 6 (Leoni); xciv, 4 (da Trezzo); Cott, p. 190; Magnaguti, no. 137, pl. xxi (Leoni); no. 138, pl. xxii (da Trezzo); no. 136, pl. xxi (unattributed medal); Valton, 'Médaille de Danaé par Leone Leoni', in *Rev. Num.*, 9 (1905) p. 497, pl. xii, 2 (for comparison with the Danae piece; I. Affò, *Memorie della vitta di Donna Ippolita Gonzaga Guastalla* (2nd ed.) 1781 (for biography. This medal is described, p. 23).

433. See Appendix.

434. PAUL III, Pope (1534–49).

Obv. Bust to left, wearing cope. Around, PAVLVS III PONT(ifex) MAX(imus) AN(no) IIII MDXXXVIII Below the shoulder, LEO

Rev. Roma, helmeted, seated on the seven hills, holding in her right hand a spear and on her knee a small column; beside her, Wolf and Twins; below, river Tiber seated, holding urn from which water flows; in the field, S(enatus) C(onsulto).

44 mm. Struck. A1171–434A

Literature: Cp. Arm. I, 166, 18; III, 70, v; Plon, pl. xxix, 4 and 5; Cott p. 190; Rizzini, no. 76.

435. (see no. 441*a*).

436. PHILIPPINA WELSER.

Obv. Bust to right, wearing flat cap, dress with fur trimming. Around, DIVAE PHILIPPINAE

Without reverse.

Lead, 56 mm. Cast hollow; not contemporary. A1173–436A

Philippina Welser was born in 1527; she first met the Archduke Ferdinand in 1556, and was secretly married to him in 1557. She died in 1580. Kenner says that the original medal was probably made in Augsburg about 1551.

Literature: Cp. Arm. II, 238, 13; III, 68, K; Domanig, *Porträtmedaillen des Erzhauses Österreich*, Vienna, 1896, no. 136; Cott p. 191; Kenner (cited above) p. 80.

ATTRIBUTED TO LEONE LEONI

436*a*. GIROLAMO CARDANO of Pavia, physician and philosopher (1501–76).

Obv. Bust to right, in doublet and robe. Around, HIER(onymus) CARDANVS AETATIS AN(no) XLVIIII On truncation of the bust, traces of a signature.

Rev. A vision of several people advancing towards a vine; below, the word ONEIPON (*Dream*).

50 mm. A1227–489A

This vision is described by Cardano in one of his works, as having been seen by him in 1534. The medal represents him in his 49th year (i.e. 1550), and has been attributed to Leone Leoni, but the signature cannot be read with certainty on any surviving specimen. The ornamental stops in the obverse legend are similar to those on the obverse of the Martin de Hanna medal, and the handling of the truncation is similar to that of the Michelangelo medal (see Habich, pls. xcii, 4 and xcii, 2).

Literature: Cp. Arm. II, 162, 21; Cott p. 191; *Museum Mazzuchellianum*, I, pp. 360–1, pl. lxxx, iv (explaining the reverse type as chosen by Cardano because his investigations of dreams were the one source of his fame, and quoting a source for this idea from Cardano's works); Hill MSS. as Leone Leoni.

JACOPO NIZOLLA DA TREZZO (b. 1515 or 1519; d. 1589)

Da Trezzo was born in Milan and died in Madrid. He was gem cutter to Cosimo III de' Medici. His first known medal is that of della Torre (441*a*, below), of 1550, after which date the artist was in Spain. In 1555 he went to the Netherlands, employed by Philip II, and in 1559 he went again to Spain, to work as a sculptor, architect, jeweller, metal-worker, gem engraver and medallist.

See Thieme-Becker, 33 (1939), pp. 392–3; Habich, p. 134, pls. xciii, 5–8, xciv, 1–4.

437. PHILIP II, King of Spain, born 1527, king 1556–1598.

Obv. Bust to right in cuirass. Around, PHILIPPVS REX PRINC(eps) HISP(aniae) AET(atis) S(uae) AN(no) XXVIII Below, IAC(obus) TREZZO F(ecit) 1555

Without reverse.

Lead, good later cast. 72 mm. A1174–437A

The reverse belonging to this medal shows the Sun-god in his car, with motto IAM ILLVSTRABIT OMNIA

Literature: Arm. I, 241, 2 (70 mm); Cott, p. 191; Alvarez-Ossorio, p. 149, no. 268 (bronze 68 mm); Lanna, lot 691 (bronze, 69 mm); Löbbecke, no. 129 (lead, uniface, 69 mm). René Graziani, 'Philip II *impresa* and Spencer's Souldan', in Warburg *Journal*, 27 (1964) pp. 322–4 (on the reverse type).

438. IPPOLITA DI FERDINANDO GONZAGA (1535–63).

Obv. Bust to left, wearing double necklace and loose drapery. Around, HIPPOLYTA GONZAGA FERDINANDI FIL(ia) AN(no) XVII; below, IAC(obus) TREZ(zo).

Rev. Aurora riding through the heavens, on a chariot drawn by winged horse, carrying torch, and scattering flowers; above, VIRTVTIS FORMAEQ(ue) PRAEVIA

69 mm. A1175–438A

Specimens in the Victoria and Albert Museum and at Oxford. See the note to no. 432 (Portrait derives from a Leoni prototype).

Collection: Signol (sale, Paris, 1 April 1878, lot 214).

Literature: Cp. Arm. I, 241, 1; Rodocanachi, *La femme italienne*, p. 220; Cott, p. 191; Alvarez-Ossorio, p. 169, no. 276 (poor bronze specimen); Magnaguti, no. 138, pl. xxii. Tervarent, cols. 78 (Car of Aurora); 182, 191 (attributes of Aurora).

439. ISABELLA CAPUA, Princess of Malfetto, wife (1529) of Ferrante Gonzaga; died 1559.

Obv. Bust to right, with veil; around, ISABELLA CAPVA PRINC(eps) MALFICT(i) FERDIN(andi) GONZ(agae) VXOR Below, IAC(obus) TREZ(zo)

Rev. Isabella, in classical attire, veiled, at a burning altar, on side of which, the sun's face and NVBIFVGO; around, CASTE ET SV[P]PLICITER

Lead, 70 mm. A good after cast. A1176–439A

Literature: Cp. Arm. I, 242, 7; Cott p. 191; Alvarez-Ossorio, p. 113, no. 274 (device on the altar absent).

440. JUAN DE HERRERA (about 1530–97), architect of the Escorial.

Obv. Bust to left, in doublet and cloak. Around, IOAN(nes) HERRERA PHIL(ippi) II REG(is) HISPP(aniarum) ARCHITEC(tus). Below, IAC(obus) TR(ezzo) 1578

Rev. Architecture seated, holding compasses and square; architectural background, with domed chapel (the Escorial). Below, DEO ET OPT(imo) PRINC(ipi).

51 mm. A1177–440A

Literature: Cp. Arm. I, 242, 8; Cott p. 191; Alvarez-Ossorio, p. 172, no. 275; J. Babelon, 'A propos de la médaille de Juan de Herrera', in *Numisma*, 13, no. 63 (1963), pp. 37–42.

441. ASCANIO PADULA.

Obv. Bust to right, in cuirass and scarf. Around, ASCANIVS PADVLA NOBILIS ITALVS MDLXXVII Below, IAC(obus) TR(ezzo).

Rev. Apollo, cloak round neck and falling behind, holding bow and lyre; on left, a blazing tripod; on right, a raven perched on a cauldron. Around, NON AB RE

50 mm. A1178–441A

Another specimen, but not fine, is in the British Museum.

Literature: Arm. I, 243, 9; Cott p. 191.

441*a*. GIANELLO DELLA TORRE, of Cremona, b. 1500, engineer in the service of Charles V, died at Toledo 1585.

Obv. Bust to right. Around, IANELLVS TVRRIAN(us) CREMON(ensis) HOROLOG(ii) ARCHITECT(us).

Rev. The Fountain of the Sciences; inscription: VIRTVS NVNQ(uam) DEFICIT

80 mm. A1172–435A

The reverse type of this medal also appears as the reverse of an unsigned medal of Philip II. The portrait type of the Philip medal derives from another medal signed by Leone Leoni, so that the della Torre piece is also sometimes given to Leoni. The medal is dated conventionally to *ca.* 1550. In 1552 Leoni wrote to the Bishop of Arras from Milan a letter which mentions della Torre in friendly terms (Plon, pp. 89–90). By 1556 however, Leoni and della Torre had disagreed, as Leoni wrote to Ferrante Gonzaga from Brussels, and made an abusive comment about the engineer (Plon p. 127). As da Trezzo copied another Leoni medal portrait, of Ippolita Gonzaga (no. 432), for his own version of the sitter (no. 438) and as both da Trezzo and the engineer had prolonged periods of work in Spain, da Trezzo is more probably the artist of the medal. The clock referred to in the legend was a celebrated piece which della Torre made for Charles V.

Literature: Cp. Arm. I, 170, 38; III, 74 *nn*; III, 115, C (as da Trezzo); Cott p. 191 (as Leone Leoni ?); Plon, pp. 273–4, pl. xxxiv, 8, 9; Habich, pl. xciii, 8 (as da Trezzo); A. Herrera, 'Medallas del principe Don Felipe y de Juanelo Turriano', in *Revista de archivos, bibliotecas y museos*, III epoca, año ix, tom. xii (Madrid, 1905) pp. 266–270 (as da Trezzo); Casto María del Rivero, 'Nuevos documentos de Juanelo Turriano', in *Revista Española de Arte*, 5, no. 1 (March 1936) pp. 17–21 (for della Torre's will, and date of death. The plates include the sculptured bust of della Torre by Monegro); Alvarez-Ossorio, p. 231, no. 270; Hill, N.I.A., no. 330 (for another medal of della Torre describing him as architect to Philip II). For the career of della Torre see Thieme-Becker 33 (1939) p. 501.

ANNIBALE FONTANA
(b. 1540; d. 1587)

Fontana was Milanese, and trained there as a gem engraver, and in Rome as a sculptor. He worked in Palermo, 1570, returned to Milan after 1574 and was active as sculptor until 1586. He was a younger contemporary of da Trezzo and was famous both as sculptor and bronze-caster. The two following medals are attributed to him by literary evidence. The problem of whether or no Fontana is to be identified with the medallists signing ANNIBAL and ANIB is still open. Both Habich (p. 137 and note 138) and Hill, 'Notes on Italian medals xxvii', in *Burl. Mag.*, 42 (1923) p. 44, only associate the medals of Castaldi and Gonsalvo de Córdoba with the two documented pieces by Fontana. See Thieme-Becker, 12, p. 169; Forrer, 2, pp. 119–120. For his sculpture, E. Kris, 'Materialien zur Biographie des Annibale Fontana und zur Kunsttopographie der Kirke S. Maria presso S. Celso in Mailand', in *Mitteilungen des Kunsthistorischen Institutes in Florenz*, III, 1930, pp. 201–253; Pope-Hennessy, *Italian High Renaissance and Baroque sculpture,* London, 1963, Text vol. p. 87, Notes vol. p. 99. For bronzework, see L. Planiscig, 'Annibale Fontana der Meister der bronze Leuchter im Dom zu Pressburg', in *Kunst und Handwerk*, 20 (1917), pp. 370–7. For his engraved work, see E. Kris, *Meister und Meisterwerke der Steinschneidekunst*, Vienna, 1929, chapter viii. There is a terracotta relief by Fontana in the Kress collection, for which see Seymour, *Masterpieces*, pp. 139–141, 181.

442. FERNANDO FRANCESCO II D'AVALOS of Aquino, Marquess of Pescara, born about 1530, died 1571.

Obv. Bust to right, in cuirass and cloak. Around, FERDINAND(us) FRAN(ciscus) DAVALOS DE AQVIN(o) MAR(chio) P(escarae).

Rev. Fernando as Hercules, his foot on the dragon, plucking the apples of the Hesperides; landscape and cities in background. Above, QVAMVIS CVSTODITA DRACONE

72 mm. A1179–442A

Lomazzo in *Trattato dell'Arte della Pittura* (Rome, 1844 edition), vol. 3, p. 218, mentions this medal as the work of Annibale Fontana.

Literature: Cp. Arm. I, 253, 1; Cott p. 191; Alvarez-Ossorio, p. 100, no. 214. Habich, pl. xcix, 2.

443. GIOV. PAOLO LOMAZZO, Milanese painter and writer on art (1538–1600).

Obv. Bust to left, cloak loosely knotted on shoulder. Around, IO(annes) PAVLVS LOMATIVS PIC(tor).

Rev. Lomazzo presented by Mercury to Fortune. Inscription: VTRIVSQVE

50 mm. A1180–443A

The attribution to Annibale Fontana is fixed by a sonnet written to him by Lomazzo (reprinted in Forrer, 2, p. 120) in which the medal is described. Lynch dates the medal to about 1559 and describes the reverse as illustrating Lomazzo's interest in Astrology. Lynch also illustrates the medal of Lomazzo by Galeotti, which he dates to early 1562, with a reverse type intended to refute the painter's critics of that time.

Literature: Cp. Arm. I, 254, 2; Hill, P.M.I.A., p. 62, no. 41, pl. xxvi; Habich, pl. xcix, 1; Cott p. 191; James B. Lynch, 'G. P. Lomazzo's self portrait in the Brera', in *Gazette des Beaux-Arts*, 64 (Oct. 1964), pp. 189–197.

ANNIBAL

A medallist of this name, possibly not distinct from Annibale Fontana (see no. 445) was working in Milan about the middle of the sixteenth century.

444. GIAMBATTISTA CASTALDI, Count of Piadena, general of Charles V, died 1562.

Obv. Bust to left, with long beard, in cuirass and scarf. Around, IO(annes) BA(ptista) CAS(taldus) CAR(oli) V CAES(aris) FER(dinandi) RO(manorum) REG(is) ET BOE(miae) RE(gis) EXERGIT(us, *sic*) DVX

Rev. Castaldi in armour, receiving sceptre from a woman, behind whom is a Turk; on right, a bearded man approaches. Around, CAPTIS SVBAC(tis) FVSISQ(ue) REG(ibus) NAVAR(ae) DACIAE ET OLIM PERSA(rum) TVRC(arum) DVCE

46 mm. A1181–444A

The signature ANIB occurs on other medals of Castaldi closely resembling this.

Castaldi distinguished himself against the French at the Battle of Pavia (1525), against the Turks at the Siege of Vienna, and afterwards as Imperial general in Siebenbürgen and elsewhere. He died at Milan in 1562.

Literature: Cp. Arm. I, 175, 3; Hill, 'The medals of Giambattista Castaldi', in *Num. Chron.*, 17 (1917), p. 167, no. 1; Cott p. 191; Löbbecke, 1908, lot 144; Kris, no. 487, pl. 124.

445. GONSALVO DE CÓRDOBA, the Great Captain (1453–1515).

Obv. Bust to left, in cuirass and scarf. Around, CONSALVVS III DICTATOR MAGNI DVCIS COGNOMENTO ET GLORIA CLARVS Incised on truncation, ANNIBAL or ANNIB ML

Rev. Battle under the walls of a city; one horseman carries Gonsalvo's banner; flag of France flying from the keep. Around, VICTIS GALLIS AD CANNAS ET LIRIM PACATA ITALIA IANVM CLAVSIT

58 mm. A1182–445A

This medal, of about 1550, is not contemporary with Gonsalvo, who died in 1515; and the portrait is not authentic. It commemorates his victories over the French at Cerignola (Cannae) and the Garigliano (Liris) in 1503. Interest in Gonsalvo was revived in Italy by a biography by Giovio, published in 1550.

On some specimens the signature reads ANNIB ML, showing that the artist was Milanese, and so perhaps to be identified with Fontana.

Literature: Cp. Arm. I, 176, 1; III, 77 *a*; Cott p. 191; Alvarez-Ossorio, p. 157, no. 181 (signed ANNIBAL); Habich, pl. xcix, no. 3; Hill, 'Notes on Italian medals, XXVII', in *Burl. Mag.*, 42 (1923) at p. 44, plate, F (specimen in the British Museum, signed ANNIB ML); cp. Middeldorf, *Morgenroth*, no. 116 (with a note concerning the legend of the 'Great Captain'). See also no. 521.

POMPEO LEONI

(b. *ca.* 1533; d. 1608)

The son of Leone Leoni, active for much of his career at the Spanish court as sculptor and medallist.

See E. Plon, *Les Maitres italiens au service de la Maison d'Autriche. Leone Leoni et Pompeo Leoni*, Paris, 1887; F. Schottmüller and G. F. Hill in Thieme-Becker 23 (1929) pp. 88–9; Habich, p. 135, pl. xciii, nos. 1 and 4.

446. ERCOLE II D'ESTE, 4th Duke of Ferrara (1508–34–59).

Obv. Bust to left, wearing cuirass with cloak. Around, HERCVLES ESTENSIS II FERR(ariae) DVX IIII and, in inner arc, POMPEIVS

Rev. Female figure standing, hands crossed on breast, chained by left foot to a rock, on which is a vase surrounded by a celestial globe; liquid flows from the spout of the vase; landscape background. Around, SVPERANDA OMNIS FORTVNA

Lead, 69 mm. A1183–446A

Literature: Cp. Arm. I, 250, 5; Cott p. 192; Habich, pl. xciii, 4; E. Molinier (ed.), *La Collection Spitzer*, Paris, 1892, vol. IV, p. 164, no. 38 (specimen with date 1554 under the shoulder); R. Wittkower, 'Vasari's "Patience" and Ercole II of Ferrara', in Warburg *Journal*, 1 (1937/8) pp. 172–3 (for the reverse type of the medal, which derives from a composition by Vasari for his painting of Patience now in the Pitti Gallery). Tervarent, cols. 173–4 (for the device, and other versions of it).

ALFONSO RUSPAGIARI

(b. 1521; d. 1576)

Ruspagiari was born at Reggio Emilia, and spent the whole of his career there, becoming the superintendent of the mint in 1571. He was the chief of a small group of delightful wax-modellers, virtuosi in very low relief, fond of portraying exquisite ladies in elaborate millinery. The other artists in the school were Agostino Ardenti, Bombarda, and Signoretti.

For Ruspagiari see Thieme-Becker, 29 (1935) pp. 225–6; Habich, pp. 138–9, pl. c, 4–6; Forrer, 5, pp. 272–5 (useful listing of works). For Ardenti (not represented in the Kress collection) see Rosenheim and Hill, 'Notes on some Italian medals', in *Burl. Mag.*, 12 (1907) pp. 141–154 (at pp. 141–7), pl. ii; Hill 'Some Italian medals of the sixteenth century', in Habich Festschrift, pp. 10–13 (at pp. 11–12, pl. ii, 1, medal of Titian, and p. 11, note 1, further bibliography); and Bange, nos. 256–9. For unattributed medals of the school see Hill, 'Notes on Italian medals, XX', in *Burl. Mag.*, 27 (1915) pp. 235–242 (at pp. 236–242, pl. ii); and nos. 461–3, below.

447, 447 *bis*. CAMILLA RUGGIERI.

Obv. Bust to right, placed on voluted bracket; fine loose drapery. Around, CAMILLAE RVGERIAE and, incised on truncation of arm, AR

Without reverse.

Lead, 68 mm. A1184–447A

There is an oval lead specimen at Oxford. The Kress collection also contains a second specimen of the medal, 69 mm, in bronze (A1185–447 *bis*), from the Joseph Fau collection (sale, Paris, 3 March 1884, lot 468).

Collection: Signol (sale, Paris, 1 April 1878, lot 203).

Literature: Arm. I, 216, 2, III, 100 *a*; Cott p. 192; Rodocanachi, *La femme italienne*, p. 220; A. Balletti, 'Alfonso Ruspagiari e Gian Antonio Signoretti, medaglisti del secolo xvi', in *Rassegna d'Arte*, 14 (1914), pp. 46–8, at p. 47, publishes an engraving exactly resembling the medal but in reverse sense, signed with monogram AH, as the portrait of Costanza Bocchi.

448. ALFONSO RUSPAGIARI, the medallist.

Obv. Half-figure to front, head to right, wearing fine loose drapery, holding syrinx. Around, ALF(onsi) RVSPAGIARII REGIEN(sis) and, below, IDEM A R

Without reverse.

Lead, 79 mm. Cast hollow. A1186–448A

Literature: Arm. I, 216, 3; Habich, pl. c, 6; Cott p. 192; Bange, no. 253 (bronze 73 mm, anepigraphic); Roberto Salvini e Alberto Mario Chiodi, *Mostra di Lelio Orsi* (catalogue of an exhibition at Reggio Emilia), 1950, p. 10, for the drawing of the medal, Galleria Estense, Modena, inv. no. 914. Another portrait medal of Ruspagiari is noted by Bernhart, *Nachträge*, p. 85, pl. xvi, 4 (lead, uniface, 47 mm).

449. UNKNOWN LADY.

Obv. Bust seen partly from behind, head to left, wearing veil, which falling behind joins drapery which covers back and breast, leaving left shoulder bare; below, A R

Without reverse.

Lead. Oval, 70 × 54 mm. Cast hollow. A1187–449A

Literature: Arm. I, 216, 4; Cott p. 192; Rosenheim sale lot 145 and Hill, 'Notes on Italian medals XX', in *Burl. Mag.*, 27 (1915), p. 241, pl. II R (circular specimen, bronze, without signature).

450. UNKNOWN LADY.

Obv. Bust to right, nude but for light drapery over left shoulder and tied in front under breasts; engraved on truncation of right arm, A R All in oval frame, out of right edge of which a beardless profile appears gazing at her; voluted mouldings filling space between oval and circular edge.

Without reverse.

Lead, 69 mm. Cast hollow. A1188–450A

Other specimens in the British Museum, and at Paris. In the Cluny Museum is an impression in reverse in horn.

Literature: Arm. I, 216, 5; Cott p. 192; Bange, no. 252; Habich, pl. c, 4; Bernhart, *Nachträge*, p. 88, fig. 2 (another similar portrait piece).

GIAN ANTONIO SIGNORETTI
(Active from 1540; d. 1602)

This artist was a medallist and die cutter at Reggio from 1540 until his death. His medals are close in style to those of Ruspagiari, and are signed S. On the school, see the note to Ruspagiari.

See Thieme-Becker, 31 (1937) pp. 14–15; Habich, p. 139, pl. c, 2; Forrer, 5, p. 500.

451. COSTANZA BOCCHI.

Obv. Bust to right, with elaborate coiffure, thin dress fastened on right shoulder. Around, CONSTANTIA BOCCHIA VIRGO ACHILLIS F(ilia) MDLX Below, S

Without reverse.

Lead, 64 mm. A1189–451A

Other specimens (Brescia, Vienna) have a reverse of the plaquette of Orpheus, Molinier, no. 526.

Costanza, daughter of the Bolognese writer Achille Bocchi, married Gianfrancesco Malvezzi and died in 1566.

Literature: Arm. I, 213, 1; III, 95 *a*; Cott p. 192; Rizzini, no. 303.

452. GABRIELE LIPPI of Reggio d'Emilia.

Obv. Half-figure to right, supported by voluted mouldings;

left hand on breast holding cornucopiae; around, GABRIEL LIPP(i) and, below, S

Without reverse.

Lead, 72 mm. Cast hollow. A1190–452A

Literature: Cp. Arm. I, 213, 2; III, 95 *b*; Bange, no. 260; Cott p. 192.

453. GIULIA PRATONIERI of Reggio d'Emilia.

Obv. Half-figure to right, on voluted bracket, helmeted, left hand on breast; voluminous thin drapery; around, IVLIA PRATONER(ia) and, on the bracket, S

Without reverse.

Lead, 66 mm. A1191–453A

Bange records a specimen in bronze, 68 mm., anepigraphic, and notes the existence of an oval stone model, German, second half of the sixteenth century, which derives from it.

Literature: Cp. Arm. I, 213, 3; III, 95 *c*; Cott p. 192; Habich, pl. c, 2; Bange, no. 261.

ANDREA II CAMBI, called BOMBARDA (Active *ca.* 1560–1575)

Bombarda was a goldsmith and medallist from Cremona. His style is similar to that of Signoretti and Ruspagiari, the three artists forming a distinct school of medallists.
See Thieme-Becker, 5 (1911), p. 428; Forrer, I, pp. 210–211. For the school, see the note to Ruspagiari.

454. LEONORA, wife of Andrea CAMBI, the medallist.

Obv. Bust to right, placed on a voluted bracket; elaborate thin dress, leaving left breast bare; around, LEONORAE CAMB(i) VXORIS; below, BOM(barda).

Without reverse.

69 mm. Cast hollow, thin bronze. A1192–454A

The portrait was doubtless originally designed to be combined with one of her husband, but only occurs singly.

Literature: Rodocanachi, *La femme italienne*, p. 41; cp. Arm. I, 214, 1; Cott, p. 192; Habich, pl. c, 7; Lanna lot 210, pl. 14 (Lead 68 mm).

455. ISABELLA MARIANI, wife of Gianfrancesco Carcass . . .

Obv. Bust to left, wearing veil, corsage with high collar and puffed sleeves. Around, ISABELLA MARIANA CARCASS

Without reverse.

Lead, 71 mm. Cast hollow. A1193–455A

The signature BOM is said to occur in front of the bust on some specimens; there is no trace of it here. Another medal of the same lady gives her husband's initials as I. F. C.

Literature: Cp. Arm. I, 214, 2; III, 98, *a*; Cott p. 182.

456. ANNA MAURELLA OLDOFREDI D'ISEO.

Obv. Bust to right, wearing veil and thin voluminous drapery. Around, ANNA MAVRELLA ISEA AET(atis) ANN(o) XV

Without reverse.

Lead, 60 mm. Cast hollow. A1194–456A

Literature: Arm. II, 208, 24; Cott p. 192; Habich, pl. c, 1.

457. *Obv.* The same bust. Around, the same inscription altered to end OLDOFREDI D(e) ISE(o) AET(atis) XV

Rev. Judgement of Paris; in the heavens, banquet of the gods. Above, HAEC DIGNIOR

63 mm. A1195–457A

Collection: Joseph Fau (sale, Paris, 3 March 1884, lot 506).

Literature: Cp. Arm. II, 207, 23; Cott p. 192.

458. The collection also contains a lead uniface version of the obverse of no. 457.

64 mm. A1196–458A

459. VIOLANTE, wife of Giambattista PIGNA.

Obv. Bust to right, placed on voluted bracket; fine loose drapery, leaving right breast bare. Around, VIOLANTIS PIGNAE ANN(o) and, in right lower corner, BOM

Without reverse.

Lead, 70 mm. A1197–459A

Violante Brasavola, wife of the Ferrarese physician, poet, and historian Giambattista Pigna, who died in 1575.

Literature: Cp. Arm. I, 215, 4; III, 98 *b*; Cott p. 192.

460. UNKNOWN LADY.

Obv. Half-figure to left; light veil at back, dress with high collar open in front, puffed sleeves. Below, on right, BOM

Without reverse.

Lead, 70 mm. A1198–460A

A medal of this sitter exists at Turin, signed by Bosius; the motto attached to it, *Quod huic deest me torquet*, suggests that she may be of the Fiamma family. Bombarda made a medal of Gabriel Fiamma, of which a signed specimen is at Madrid, similar in the handling of the bust to the medal of Isabella Mariani (no. 455). Fiamma was bishop of Chioggia, 1584–5.

Literature: Hill, 'Some Italian medals of the sixteenth century', in Habich Festschrift, pp. 10–3 (at p. 12, pl. ii, 6); Alvarez-Ossorio, p. 160, no. 212 (medal of Gabriel Fiamma); Cott p. 192.

EMILIAN SCHOOL

The three following medals belong to the school of artists of which Ruspagiari is the principal member, centred in Emilia.

Apart from the works on the three artists Ruspagiari, Signoretti and Bombarda, who are the main members of the school, the related and anonymous medals are discussed by Rosenheim and Hill, 'Notes on some Italian medals', in *Burl. Mag.*, 12 (1907), pp. 141–154 (at pp. 141–7, pl. ii, group of pieces given to Ardenti), and by Hill, 'Notes on Italian Medals, XX', in *Burl. Mag.*, 27 (1915), pp. 235–242 (at pp. 236–242, pl. ii).

461. UNKNOWN LADY.

Obv. Half-figure to right, in thin dress, scarf over left shoulder and arms, passing behind and round to front.

Without reverse.

Lead, 65 mm. A1199–461A

Literature: Cp. Arm. III, 276, Y; Cott p. 192.

462. UNKNOWN LADY.

Obv. Half-figure to left, hair dressed with voluted ornaments and a string of pearls hanging from the back; light drapery.

Without reverse.

Lead, 55 mm. Cast hollow. A1200–462A

Literature: Cott p. 192.

463. UNKNOWN LADY.

Obv. Bust to right, wearing thin voluminous dress.

Without reverse.

76 mm. A1201–463A

Another specimen (72 mm.) is in Berlin, *Simon collection*, no. 368. It is true that a later lead casting in the British Museum has the inscription CAMILLA PALLAVICINA, but that is of doubtful authenticity; nor is it certain which of the four ladies of that name is meant. It is better therefore to regard this portrait as unidentified.

Literature: Rodocanachi, *La femme italienne*, p. 40; Cott p. 192.

ANTONIO ABONDIO
(b. 1538; d. 1591)

Abondio was born at Riva di Trento, and died in Vienna. His work began in Italy between 1552–65, and shows him to have been influenced by Milanese, Florentine, and Emilian artists. From 1565 Abondio worked at the courts of Vienna or Prague with excursions to the Netherlands, Spain, Bavaria and north Italy. He was a most accomplished wax-modeller, and exercised a great influence on the development of the later German-Austrian school.

The latest monograph on Abondio is Fritz Dworschak, *Antonio Abondio, medaglista e ceroplasta (1538–1591)*, (in the series *Collana di Artisti Trentini*) Trento, 1958, with full bibliography. To this may be added U. Schlegel, 'Einige italienische Kleinbronzen der Renaissance' in *Pantheon*, 24, VI (1966), pp. 388–396. The earlier studies remain important, E. Fiala, *Antonio Abondio Keroplastik a Medajlér*, Prague, 1909; G. Habich, *Die deutschen Schaumünzen des XVI Jahrhunderts*, 1929–34 (vol. ii, 2, pp. 486–507) which deals fully with the German work by Abondio.

Three pieces ascribed to Abondio are published by G. Probszt, 'Unbekannte Renaissance-Medaillen', in *Numismatische Zeitschrift*, 74 (1951), pp. 86–95, nos. 2, 10, 15.

464. MAXIMILIAN II, Emperor (1527–64–76), and MARIA (1528–48–1603).

Obv. Bust of Maximilian to right, in cuirass and mantle, with collar of the Fleece. Around, IMP(erator) CAES(ar) MAXIMIL(ianus) II AVG(ustus) and behind, in outer arc, AN(tonius) AB(ondius).

Rev. Bust of Maria to left, hair in coif; ruff and gown with high collar. Around, MARIA IMPER(atrix) MDLXXV and, in outer arc, AN AB

Silver, 56 mm., in corded mount making 64 mm., with loop. A1202–464A

A wax model of the bust of Maria is published by Menadier. It differs in detail from the medal portrait. A unique variant of this medal, with reverse the emperor in the guise of St George, formerly in the Katz collection, is Salton collection, no. 112.

Literature: Dworschak, p. 86; Fiala, p. 36, no. 38, pl. II, 6; cp. Arm. I, 268, 4 and 5; K. Domanig, *Porträtmedaillen des Erzhauses Österreich*, Vienna, 1896, 102; H. Kervyn de Lettenhove, *La Toison d'Or*, Brussels, 1907, pl. 99, 14; Cott p. 193. Menadier, 'Medaillenmodelle der Renaissance aus farbigem Wachs', in *Amtliche Berichte aus den königlichen Kunstsammlungen*, XXXI (1910), cols. 314–320 (at col. 318, fig. 161, wax model).

465. RUDOLPH II, Emperor (1552–76–1612).

Obv. Bust to right, in ruff, cuirass, and cloak. Around, RVDOLPHVS II ROM(anorum) IMP(erator) AVG(ustus).

Rev. An eagle flying upwards into clouds which in opening disclose a radiant wreath. Above, SALVTI PVBLICAE

Silver, 45 mm. Loop soldered on. A1203–465A

Some specimens (e.g. Löbbecke Sale, no. 547) show the signature AN AB behind the bust in an outer arc.

Literature: Cp. Arm. I, 269, 7; Fiala, p. 37, no. 45, pl. V, 1;

Dworschak, p. 92 (illustrated, Vienna specimen); Cott p. 193.

466. JOHANN BARON VON KHEVENHÜLLER (1538–1606).

Obv. Bust to right, in cuirass, mantle, and ruff; below, on left, AN AB; around, IOANNES KEVENHVLLER BARO

Rev. Minerva walking, leading by the hand Hercules; he raises his left hand in farewell to Vice who slinks away to right; hilly landscape background.

53 mm. A1204–466A

Dated by Fiala about 1571, during Abondio's journey in Spain in the suite of Khevenhüller who was imperial ambassador in Madrid.

Literature: Cp. Arm. I, 271, 21; Fiala, p. 32, no. 25, pl. iii, 3; Dworschak, p. 51; Cott p. 193.

467. CATERINA RIVA.

Obv. Half-figure to right, holding lap-dog, right breast bare, left hand on bosom. Around, CATHERINA RIVA and, in right corner, AN(tonius) AB(ondius).

Without reverse.

Lead, 70 mm. Cast hollow. A1205–467A

Belongs to Abondio's Italian period, before 1565. Wrongly dated by Dworschak to 1577. In style, the handling of the figure clearly derives from the Emilian school of medallists.

Literature: Cp. Arm. I, 272, 25; Dworschak, p. 64, illustrated; Cott p. 193.

468. JACOPO ANTONIO SORRA.

Obv. Bust to left in doublet with turn-down collar, and gown. Around, IAC(obus) ANT(onius) SORRA 1561

Rev. Sorra, nude, shooting at a mark; two arrows have missed the target; behind, a tree. Above, NON SEMPER

50 mm. A1206–468A

Amongst the earliest authentic work by Abondio.

Literature: Cp. Arm. II, 233, 22; Habich, 'Beiträge zu Antonio Abondio, II, Nachträge und Berichtigungen', in *Archiv für Medaillen- und Plakettenkunde*, I (1913–14) pp. 100–9 (at p. 101, pl. xi, 7); Dworschak, p. 50 (illustrated p. 65); Cott p. 193.

469. SEBASTIAN ZÄH (1527–98) and his wife SUSANNA SCHLECHT.

Obv. Bust to right, in small ruff, doublet and gown. Around, SEBASTIAN ZÄH [A]NNO AET(atis) XXXXV 1572 Incised on truncation, AN AB

Rev. Bust to left, wearing flat cap, hair in net. Around, SVSANNA SCHLECHTIN SEIN HAVSFRAW IRS ALTERS IM XXXI IAR Incised on truncation, 1572

39 mm. A1207–469A

Zäh married Susanna, daughter of Otmar Schlecht, in 1560.

Literature: Cp. Arm. I, 273, 33; Fiala, p. 34, no. 33, pl. iv, 2, where it is said to be signed AN AB on the reverse. Dworschak, p. 81 (illustrates another medal of Zäh, dated 1572, rev. RESPICE FINEM, Vienna, 40 mm); Cott p. 193.

469*a*. FAUSTINA ROMANA (?).

Obv. Bust to left; around, FAVSTINA RO(mana) O(mnium) P(ulcherrima) ?

Rev. Leda and the swan. Around, SI IOVI QVID HOMINI

47 mm. A late cast. A1229–491A

There is a fine specimen in the British Museum. Blanchet identifies the lady with a courtesan celebrated by Joachim du Bellay, who was in Rome from 1553 to 1558, and possibly identical with the Faustina who excited the passion of Brantôme. Abondio worked in such variety of style that the attribution is possible. The Milanese school of Leoni is the most probable influence for the bust, but the reverse could be Venetian.

Literature: Cp. Arm. II, 170, 32 (misread); III, 231, *e*; Habich, pl. lxxxiii, 7 (unknown master); Dworschak, p. 50 (no discussion of the attribution); Cott, p. 194. A Blanchet, 'Une Faustine à Rome au milieu du XVIe siècle', in *Arethuse*, fasc. 7 (1925) pp. 41–9.

ANTONIO VICENTINO

An artist of whom nothing is known except that he signed a medal of Ascanio Gabuccini of Fano which makes possible the attribution to him of a number of other medals in the same style, formerly assigned to Nicolò Cavallerino of Modena. The other medals in the group besides the Kress pieces are of Laura Pallavicini, Marino Grimani, Girolamo Beltramoti, and Giovanni Battista Casali.
See Hill, 'Nicolò Cavallerino et Antonio da Vicenza', in *Rev. Num.*, 19 (1915) pp. 243–255, pls. viii, ix.

470. ALTOBELLO AVEROLDO (d. 1531), Bishop of Pola, thrice Governor of Bologna.

Obv. Bust to right in berretta and cape. Around, ALTOBELVS AVEROLDVS EPIS(copus) POLEN(sis) BONON(iae) ETC TER GVBERN(ator).

Rev. A prince seated, receiving a man who holds a bridle; two other persons, one with cornucopiae, in background. Inscription: MATVRA CELERITAS

67 mm. A1208–470A

The date is fixed by the mention of Averoldo's third

governorship to 1530–1, in which latter year he died. The reverse is similar in composition and handling to that of the medal of Giovanni Battista Casali published by Hill from the unique specimen in Cambridge.

Literature: Arm. III, 55 B; 196, *a*; Cott p. 193; Alvarez-Ossorio, p. 101, no. 128 (as Cavallerino); Hill (cited above) p. 244, pl. ix, 1 (for the medal of Casali).

471. GUIDO RANGONI (1485–1539), Lord of Spilimberto.

Obv. Bust to left, in close-fitting cap tied under chin, and cuirass. Around, GVIDVS RANGONVS BELLO PACEQ(ue) INSIGNIS

Rev. Female figure, holding palm-branch and thunderbolt, riding on bull galloping to right; a flying angel lays a wreath on her head. On the ground, baskets of fruit, cornucopiae, etc. Around, EXTENSIO ALARVM DEI

Lead, 67 mm. A1209–471A

The reverse appears as a plaquette, at Modena. There is another medal of Guido Rangoni, by Vicentino, struck, 32 mm.

Literature: Cp. Arm. I, 142, 1; Cott p. 193; Hill (cited above), p. 243, pl. viii, 1 (cast medal) and p. 243, pl. viii, 2 (struck medal, similar reverse type); *Le Gallerie Nazionali Italiane*, II (1896) pl. xxi (plaquette at Modena).

472. ARGENTINA PALLAVICINI, wife of Guido Rangoni, poetess and botanist, died 1550.

Obv. Bust to left; back hair in large puffed-out net; dress with frilled edge. Around, ARGENTINA RANGONA PA(llavicina) DICAVIT

Without reverse.

64 mm. A1210–472A

The reverse of this medal depicts Argentina seated by a river (the Parma or Panarus), and being crowned by Fame; around, FIDES ET SANCTA SOCIETAS.

Literature: Cp. Arm. I, 142, 4; Cott p. 193; *Museum Mazzuchellianum*, I, pp. 179–180, pl. xl, no. vii (for obverse and reverse).

IAC. URB.

473. GIULIA ORSINI, wife of Baldassare Rangoni, born 1537, married about 1554, died 1598.

Obv. Bust to left, hair braided, wearing light drapery fastened on left shoulder. Around, IVLIA VRSINA RANGONA CAMILLI FILIA ANN(o) ATAT(is) SVE XVII

Rev. In a landscape a large two-handled vase; above, PANTAGATON; around, MORTALIBVS AB INMORTALIBVS ANTIPANDORA 1554; below, IAC VRB

51 mm. A1211–473A

Giulia, born in 1537, married (as the medal shows) in 1554 or soon before, and died in 1598. The device describes her as a vessel full of all blessings, given by the gods to men as an antidote to Pandora's vase. Another specimen is at Milan. Nothing is known of the artist Jacopo, who may have been either of Urbino (*Urbinas*) or Orvieto (*Urbevetanus*). See also no. 497.

Literature: Cp. Arm. I, 185; III, 81; Litta, *Orsini*, no. 31 and, *Rangoni*, no. 6; Cott p. 193.

T. R.

Nothing is known of this medallist, except that he signed a number of medals about the 'seventies of the sixteenth century. He used to be wrongly identified with the medallist Timotheus Refatus of Mantua.

See G. F. Hill, 'Timotheus Refatus of Mantua and the medallist "T.R.",' in *Num. Chron.*, 2 (1902), pp. 55–61, pls. i, ii; Hill, 'Some Italian medals of the sixteenth century' in Habich Festschrift, pp. 10–3 (at p. 13); Bernhart, *Nachträge*, p. 78.

474. BENEDETTO LOMELLINI of Genoa, born 1517, cardinal 1565, died 1579.

Obv. Bust to right, in cape with hood. Around, BENEDICTVS CARD(inalis) LOMELLINVS T R

Rev. Gentleness standing on a serpent, and holding a dove. Around, MANSVETVDO; below, on left, ꓤ T

Lead, 34 × 28 mm. Oval. A1212–474A

Other specimens are in the British Museum and the Cabinet des Médailles, Paris.

Literature: Cp. Arm. I, 287, 4; Hill (cited above) p. 59, pl. ii, 2; Cott p. 193.

475. GIOVANNI PICO DELLA MIRANDOLA, philosopher and poet (1463–94).

Obv. Bust to right, with long hair, wearing cap and gown. Around, IO(annes) PICVS MIRANDVLE DOM(inus) PHIL(osophus) ACVTIS(simu)S. On truncation, T R

Without reverse.

48 mm. A1213–475A

A 'restitution' portrait of the fifteenth-century humanist.

Literature: Cp. Arm. I, 82; III, 139, E; Cott p. 193.

FELICE ANTONIO CASONI
(b. 1559; d. 1634)

Architect, sculptor, wax-modeller, and medallist, born at Ancona 1559. He was working at Bologna as early as 1592, and died in Rome 1634.

476. DIONISIO RATTA of Bologna (d. 1597).

Obv. Bust to right, in doublet. Around, +DIONYSIVS DE RATA VTR(iusque) SIG(naturae) REF(erendarius) ET S(acrae) INQVISIT(ionis) PRAELATVS CONS. Signed on truncation ANTONIO CASONI F

Rev. Inscription recording building of Church of St Peter Martyr (at Rome) and of his own tomb in 1592. DIVO PETRO MARTYRI TEMPLVM EREXIT ET SEPVLCHRVM SIBI CONSTRVXIT SEDENTE CLEMENTE VIII PONT MAX A D MDXCII

67 mm. A1214–476A

Some specimens of the medal are recorded as bearing the signature CASONIVS. There are three other reverses recorded with this portrait type.

Literature: Cp. Arm. III, 147, D; *Museum Mazzuchellianum,* I, p. 416, pl.xciii, no. viii (the other reverses also illustrated); Cott p. 193.

477. LAVINIA FONTANA, Bolognese painter (1552–1612).

Obv. Bust to left, light veil at back, puffed sleeves. Around, LAVINIA FONTANA ZAPPIA PICTRIX 1611 and, below, ANT(onio) CASONI

Rev. Lavinia, with flying hair, seated to left painting at an easel; implements of her art on the ground and in margin below. Around, PER TE STATO GIOIOSO MI MANTENE

65 mm. A1215–477A

Another specimen in the British Museum. The artist in this portrait recalls the manner of the Emilian school. Lavinia, a representative of the Bolognese mannerists, worked for some time in Rome, where she married Zappi.

Literature: Hill, P.M.I.A., p. 81, no. 66, pl. xxxi; Cott p. 193.

CAMILLO MARIANI
(b. 1556; d. 1611)

Mariani was born in Vicenza, and practised as sculptor, painter, architect, and medallist. He died in Rome in 1611. According to a seventeenth century tradition he made a number of fancy medals of ancient worthies whom he supposed to be connected with Vicenza, the inspiration for the series being *La historia di Vicenza,* by Giacomo Marzari, published in 1590.

See Thieme-Becker, 24 (1930) p. 93 (the bibliography giving full references to the four important articles by B. Morsolin in *Rivista Italiana di Numismatica*); Hill, 'Classical influence on the Italian medal', in *Burl. Mag.,* 18 (1911), p. 259 (on the medal of Q. Remmius Palaemon in the series of worthies).

478. AULUS CAECINA ALIENUS, general of Vitellius in A.D. 68.

Obv. Bust to right, in cuirass; around, A(ulus) CAECINVS VICENT(inus) MENE VIT(ellii) EXERC(itus) IMPERAT(or).

Rev. G E across the field.

50 mm. A1216–478A

Another specimen was in the Bardini collection. MENE and G E have not been explained.

Literature: B. Morsolin, 'Camillo Mariani, coniatore di medaglie', in *Rivista Italiana di Numismatica,* iv (1891) at p. 178; Cott p. 193.

MONOGRAMMIST AG

479. PAULA CARLINA.

Obv. Half-figure to left seated in chair (on back of which is a satyric mask); she holds in her right hand jewels (?). Seated on a table facing her, and chucking her under the chin with his left hand, a Cupid, his right hand on his quiver. On the table-cloth a monogram of A G. Above, PAVLA CARLINA

Without reverse.

Lead, 94 mm. Cast hollow. A1217–479A

Judging by the lady's head-dress, about 1590–1600. The monogrammatic signature is entirely in the German fashion (compare the Aldegrever monogram), but the style of the piece is Italian or at least Italianate.

Literature: Cott p. 193.

M. A. S.

480. ERCOLE TEODORO TRIVULZIO, Prince of the Holy Roman Empire and of Valle Misolcina, Count of Mesocco 1656–64.

Obv. Bust to right, in cuirass, open collar, and cloak over left arm. Around, THEOD(orus) TRIVVLTIVS S(acri) R(omani) I(mperii) MESOCHII ET VAL(lis) MES(olcinae) PRIN(ceps) ETC. On truncation of arm, M. A. S. F.

Without reverse.

41 mm. A1218–480A

There are other specimens at Brescia and in the Victoria and Albert Museum. Mazzuchelli wrongly identifies the sitter and Rizzini ascribes the medal to Alberto Hamerani and reads the signature H. A. F. R. On the London specimen the signature is less clear than on the Kress piece. The initials may represent Maria Aurelio Soranzo, mint-master of Venice in 1659.

Literature: Cott p. 193; Rizzini, no. 816; *Museum Mazzuchellianum* 2, p. 15, pl. civ, i; Thieme-Becker, 31 (1937) p. 288 (for Soranzo).

JOHANN JAKOB KORNMANN, called CORMANO (d. 1649)

The artist was born in Augsburg, and is believed to have married at Landsberg in 1620. From about 1630 he was in Venice, as he signed a medal of Antonio Marta who died in that year. He worked as a papal medallist, a rival to Gaspare Mola and to his successor Morone-Mola. Cormano's skill is said to have excited the jealousy of Mola. Cormano's medals include the following—Henri de Fois, duc de Candalle (N. Rondot, *Les médailleurs et les graveurs de monnaies, jetons, et médailles en France*, Paris, 1904, pl. 29, 1); Dr Johann Heins of Augsburg; Paolo Giordano Orsini, Duke of Bracciano, 3 medals, one only signed and dated 1635 (*Museum Mazzuchellianum*, 2, p. 51, pl. 111, 2, 4, 7); Ferdinando Carli, 1639 (*Museum Mazzuchellianum*, 2, p. 25, pl. 106, 2); Filippo Pirovani, dated 1641 (*Museum Mazzuchellianum*, 2, p. 25, pl. 106, 1; Forrer, 3, pp. 206–207); Accession medal of Pope Innocent X, 1644, there being another with similar reverse signed by Mola (Martinori, *Annali*, fasc. 15, p. 35); Jubilee medal of Pope Innocent X, 1650 (Martinori, *Annali*, fasc. 15, p. 37); Cardinal Widman, 1648 (reverse ODIT TAMEN OTIA VICTOR, diam. 35 mm., specimens in the British Museum and at Cambridge).

The biographical accounts of Cormano remain Forrer, 3, pp. 206–8; Thieme-Becker, 21, p. 319. The medals of the duke of Bracciano have the incidental utility of dating the marble and bronze busts of the duke attributed to Bernini. See R. Wittkower, *Gian Lorenzo Bernini*, London, 1966, catalogue nos. 36a, b.

481. FRANCESCO MOROSINI, Venetian admiral, born 1618, Doge 1688, died 1694.

Obv. Bust to left, in cuirass and cloak. Around, FRAN(ciscus) MAVROC(enus) VEN(etus) REGNI CRETAE PROCONSVL Below, CORMANO F(ecit).

Without reverse.

52 mm. Cast hollow. A1219–481A

Literature: Cott p. 194.

482. FRANCESCO MARIA BRANCACCI, cardinal 1634, died 1675.

Obv. Bust to right, in cape with small hood. Around, FRANC(iscus) MARIA S(anctae) R(omanae) E(cclesiae) CARDINALIS BRANCATIVS Below, CORMAN F(ecit) A(nno) 1636

Without reverse.

83 mm. A1220–482A

Literature: Cott p. 194; *Museum Mazzuchellianum*, 2, p. 111, pl. 126, 1 (with reverse, swarm of bees issuing from a dead lion, legend NEC. IPSA. IN. MORTE. RELINQVAM. referring to the cardinal's devotion to the Barberini). A specimen in the British Museum bears the same reverse type, with legend QVIS NOS SEPARABIT.

ANTON FRANCESCO SELVI (b. 1679; d. 1753)

Little seems to be known of Selvi's biography. He is believed to have been Venetian, and to have come to Florence relatively late in life. He is also recorded as a bronze caster, although nothing attributable to him has survived. He was one of the two important pupils of Massimiliano Soldani-Benzi, and by far the more prolific, as he is credited with more than one hundred medals. Early in his association with Soldani he produced a fine portrait medal of his master, closely in his style and based on Soldani's own prototype. It is dated 1715, and is much above the general level of Selvi's production. The medal in the Kress collection is one of a large series of medals commemorating the house of Medici, announced in 1740 by Selvi and Bartolomeo Vagelli, as being based on earlier medals, and on painted and graphic sources. The series numbers seventy-six, and is ascribed as a whole to Selvi alone.

See Klaus Lankheit, *Florentinische Barock Plastik*, Munich, 1962, pp. 195–7; Grotemeyer, Thieme-Becker 30 (1936) p. 483; Forrer, 5, pp. 472–4.

483. GIOVANNA D'AUSTRIA, first wife (1565) of Francesco I de' Medici. Died 1578.

Obv. Bust to left; around, IOANNA AVSTRIACA MAG(na) DVX ETRVRIAE

Without reverse.

86 mm. A1221–483A

The reverse should show an eagle bearing five eaglets above the clouds, motto AD AETHERA

Literature: Cott p. 194; *Corpus*, pp. 284–5; Lankheit, *Florentinische Barock Plastik*, pp. 196–7 (for the advertisement for this series of medals).

UNATTRIBUTED ITALIAN MEDALS OF THE XVI CENTURY

484. MARIA OF ARAGON, wife of Alfonso II d'Avalos. Died 1568.

Obv. Bust to right, hair braided; dress with square opening to bodice and puffed sleeves.

Rev. Assembly of the Gods—Mars, Cupid at his knee, Venus (holding tall torch), Jupiter (?) with globe, Mercury, Vulcan, etc.

Slightly oval, 42 × 41 mm. A1222–484A

The medal is a hybrid, the reverse being ill-adapted to the obverse. The portrait is identified by its likeness to that on an inscribed medal published by Armand, and another variety exists without the ornament on the breast. The handling of the portrait is in the manner of Leone Leoni. There are uniface specimens at Munich and in the Victoria and Albert Museum, and a specimen similar to the Kress at Brescia.

Literature: Cp. Arm. II, 163, 2; Habich, pl. xcvii, 5 (as manner of Leoni); Rizzini no. 606; Cott p. 191 (as manner of Leoni); Habich, in *Münchner Jahrbuch der bildenden Kunst*, 5 (1910) p. 137, pl. c, 13 (as style of Leoni); Löbbecke collection, lot 70, pl. vii (oval specimen); Bernhart, *Nachträge*, p. 89, pl. xvi, 7 (without the ornament on the breast).

484*a*. PIETRO BACCI, called Aretino, the satirist (1492–1557).

Obv. Bust to left, wearing gown and chain. Around, DIVVS PETRVS ARETINVS

Rev. Truth, nude, seated, crowned by Victory; before her, a satyr (Hatred) crouching; she points at him and looks up at Jupiter (?) in the clouds. Around, VERITAS ODIUM PARIT.

60 mm. A1164–427A

The medal is often attributed to Leone Leoni, who signed a medal of Aretino dated 1537, and was making another in 1546. A specimen of the Kress piece (recorded by Hill) formerly in the T. W. Greene collection was dated on the truncation of the arm, 1542. Habich ascribes the medal to an unknown master. The handling and invention of the piece seem too poor to have any connection with Leoni, the obverse conforming in a general way to the type of Titian's portrait in the Frick Collection. Professor Middeldorf (private communication) suggests that the medal may be associated with the sculptor Francesco Segala, who made a bronze bust of the sitter (Widener collection). Wind has pointed out that the reverse legend is a parody of a medal of Federigo Gonzaga, GLORIAM AFFERTE DOMINO (*Corpus* no. 267). The type illustrates Aretino's opinion that Truth engendered Hate.

Literature: Cp. Arm. II, 153, 11; III, 72, Q; E. Plon, *Les Maitres italiens au service de la Maison d'Autriche. Leone Leoni et Pompeo Leone*, Paris, 1887, pl. xxix, nos. 11–12; Habich, pl. lxxxvii, 8 (unknown master); Supino, no. 287 (as L. Leoni); Alvarez-Ossorio, p. 101, no. 169; Cott p. 190 (as L. Leoni). *Paintings and sculptures from the Widener collection*, National Gallery of Art, Washington, 1948, p. 126 (for the bust, ascribed to Sansovino, which is similar to the works of Segala); Wind, p. 73 n. (on reverse legend). For the struck medal of Aretino, 1537, by Leone Leoni, see Plon (cited above), pl. xxix, 10. It is wrongly identified by Habich, p. 130, pl. xcii, 8 (but explained in his note 135, as possibly the work of Battista Baffo). Tervarent, col. 336 (on reverse type).

484*b*. PIETRO BEMBO, born 1470, promoted cardinal 1538, died 1547.

Obv. Bust to right, with long beard, in habit. Around, PETRI BEMBI CAR(dinalis).

Rev. The fountain Hippocrene starting from the ground under the hoofs of Pegasus.

55 mm. A1159–422A

Cellini modelled Bembo in 1537, in preparation for a struck medal, but there is no documentary evidence for his having cast a medal of Bembo. Plon followed Armand, suggesting that Cellini made the piece in *ca.* 1539 from the earlier model. Rizzoli proposed Danese Cattaneo as the artist, but Hill (in 1910) accepted the view of Plon and suggested a grouping of pieces (on rather tenuous similarities between them) based on a figure on the reverse of Cellini's documented medal of Clement VII. Habich accepted the grouping, but denied Cellini's connection with it, and Hill followed this view in publishing this piece in 1930, placing the Bembo with medals nos. 423–425. Pope-Hennessy supports the ascription to Cellini, but does agree (private communication) that the style is not Milanese.

Literature: Cp. Arm. I, 146, 1; Habich, p. 121; Cott p. 190; Middeldorf, *Morgenroth*, no. 127 (as Milanese); Plon, *Benvenuto Cellini, Orfèvre, Médailleur, Sculpteur*, Paris, 1883, pp. 328–334; Rizzoli, 'Una medaglia del Bembo che non è opera di Benvenuto Cellini', in *L'Arte*, 8 (1905) pp. 276–280; *The Life of Benvenuto Cellini* (ed. Pope-Hennessy), London, 1949, p. 484 (Note to plate VIII).

484*c*. CHARLES V, born 1500, King of Spain 1516, Emperor 1519–56, died 1558. Coronation medal, 1530.

Obv. Bust three-quarters to right, head to right, bearded, wearing flat cap and robe. Around, CAROLVS V IMP(erator) BONON(iae) CORONATVS MDXXX

Without reverse.

83 mm. A1101–364A

Vasari says that Giovanni Bernardi da Castelbolognese

made a medal, from engraved dies, at the coronation of Charles. This medal however, is cast, shows little affinity to the other work of Bernardi, and must be by another artist.

Literature: Cp. Arm. I, 137, 1; Cott p. 185 (as Bernardi ?); Löbbecke, lot 61 (as Bernardi); Alvarez-Ossorio, p. 116, no. 125 (as Bernardi). W. M. Stirling, *The procession of Pope Clement V after the coronation at Bologna ... designed and engraved by Nicolas Hogenberg* (Edinburgh, 1875) plate 23, depicts a herald throwing medals to the crowd. It is probable that the medal for the emperor by Bernardi would also have been small enough to be distributed in this way.

485. VITTORIA COLONNA (1490–1547), married, 1507, to Fernando Francesco I d'Avalos (*ca.* 1490–1525) Marquis of Pescara.

Obv. Bust to left, with floating hair and top-knot, drapery fastened on left shoulder. Around, VICTORIA COLVMNIA DAVALA

Without reverse.

49 mm. Late chasing. A1223–485A

Literature: Cp. Arm. II, 107, 7 (the Paris specimen); Cott p. 194.

486. LUCIA BERTANI, Bolognese poetess (1521–67), née dall'Oro, married Gurone Bertani.

Obv. Bust to right. Around, LVCIA BERTANA

Rev. The three Graces. Around, NVLLI LARGIVS

Lead, with bronze rim, 73 mm. A1224–486A

Third quarter of the sixteenth century.

Literature: Arm. II, 219, 28; III, 268, *k*; Cott p. 194.

487. (See 347*a*).

488. (See 347*b*).

489. (See 436*a*).

490. (See 338*a*).

491. (See 469*a*).

492. MATHIAS CORVINUS, King of Hungary (1458–90).

Obv. Bust to right, wearing oak-wreath. Around, MATHIAS REX HVNGARIAE

Without reverse.

86 mm. A1230–492A

Hill believed the medal to be probably sixteenth century, based on a marble relief. Middeldorf (private communication) is uncertain whether the medal is contemporary or posthumous.

Collection: Signol (sale, Paris, 1 April 1878, lot 280).

Literature: Arm. II, 81, 7; III, 187 *a*; *Les Arts*, Aug. 1908, p. 13, no. xii; cp. Corpus, no. 1281; Cott p. 194; Balogh (cited under no. 255) p. 449, fig. 1, p. 462.

493. LORENZINO DE' MEDICI, son of Pierfrancesco II (1514–47).

Obv. Bust to right, drapery fastened on shoulder. Around, LAVRENTIVS MEDICES

Rev. Cap of Liberty between two daggers. Below, VIII ID(us) IAN(uarias)

37 mm. Struck. A1231–493A

The medal is sometimes attributed to Cavino (as by Habich), but lacks his dry precision. The reverse, borrowed from a well-known denarius of Brutus with the words EID. MAR. commemorating the murder of Caesar, here of course alludes to the murder of Alessandro de' Medici in 1537. The medal was popular and exists in many examples.

Literature: Cp. Arm. II, 151, 3; Habich, pl. lxxvi, ii; Alvarez-Ossorio, p. 197, no. 395; Cott p. 189 (as Cavino ?).

494. Omitted.

495. CORNELIO MUSSO of Piacenza, a Franciscan, Bishop of Bitonto 1544, died 1574.

Obv. Bust to left, in cape. Around, CORNELIVS MVSSVS EP(iscop)VS BITVNT(inus).

Rev. SIC VIRVS A SACRIS Unicorn purifying a stream by dipping his horn in it; landscape with shepherd, etc. Below, shield of arms between two horns of plenty.

60 mm. A1232–495A

The unicorn expelled poisonous creatures from fountains by virtue of his horn. An attribution of the medal to Galeotti is doubtful, although no alternative artist has been suggested.

Literature: *Les Arts*, Aug. 1908, p. 12, no. vii; cp. Arm. II, 212, 46; *Museum Mazzuchellianum*, I, p. 353, pl. lxxvii, iv (with three other medals of Musso); Alvarez-Ossorio, p. 202, no. 408; Cott p. 185 (as Galeotti ?). Tervarent, cols. 235–6 (Unicorn as purifyer).

495 *bis*. GIOVANNI DE NORES, Count of Tripoli.

Obv. Bust to left, bearded, wearing robe with broad fur collar, and chain. Around, IOANNES DE NORES COMES TRIPOLIS

Without reverse.

95 mm. A1233–495 *bis* A

Nores was a distinguished Cypriote family. Tripolis in Syria was captured by the Sultan of Egypt in 1288, when the actual dynasty of the Counts of Tripolis came to an end. Giovanni de Nores received from the Republic of Venice in 1489 the hereditary title of Count of Tripoli;

he was succeeded by his son Lodovico in 1544. This medal is of about 1530–40, perhaps of Venetian origin. One of two known specimens.

Literature: Arm. II, 164, 10; Cott p. 194; Middeldorf, *Morgenroth*, no. 118 (legend almost obliterated).

496. ENRICO ORSINI.

Obv. Bust to right, in cuirass and cloak; around, HENR(icus) VRSIN(us).

Rev. Bees flying round a hive; around, NON NISI LAEDENTEM LAEDIMVS

Oval, 35 × 28 mm. A1234–496A

Other specimens were in the Borghesi and Sambon collections.

Literature: Arm. II, 218, 24; Cott p. 194; *Ancienne Collection Borghesi*, sale catalogue, Sambon & Canessa, Paris, 25–27 May, 1908, lot 760; Arthur Sambon collection sale catalogue, Hirsch, Munich, 9 May 1914, lot 44, plate ii.

497. GIULIA ORSINI.

Obv. Bust to left; around, IVLIA VRSINA

Without reverse.

52 mm. A1235–497A

Possibly the Douglas specimen described by Armand. Perhaps, says Armand, the wife of Baldassare Rangoni, see no. 473. But the resemblance between the two portraits is not convincing.

Literature: Arm. III, 265, MMM; Cott p. 194.

498. GIROLAMO PRIULI (Doge of Venice 1559–67) and ALVISE or LODOVICO DIEDO (1539–1603), 1566.

Obv. Bust of Priuli to right, in ducal cap and robes. Around, HIERONIMVS PRIOL(us) VENE(tiarum) DVX AN(n)O P(rincipatus) VIII AE(tatis) LXXX and, in field, 1566

Rev. Bust to right of Diedo in gown. Around, ALOY(sius) DIEDO PRIMICE(rius) S(ancti) MAR(ci) VE(neti) AN(no) III AE(tatis) XXVII and, in field, 1566

96 mm. Much tooled. A1236–498A

Diedo, scholar and poet, was appointed *Primicerius* of St Mark's in 1563 by the Doge. The obverse occurs with its own reverse of Justice and Peace embracing. A specimen like the present with the two portraits is in Brescia and another was formerly in the Rosenheim collection. The portraits are by the same hand as that of a medal of Francesco da Ragogna.

Literature: Cp. Arm. II, 225, 3 (obv.) and 226, 9 (rev.); Cott p. 194. *Museum Mazzuchellianum*, I, p. 345, pl. lxxv, 2; and Rizzini, no. 689 (specimen at Brescia); Rosenheim sale (London, Sotheby, 1 May 1923, lot 213). Hill, 'Eight Italian medals', in *Burl. Mag.*, 14 (1909), pp. 210–7 (at p. 216 for the medal of Ragogna).

499. BEATRICE ROVERELLA, wife of Ercole Rangoni; died 1573.

Obv. Bust in high relief to front, inclined to left, coif at back of head. Inscription: BEATRIX RANGONA ROVO-RELLA

Rev. Three-masted ship, without sails, in a stormy sea; inscription: FIDE ET PIETATE EGREDIAR

Rectangular, 61 × 58 mm. A1237–499A

Another specimen is in the Medagliere, Palazzo Pubblico, Siena. Ossbahr (cited below) published another of these curious rectangular portrait pieces.

Literature: Cp. Arm. II, 196, 17; Bange, no. 275 (as school of Modena, *ca.* 1550); C. A. Ossbahr, 'Nachtrag zu Armand', in *Archiv für Medaillen- und Plakettenkunde*, 4 (1923/4) pp. 93–4 (materials in Stockholm; p. 93, no. 2, pl. x, another rectangular portrait piece of different size and format); Cott p. 194.

500. (See 417*a*).

501. (See 420*a*).

502. (See 417*b*).

503. See Appendix.

504. MARCANTONIO TREVISAN, Doge of Venice, 1553–4.

Obv. Bust to right, in ducal cap and robe. Around, MARCVS ANT(onius) TRIVISANO DVX V(enetiarum).

Rev. In wreath, inscription, MARCVS ANTONIVS TRIVIX-ANO DEI GRATIA DVX VENETIARVM ET C VIXITANO I IN PRINCIPATV OBIT MDLIIII.

63 mm. A1242–504A

Another specimen is in the Victoria and Albert Museum.

Literature: Cp. Arm. II, 224, 1; Cott p. 194.

505. (See 360*a*).

506. LAURA GONZAGA TRIVULZIO (b. 1525/1530).

Obv. Bust to right, wearing veil. Around, LAVRA GONZ(aga) TRIVL(tia).

Rev. The river-god Mincio (MINC) reclining to right, hand on urn from which water flows; on left, tree, in background, town on hill; above, SEMPER ILLAESA

47 mm. A1244–506A

The medal has been attributed to Annibale Borgognone da Trento. The lady married first Giovanni Trivulzio, and then, after 1549, Giangiacomo Trivulzio. If the veil is a widow's veil, as seems probable, the medal dates from her first widowhood. She is supposed to have been born between 1525 and 1530, and looks here to be between 25 and 30.

Literature: Cp. Arm. II, 206, 14; Habich, pl. xcvi, 4; J. Babelon, 'Médailles et plaquettes artistiques', in *Rev.* Num., 23 (1920), at p. 137, no. 4; Cott p. 194.

507. ANDREA DELLA VALLE, Roman cardinal, 1517–34.

Obv. Bust to left, wearing cape with hood. Around, ANDREAS CAR(dinalis) DE VALLE AR(chipresbyter ?) ANNO IVBILEI

Rev. Faith, pointing to heaven, extends her left hand over a chalice on an altar; on the left the golden door of St Peter's, incised with a cross, and surmounted by a cherub's head. Around, PORTA AVRE(a) FIDES PVBLICA and, below, CONSECRACIO

39 mm. A1245–507A

Other specimens in the British Museum, and at Brescia and Modena.

Andrea was promoted cardinal in 1517. He became Archipresbyter of S. Maria Maggiore in 1520, and died in 1534. Yet the style of the medal forbad Hill to date it as early as 1525, to the Jubilee of which year it must refer.

Literature: Cp. Arm. II, 170, 33; Alvarez-Ossorio, p. 233, no. 446; Rizzini, no. 610; Cott p. 194.

507 *bis.* PIERIO VALERIANO BOLZANIO of Belluno, scholar (1475–1558).

Obv. Bust to right, in embroidered robe. Around, PIERIVS VALERIANVS BELLVNENSIS

Rev. Mercury, holding caduceus and resting left hand on a broken obelisk inscribed with hieroglyphics; between, INSTAVRATOR

61 mm. A1246–507 *bis* A

Made about 1545–50, probably at Padua; other medals by the same hand represent Fra Urbano Bolzanio and Florio Maresio. The reverse alludes to Pierio's work *Hieroglyphica* (published at Basel in 1556).

Literature: Cp. Arm. II, 176, 14; Hill, 'Medals of the Bolzanio family', in *Archiv für Medaillen- und Plakettenkunde*, I (1913–14), p. 3; Cott p. 187.

508. DON NICOLA VICENTINO (b. *ca.* 1511; d. 1572).

Obv. Bust to left, with long beard, wearing gown. Around, NICOLAS VINCENTINVS

Rev. An organ (ARCIORGANVM incised) and cymbalum (ARCHICEMBALVM incised). Around, PERFECTAE MVSICAE DIVISIONISQ(ue) INVENTOR

50 mm. A1247–508A

Nicola was born at Vicenza and became a priest. He invented the *archicembalo* for combining the ancient and modern harmonies. His theoretical treatise *L'antica musica ridotta alla moderna prattica* was printed at Rome, 1555, and his work on the *archicembalo*, *Descrizione dell'archiorgano* (n.p.) in 1561. Habich ascribes the medal to the circle of Leone Leoni, Hill cited the opinion of P. H. C. Allen for the medal being by Vittoria, Dworschak gives it to Antonio Abondio. There are other specimens in the British and Victoria and Albert Museums, at Vienna, and at Brescia.

Literature: Cp. Arm. II, 299, 24; III, 271 *f*; *Museum Mazzuchellianum*, I, p. 271, pl. lix, v; Rizzini, no. 695; K. Andorfer u. R. Epstein, *Musica in Nummis*, Vienna, 1907, p. 155, no. 799; Habich, pl. xcvii, 3; Dworshak, *Antonio Abondio, medaglista e ceroplasta* (1538–1591), (in the series *Collana di Artisti Trentini*) Trento, 1958, p. 50, illustrated p. 28; Cott p. 189 (as Vittoria ?).

509. CALIDONIA VISCONTI, wife of Lucio Cavanago.

Obv. Bust to right, in rich dress with high collar; behind, the Visconti *biscione*. Around, CALIDONIA VICECOMES VIRAGO

Rev. Eagle standing on arms and looking up at sun above clouds; landscape background. Around, VISVS ET ANIMVS IDEM

41 mm. A1248–509A

Calidonia was the daughter of Gasparo Visconti, who died in 1535.

Literature: Cp. Arm. II, 160, 10; Cott p. 195.

510. CARLO VISCONTI, born 1523, cardinal 1565, died same year.

Obv. Bust to right, in cuirass. Around, CAROLVS VICECOMES

Rev. A stalk of branching coral. Below, COR ALIT

69 mm. A1249–510A

The medal has been attributed with little reason to Leone Leoni; also by Milanesi to Francesco Tortorino, who made many works in rock-crystal for Cardinal Carlo Visconti.

Literature: Cp. Arm. II, 206, 15; III, 255, *c*; Cott p. 195; Löbbecke lot 123 (as Leone Leoni); Alvarez-Ossorio, p. 238, no. 445.

511. UNKNOWN LADY.

Obv. Bust to right, hair braided, thin dress, scarf fastened with brooch on right shoulder.

Without reverse.

67 mm. Thrice pierced. A1250–511A

North Italian, second half of sixteenth century.

Literature: Cott p. 195.

512. UNKNOWN LADY.

Obv. Bust to left, hair braided; dress open in front. The bust in very high relief.

Without reverse.

81 mm. A1251–512A

North Italian, second half of sixteenth century.

Literature: Cott p. 195.

513. UNKNOWN LADY.

Obv. Bust to right, hair in small chignon, dress laced in front, sleeves puffed and slashed.

Without reverse.

57 mm. A1252–513A

Another specimen in the Victoria and Albert Museum (730–'65).

About 1550. In some ways close to the Berlin specimen, which is oddly described as in the style of Pastorino.

Literature: Bange, no. 237; Cott p. 195.

514. UNKNOWN LADY, about 1550–75.

Obv. Bust to left of lady, hair braided and confined with string of pearls across top of head; dress with high collar open in front; puffed sleeves. Guilloche border.

Without reverse.

62·5 mm. Cast hollow. A1253–514A

The only specimen known. Middeldorf (private communication) suggests that in spite of the unusual border the piece might be by Pastorino.

Literature: Les Arts, Aug. 1908, p. 12, no. vi; Cott p. 195.

515. A TURK.

Obv. Bust to left, in turban and robe.

Without reverse.

Ht. 93 mm. Cast hollow, without background. A1254–515A

The medal was described by Migeon in his account of the Dreyfus collection as depicting a courtier of Mahomet II. The style is rather of the sixteenth century. The portrait may be compared with that on the medal of Soliman (reigned 1520–66) formerly in the Oppenheimer collection, although nose and chin are more pointed. Hill also suggested that the portrait could be that of an official rather than of a sultan.

Literature: Les Arts, Aug. 1908, p. 8, no. ix (as 'courtisan de Mahomet II'); Cott p. 195. For the medal of Soliman, see Oppenheimer sale, lot 223 (formerly Lanna, lot 329; illustrated in both catalogues). Hill, 'Medals of Turkish Sultans', in *Num. Chron.*, 6 (1926), pp. 287–298 (at p. 298, fig. 2).

516. ANTINOUS.

Obv. Nude bust to left; around, ANTINOOC HPΩC

Rev. Antinous reclining on the back of a griffin. Above, ΚΑΔΧΑΔΟΝΙΟΙC (sic); below, ΙΠΠΩΝ

42 mm. A1255–516A

Sixteenth century?

Another specimen is in the British Museum. The types are based on a Greek imperial coin of Calchedon, Bithynia.

Literature: Cott p. 195; Blum, 'Numismatique d'Antinoos', in *Journal International d'Archéologie Numismatique*, 16 (1914) pp. 33–70 (at p. 47, no. 1, for the coin prototype).

517. (See 416*a*).

MISCELLANEOUS FICTITIOUS PORTRAITS

518. ENRICO AMBANELLI.

Obv. Bust to left, with long beard. Around, incised, 1423 ENRICVS DE AMBANELIS ANN(O) 58 D

Without reverse.

69 mm. A1257–518A

The numerals, the forms of the letters, etc., are not earlier than the late sixteenth century; how much earlier the bust may be, is uncertain.

Literature: Arm. III, 158, H; Cott p. 195.

519. CATERINA CAPALLA.

Obv. Bust to right copied from the portrait of Isabella Capua Gonzaga by Trezzo (no. 439). Around, CATERINA CAPALLA

Rev. Branch of coral; below, COR ALIT (All from the medal of Carlo Visconti, no. 510.)

69 mm. A1258–519A

Perhaps the Montigny specimen.

Literature: Cp. Arm. II, 230, 6 (Montigny); Cott p. 195.

520. FILIPPO CASOLI.

Obv. Bust to left, wearing cap with cloth hanging behind, and furred robe. Around, DOCTORI DOCTOR(um) NOB(ilissimo) PHILIPPO DE CASOLIS

Rev. A young man in antique cuirass, walking round the walls of a fortified town, holding fiddle and bow; around, OMN(ibus) ITALIAE GYMNAS(iis) LECTORI; below, D P I

68 mm. A1259–520A

This is now generally considered to be a later invention in fifteenth-century style.

Literature: Arm. I, p. 101; Cott p. 195.

521. ELVIRA, daughter of Gonsalvo de Córdoba, died 1524.

Obv. Bust in very high relief, to front, head inclined to left. Around, ALVIRA CONSALVI AGIDARI(i) MAGNI FIL(ia).

Rev. Before a round temple, Time carrying scythe, and another person. Around, TEMPLVM BELLI PAC(is)

46 mm. A1260–521A

Obviously a late invention, for which a bust, possibly of Lucretia, has been borrowed. The Morgenroth catalogue explains the posthumous reputation of the 'Great Captain', especially in Venice. See also no. 445.

Literature: Arm. II, 138, 15; *Corpus*, no. 1261; Middeldorf, *Morgenroth*, no. 116 (with note on the type); Cott p. 195. For the type of Lucretia cp. *Kress Bronzes*, no. 185, fig. 205.

522. See Appendix.

523. See Appendix.

III

FRENCH MEDALS

This series is arranged on the plan of the standard work on the subject by Mazerolle. The most recent general account of the school is J. Babelon, *La médaille en France,* Paris, 1948.

PARISIAN SCHOOL
between 1400–1402

524. CONSTANTINE THE GREAT, Emperor, 307–337.

Obv. Constantine, crowned, in long robes, riding to right; around, CONSTANTINVS IN XPO DEO FIDELIS IMPERATOR ET MODERATOR ROMANORVM ET SEMPER AVGVSTVS

Rev. The Fountain of Life, surmounted by a cross; beside it, two figures representing the Church and Paganism; around, + MIHI ABSIT GLORIARI NISI IN CRVCE DOMINI NOSTRI IHV XPI

95 mm. A1263–524A

This and the following medal are part of a group of pseudo-antique medallions produced to form a series depicting the history of Christianity, probably by Michelet Saulmon, of which the Duc de Berry acquired specimens in gold between 1400 and 1402.

Literature: Les Arts, Aug. 1908, p. 10, no. xii; cp. Arm. II, 8, 5; Seymour, *Masterpieces,* p. 39, Notes 7–8 (as Burgundian); Cott p. 195 (as Burgundian or North French). The group of medals has been studied by R. Weiss, 'The medieval medallions of Constantine and Heraclius', in *Num. Chron.,* 3 (1963) pp. 129–144, pls. xi–xv (where the earlier opinions and literature are fully discussed, dating proposed for the several versions of the medals, the copies of the medals in MS illumination examined, and the Parisian origin proposed). Medal no. 524 is Weiss no. Cl.

525. HERACLIUS I, Emperor, 610–611.

Obv. Bust to right, with long beard, crowned, looking up at sun's rays, his fingers in his beard, all placed on a crescent, which is inscribed SVPER TENEB(R)AS NOSTRAS MILITABOR IN GENTIBVS; around, name and titles of Heraclius in Greek; across field, ΑΠΟΛΙ(Π)ΙC and ILLVMINA VVLTVM TVVM deu'.

Rev. The Emperor holding a cross, in a car, drawn by three horses; around, SVPER ASPIDEM ET BAZILISCVM etc., and, in field, Greek inscr. 'Glory to God in the Highest', etc.

98 mm. A1264–525A

A companion to the preceding piece. It commemorates the recovery of the Holy Cross from Persian captivity in 629.

Literature: Cp. Arm. II, 8, 6; Seymour, *Masterpieces,* p. 38, Notes 7–8 (as Burgundian); Cott p. 195 (as Burgundian or North French); Weiss (cited above) no. H. 1; V. Tourneur, 'La médaille d'Héraclius', in *Rev. Belge de Num.,* 65 (1923) pp. 67–76 (for the variant legends on the medal).

LOUIS LEPÈRE (Active 1456–1500), NICOLAS DE FLORENCE, and JEAN LEPÈRE (Active from 1492; d. 1534/7).

See Grotemeyer in Thieme-Becker 23 (1929) pp. 97–8 (for the Lepère family and for Nicolas de Florence).

526. CHARLES VIII (1483–98) and ANNE DE BRETAGNE (1477–1514).

Obv. Bust of Charles to right, crowned and wearing Order of St Michael; field semé with fleurs-de-lis. Around, FELIX FORTVNA DIV EXPLORATVM ACTVLIT 1493

Rev. Bust of Anne, crowned and wearing ermine robe; field mi-parti of fleurs-de-lis and ermines. Below, in margin, a lion. Around, R(es) P(ublica) LVGDVNEN(sis) ANNA REGNANTE CONFLAVIT.

40 mm. Struck. A1265–526A

On the passage through Lyon of the King, on his way to the first Italian campaign, the city of Lyon offered a golden lion holding a cup containing 100 examples of this medal in gold to him and Anne on 15 March 1494 (new style). Both the lion and the medal are claimed to have been designed by the queen's painter Jean Perréal, although the monograph by Grete Ring (cited for the next medal) does not discuss the attribution. The piece was modelled by Jean Lepère, and the dies cut by his father Louis and his brother-in-law Nicolas de Florence.

Literature: Cp. Mazerolle, no. 22; Tricou, no. 2; Cott p. 195. Tervarent, cols. 212–13 (ermine as a personal device of Anne).

NICOLAS LECLERC (Active in Lyon 1487–1507) and JEAN DE SAINT-PRIEST (Active in Lyon 1490–1516)

Queen Anne of France was offered a gold medal by the city of Lyon when she entered the city for the second time in March 1500. The medal was designed by Jean Perréal (b. 1455/60; d. 1530), modelled by Leclerc and Saint-Priest, and cast by Jean Lepère (active 1492; d. 1534/37). See Grete Ring, 'An Attempt to reconstruct Perréal', in *Burl. Mag.*, 92 (1950) pp. 255–261; Thieme-Becker, 22 (1928) p. 523 (Leclerc); 29 (1935) p. 328 (Saint-Priest); 23 (1929) pp. 97–8 (Lepère family: in the article Saint-Priest is wrongly identified with Perréal).

527. LOUIS XII (b. 1462) King of France (1498–1515), and ANNE DE BRETAGNE (b. 1477) Queen of France (1499–1514).

Obv. On a field semé with fleurs-de-lis, bust of Louis XII to right, wearing crown over cap, robe and collar of St Michael; below, lion of Lyon; around, FELICE LVDOVICO REGNA(n)TE DVODECIMO CESARE ALTERO GAVDET OMNIS NACIO

Rev. On a field mi-parti of ermines and fleurs-de-lis, bust of Anne to left, crowned and veiled; below, lion of Lyon; around, LVGDVN(ensi) REPVBLICA GAVDE(n)TE BIS ANNA REGNA(n)TE BENIGNE SIC FVI CONFLATA 1499

114 mm. A1266–527A

Many bronze casts of the gold medal have survived. There are two specimens in the Victoria and Albert Museum, and others in the British Museum, Wallace collection, and at Cambridge. The many bronze casts which exist of the medal may have been produced for antiquarian purposes. The only dated reproduction is that in silver recorded in the Clemens collection.

Literature: Cp. Mazerolle, no. 27; Tricou, no. 4 (with references to the literature by Rondot on the medal; Cott p. 196; Middeldorf, *Morgenroth*, no. 149; Ring (cited above) p. 260, no. 11; J. G. Mann, Wallace collection catalogue: *Sculpture, marbles, terra-cottas and bronzes*, London, 1931, p. 134, no. S. 362, pl. 83 (ex. Nieuwerkerke collection); C. Winter, *The Fitzwilliam Museum, an illustrated survey*, 1958, no. 40 (ex. Maurice Rosenheim, 1912); Gilt bronze specimens are recorded also, there is one in the Widener collection (A1480), and one at Cambridge (second specimen). Exhibition catalogue, Cologne, *Die Sammlung Clemens*, May-September 1963, Kunstgewerbemuseum der Stadt Köln, no. 282 pl. 37 (silver medal, diam. 113 mm., signed under the sleeve of Louis XII, C W 1603). Tervarent, cols. 212–13 (ermine as a personal device of Anne).

JEAN MARENDE

Goldsmith of Bourg-en-Bresse. See Forrer, 3, pp. 567–8 (with bibliography); Thieme-Becker, 24, p. 85.

528. PHILIBERT II LE BEAU, Duke of Savoy (1840–97–1504) and MARGARET OF AUSTRIA (married 1501, died 1530).

Obv. On a field semé with knots of Savoy and marguerites, busts confronted, rising from a wattle palisade, of Philibert and Margaret. Around, PHILIBERTVS DVX SABAVDIE VIII MARGVA(rita) MAXI(miliani) CAE(saris) AVG(usti) FI(lia) D(ucissa) SA(baudiae).

Rev. Arms of Philibert impaling those of Margaret; in margin Savoy knots and marguerites and across field the Savoy motto FERT Around, GLORIA IN ALTISSIMIS DEO ET IN TERRA PAX HOMINIBVS BVRGVS

103 mm. A1267–528A

When on 2 August 1502 Margaret of Austria entered Bourg-en-Bresse as Duchess of Savoy, the city presented her with a medal, made by the local goldsmith Jean Marende. The second version is represented by many bronze casts, of which this is one; the flat treatment was adapted for enamelling, and some specimens have been so treated.

Literature: Les Arts, Aug. 1908, p. 14, no. i; cp. Mazerolle, no. 30; Cott p. 196.

UNIDENTIFIED MEDALLIST

529. LOUIS XII, King of France, 1498–1515.

Obv. Bust to left, wearing cap, with medallion with cross on edge, and encircled with crown, and robe. Around, LODOVICVS REX FRANCORVM MCCCCC

Without reverse.

59 mm. A1268–529A

Not Italian, but inspired by an Italian medal of Charles VIII. Armand mistook the robe for a cuirass. Another specimen is in the Cabinet des Médailles, Paris.

Collection: Signol (sale, Paris, 1 April 1878, lot 261).

Literature: Les Arts, Aug. 1908, p. 14, no. iv; cp. Arm. II, 139, 3; Cott p. 196.

THE MEDALLIST OF 1518

The author of the three following medals, and of others, was a Lyonnese, and possibly Jéronyme Henry, a goldsmith known to have been working at Lyon from 1503 to 1538. All but one of his medals are dated 1518, the other 1524. He shows the influence of Candida and the Low Countries. The three following pieces are all dated 1518 and depict humanists of the city of Lyon.

530. JEAN DE TALARU (d. 1550), Canon of Fourrière (1517).

Obv. Bust to right, in large cap. Around, D(ominus) IOHANNES DE TALARV Below, 1518

Without reverse.

47 mm. A later cast. A1269–530A

There should be a reverse with a putto holding the arms of Talaru, motto *Accelera ut eruas me.*

Literature: cp. Mazerolle, no. 40; Cott p. 196; Tricou, no. 10 (with reverse); Tricou, 'Médailles de personnages ecclésiastiques lyonnais du XVe au XVIIe siècles', in *Rev. Num.*, 12 (1950) at pp. 186–8, no. 18.

531. JACQUES DE VITRY-LA LIÈRE (d. 1515) Canon of Lyon, 1492–9; 1501–15.

Obv. Bust to left, in large cap. Around, D(ominus) IACOBVS DE VITRI and, below, 1518

Rev. Putto holding arms of Vitry. Around, NON CONFVNDAS ME AB EXPECTACIONE MEA

48 mm. A1270–531A

Literature: Cp. Mazerolle, no. 41; Cott p. 196; Tricou, no. 11; Tricou, 'Médailles de personnages ecclésiastiques lyonnais du XVe au XVIIe siècles, in *Rev. Num.*, 12 (1950) at pp. 188–9, no. 19.

532. ANTONIO GONZALO DE TOLEDO (1480/3–1524) physician at Lyon.

Obv. Bust to right, in large cap. Around, ANTHONIVS DE TOLEDO MEDICINE DOCTOR and, below, 1518

Rev. Nude woman, a basket of fruits on her head, sits on a saddle (with stirrups attached) and holds a vase of flowers and some plants. Around, NON TOLEDI TABVLA EST ISTA SED EST SPECVLVM

48 mm. A1271–532A

The only specimen mentioned by Mazerolle was in the Fillon collection.

Literature: Cp. Mazerolle, no. 43; Middeldorf, *Morgenroth*, no. 150; Cott p. 196; Fillon sale (Paris, 20 March 1882, lot 190); Tricou, no. 9 (reproducing a modern specimen).

JACQUES GAUVAIN
(Active *ca.* 1501–1547)

Worked for more than 30 years at Lyon, was engraver to the mint at Grenoble 1521–6, and died after 1547. See Thieme-Becker, 13 (1920) p. 294.

533. BARTOLOMMEO PANCIATICHI, of Florence, born 1468, died at Lyon 1533.

Obv. Bust to right, in cap and gown. Around, BARTHOLOMEVS PANCIATIC(us) CIVIS FLORE(n)TI(nus).

Rev. Arms of Panciatichi, with L X above. Around, HANC CAPPELLA(m) FVNDAVIT AN(n)O D(omi)NI MDXVII

45 mm. A1272–533A

A specimen was found in the foundations of a chapel of the Church of the Jacobins at Lyon (cp. the Guadagni medal, no. 534). It has been attributed to Jacques Gauvain; and it has been compared to the Guadagni medal, which it does not in the least resemble, and to the Francesconi medal (no. 309), which it does resemble, though not so closely as to force one to accept the same authorship for the two. Since this was made for a chapel at Lyon and the Francesconi piece for one at Siena, the two may remain in their several countries.

Literature: Cp. Mazerolle, no. 49; Arm. II, 97, 16; III, 192, F; Rondot, *Jacques Gauvain*, Lyon, 1887, p. 55; Cott p. 196; Tricou, no. 7; Tricou 'Médailles religieuses de Lyon', in *Rev. Num.*, 13 (1951) at pp. 115–16, no. 32.

UNIDENTIFIED MEDALLIST

534. TOMMASO GUADAGNI (1454–1533), Florentine consul at Lyon 1505, municipal councillor 1506–27, councillor and major-domo of Francis I in 1523.

Obv. Half-figure to left, wearing cap and robe with turn-down collar. Around, NOBILIS THOMAS DE GVADAGNIS CIVIS FLORENTINVS

Rev. Shield of Guadagni.

103 mm. Moulded border on both sides. The only recorded specimen. A1273–534A

The portrait is from the same model as on another medal (Arm. II, 96, 11) which describes Guadagni as councillor, etc., of Francis I, and records the foundation of the chapel of the Guadagni in the Church of the Jacobins at Lyon in 1523. See Mazerolle, ii, p. 15, no. 53. Nevertheless, judging from the style, the medal may be by an Italian hand. The attribution to Jacques Guavain seems in the circumstances hazardous.

Literature: Arm. II, 96, 12; Heiss, *Florence*, i, p. 162, 2, pl. xxi, 2; Tricou no. 14; Cott p. 196.

MATTEO DAL NASSARO
(Active *ca.* 1515; d. 1548)

The artist was born in Verona, and practised as goldsmith, gem cutter, medallist, painter and musician. From *ca.* 1515 until his death he was employed at the court of Francis I. See Thieme-Becker 25 (1931), p. 350.

535. FRANCIS I, King of France (1494–1515–47).

Obv. Bust to left, with long beard; richly decorated cuirass and scarf fastened on each shoulder. The bust is placed on a crown. Around, FRANCISCVS PRIMVS F(rancorum) R(ex) INVICTISSIMVS All in narrow wreath.

Without reverse.

41 mm. A1274–535A

There should be a reverse of the coronation of the King by Victory and Mars (VIRTVTI REGIS INVICTISSIMI). The medal, which is inspired by Cristoforo di Geremia's of Alfonso V (no. 210), was probably made between 1538 (Treaty of Nice) and 1544 (Battle of Ceresole). The original was struck.

Literature: Cp. Arm. II, 188, 11; H. de la Tour, 'Matteo dal Nassaro', in *Rev. Num.*, 11 (1893) pp. 517–561 (at p. 552, no. 5); Cott p. 196.

536. (See 604*a*).

UNATTRIBUTED

537. FRANCIS I, King of France (1494–1515–47).

Obv. Bust three-quarters to right, bearded, wearing flat cap with falling plume, and slashed doublet. Around, FRANCISCVS I FRANCORVM REX

Rev. Unicorn dipping its horn into a stream at the foot of a high rock. Around, CHRISTIANAE REIP(ublicae) PROPVGNATORI

39 mm. Struck. A1276–537A

The unicorn expelled poisonous creatures from fountains by dipping in his horn. Another specimen was in the T. W. Greene collection.

Literature: Cp. Arm. III, 242, B; Cott p. 196; T. W. Greene sale (London, Sotheby, 31 Oct. 1933, part lot 137). Tervarent, cols. 235–6 (Unicorn as purifyer).

538. FRANCIS, Dauphin, eldest son of Francis I; born 1517; Duc de Bretagne 1532, died 1536.

Obv. Bust to left, wearing broad-brimmed hat with plume. Around, FRANCISCVS II FRANC(iae) DELPHI(nus) BRITA(nniae) DVX I

Without reverse.

52 mm. A1277–538A

Other specimens have a reverse with Hercules fighting the hydra, HERCVLI GALLIAE PACATORI, but it does not seem to have been made for this portrait. Another specimen of the obverse only was formerly in the Henry Oppenheimer collection.

Literature: Cp. Arm. II, 189, 14; Cott p. 196.

539. ANTOINE, DUC DE LORRAINE (1489–1508–44), and RENÉE DE BOURBON, his wife (married 1515, died 1539).

Obv. Bust to right, hair in net, broad-brimmed hat, with A in medallion under brim. Around, ANTHONIVS D(ei) G(ratia) LOTHOR(ingiae) ET BA(ri) DVX

Rev. Bust to left of Renée, wearing coif with veil. Around, RENATA DE BORBO(n)IA LOTHOR(ingiae) ET BA(ri) DVCISSA

42 mm. Gilt. A1278–539A

Has been attributed to Florentin Olriet, engraver to the Mint of Nancy.

Literature: Cp. Mazerolle, no. 75; Cott p. 196; Middeldorf, *Morgenroth*, no. 151 (attributed to Olriet).

REGNAULT DANET

Goldsmith working in Paris from 1529 to 1538. See Forrer, I, p. 502; 7, pp. 202–203.

540. UNKNOWN COUPLE.

Obv. Bust of man to right, in cap; around, TAIRE OV BIEN DIRE

Rev. Bust of woman to left, in coif; around, SANS VARIER

36 mm. A1279–540A

Supposed, without certainty, to represent Pierre Briçonnet and his wife Anne Compaing. It is from the same hand as the portrait of Regnault Danet and his wife Marguerite, presumably therefore by Danet himself.

Literature: *Les Arts*, Aug. 1908, p. 14, nos. XV, XVI; cp. Mazerolle, no. 86; Arm. II, 143, 19; *Corpus*, no. 847 *ter* note; J. de Foville, 'Regnault Danet orfèvre et médailleur de Francois Ier', in *Rev. Num.*, 14 (1910) pp. 392–9; Cott p. 196.

ETIENNE DE LAUNE
(b. 1518/19; d. 1583)

Born 1518/19, was appointed in 1552 engraver to the newly installed Paris Mint; he, however, only held the office for a few months. He afterwards became famous as an engraver on copper, and died in 1583. On his medals see H. Stöcklein in Thieme-Becker, 9 (1913) pp. 2–3; H. Stöcklein, 'Die Medaillen von E. Delaune in der Staatlichen Münzsammlung München', in Habich Festschrift, pp. 53–62.

541. HENRY II, King of France (1519–47–59).

Obv. Bust to right, laureate, cloak fastened on right shoulder. Around, HENRICVS II DEI G(ratia) FRANCO(rum) REX

Rev. Victory seated on globe, holding palm and wreath. Around, SIC FAMA VIRESCIT 1552 E and, to right of globe, S

Silver, 20 mm. Struck. A1280–541A

Cp. Mazerolle, no. 98, who reads L (for Launius) instead of E. But the reading given above is confirmed by his note on his no. 96, where E is read in the same place on the Munich specimen of a similar medal with Diana. S is for Stephanus.

Literature: Cp. Mazerolle, no. 98; Cott p. 196.

542. *Obv.* Bust to right, laureate, in cuirass. Around, HENRICVS II FRANCOR(um) REX INVICTISS(imus) P(ater) P(atriae).

Rev. Fame, holding trumpet, with banner of France modern attached, in quadriga to right; with her Abundance and Victory. Below, NV(m)I(n)A and, around, TE COPIA LAVRO ET FAMA BEARVNT

52 mm. Late cast. A1281–542A

Literature: Cp. Arm. III, 285, D; Mazerolle, no. 103; Cott p. 196.

543. See Appendix.

PIERRE II WOEIRIOT DE BOUZET
(b. 1532; d. after 1596)

Goldsmith and engraver working at Lyon. See Thieme-Becker, 36 (1947) p. 163.

544. SIMON COSTIÈRE of Lyon, born 1469, goldsmith and jeweller, still living 1572.

Obv. Bust to left, wearing flat cap and doublet. Around, SIMON COSTIERE AN(no) ET AE 97 and, on truncation, 1566

Without reverse, but engraved with intersecting circles.

67 mm. A1283–544A

Tourneur maintained (for rather unconvincing reasons) that this medal was an early seventeenth century recasting, with modified legend (ET AE being unintelligible). The original bears the artist's monogram on the truncation of the arm. There is another specimen from the Valton collection in the Cabinet des Médailles, Paris.

Literature: Mazerolle no. 439; cp. V. Tourneur, 'Simon Costière et Pierre Woeiriot', in *Arethuse*, fasc. 8 (1925) pp. 85–8; Tricou, no. 28 (Valton specimen, illustrated); Cott p. 197.

UNIDENTIFIED MEDALLISTS

545. HENRY II of France.

Obv. Bust to left, cloak clasped on left shoulder. Around, HENRICVS II FRANCORVM REX

Rev. Perseus rescuing Andromeda. Around, ΟΛΟΣ ΔΓΟ ΜΗΧΑΝΗΣ

49 mm. Late cast. A1284–545A

The blundered words on the reverse are for *θεὸς ἀπὸ μηχάνης*, as earlier versions show. The medal has been attributed to Cesati, without much probability; in its present form it is generally included in the French series.

Literature: Cp. Arm. II, 248, 2; Mazerolle, no. 340; Löbbecke sale, lot no. 93, pl. viii; Cott p. 197.

546. FRANCIS I, HENRY II, and FRANCIS II of France.

Obv. Bust of Henry II between Francis I and Francis II, all laureate, jugate to left. Around, PR(anciscus, *sic*) HEN(ricus) ET FR(anciscus) REGES FRANC(orum).

Without reverse.

38 mm. A1285–546A

Another specimen is in the British Museum, with the correct reading FR(anciscus) at the beginning of the inscription. There should be a reverse with the busts of Carlo Emanuele, Filiberto and Margherita of Savoy.

Literature: Cott p. 197; *Trésor, Méd. fr.*, part I, pl. xv, 7 (for the reverse type).

547. CATHERINE DE MÉDICIS, wife of Henry II of France (1519–33–59).

Obv. Bust to left, in jewelled head-dress, dress with high collar. Around, CATERINA [R]EGINA FRANCIAE

Without reverse.

Lead, 90 mm. Cast hollow. A1286–547A

A rough casting after the wax medallion at Breslau. The bronze casting in the Louvre and this piece derive from the same original.

Literature: cp. Arm. II, 249, 7; Mazerolle, no. 346; Cott p. 197. Courajod, 'La collection de médaillons de cire du Musée des Antiquités silesiennes a Breslau', in *Gazette des Beaux-Arts*, 29 (1884) pp. 236–241 (at p. 238 for the Breslau wax); M. Zimmer, 'Die Wachsbossierungen im Museum schlesischer Altertümer', in *Schlesiens Vorzeit in Bild und Schrift*, 4 (1887) pp. 591–5 (for the Breslau wax, p. 593, no. 1).

548. ISABELLE (ELISABETH) DE VALOIS (1545–68), third wife of Philip II of Spain, 1559.

Obv. Bust to left in jewelled head-dress, dress with high collar, chain across breast. Around, incised, ISABELLA FILIA HENRICI II REX (*sic*) VXOR PHILIPPI HISPA(niarum) REX (*sic*) 1559

Without reverse.

Lead, 85 mm. Cast hollow. A1287–548A

Although the incised inscription is not contemporary, the portrait goes back to a good model, perhaps one of the series to which no. 547 of Catherine de Médicis belongs. But the medal of Isabelle that is exhibited with the wax medallions at Breslau is by Giampaolo Poggini. As Middeldorf notes, the awkward junction of head and body appears in another piece, of Livia Bentivoglio, of Italian workmanship.

Literature: Cott p. 197; cp. Middeldorf, *Morgenroth* no. 135; Zimmer (cited above) p. 593.

549. 'CHARLES IX', King of France, 1550–60–74.

Obv. Bust to right, youthful, wearing flat cap with plume, robe with high standing collar open in front. Around, incised, CHARLE IX D(ei) G(ratia) FRANCOR(um) REX 1561

Without reverse.

Lead, 90 mm. Cast hollow. A1288–549A

This is really a medal of Francis II from which the proper inscription FRANCISCVS II D. G. FRANCOR. REX has been removed, the present one being substituted.

Literature: Arm. II, 251, 15; III, 290 *a*; Mazerolle, note on no. 351; Cott p. 197; Engel-Gros collection sale catalogue, Paris, 17 Dec. 1921, lot 106, pl. X (anepigraphic bronze medal, 72 mm, with the same portrait type, different dress).

550. CHARLES III DE LORRAINE (1543–1608) Duc de Guise.

Obv. Bust to right, laureate, in cuirass. Around, CHARLES DE LOR(raine) DVC DE GVISE

Rev. In a landscape, a man ploughing; above, sun dispelling clouds. Around, DISCVTIT VT COELO PHOEBVS PAX NVBILA TERRIS

Silver, 48 mm. A modern strike. A1289–550A

For the reverse, cp. Mazerolle, no. 409; *Trésor, Méd. fr.*, Part I, xxvii, 1 and 2; *Médailles françaises dont les coins son conservés au Musée monétaire*, Paris, 1892, no. 455. This is from the same hand as the medal of Henri Duc de Guise there figured, and both appear to be modern 'restitutions'.

Literature: Cott p. 197.

551. DIANE DE POITIERS, wife of Louis de Brézé (1499–1566), Duchess of Valentinois 1548.

Obv. Bust to left, wearing cap. Around, DIANA DVX VALENTINORVM CLARISSIMA; below, AE(tatis) 26

Rev. Diane, with bow, standing to right, trampling on Cupid. Around, OMNIVM VICTOREM VICI

53 mm. Late cast. A1290–551A

The original should be struck, but it is doubtful whether it was made at the time.

Literature: Cp. Arm. II, 250, 10; Mazerolle, no. 431; Cott p. 197.

552. MICHEL DE L'HÔPITAL (1503–73), Chancellor of France 1560–8.

Obv. Bust to left in gown. Around, M(ichael) OSP(italis) FRAN(ciae) CANCEL(larius).

Rev. A tower on a rock in the sea, struck by lightning. Around, IMPAVIDVM FERIENT RVINAE

35 mm. A1291–552A

Literature: Cp. Arm. III, 288, x; Mazerolle, no. 453; Cott p. 197.

553. ANNE DE MONTMORENCY (1493–1567), Constable of France in 1538.

Obv. Bust to left. Around, ANNAS MOMMORANCIVS MILITIAE GALLICAE PRAEF(ectus).

Rev. Three nude female figures, the middle one, winged (Prudence), bringing together one (Courage), who holds banner, arms at her feet, and the other (Fortune) who carries a sail, anchor at her feet. Around, PROVIDENTIA DVCIS FORTISS(imi) AC FOELICISS(imi).

54 mm. A1292–553A

Mazerolle describes one, formerly in the Pichon Collection, as struck.

Literature: Cp. Arm. II, 190, 20; Mazerolle, no. 461; Cott p. 197.

554. JEAN VIRET, scholar and mathematician.

Obv. Bust, elderly, nearly facing, in fur cloak and flat cap. Incised on left and right, IOANNES VIRETVS

Without reverse.

67 mm. With loop. A1293–554A

Viret died at Paris of plague in 1583. The medal identifies a sculptured portrait medallion in black stone (diam. 11·5 cms.) with legend ANNO AE[TA]TIS SVAE LXXII which was in commerce, 1927.

Another specimen of this medal in lead (diam. 55 mm) appeared in commerce, 1966, from a seventeenth century collection, with the identification 'Bishop Fisher' scratched on the back.

Literature: Cott p. 197; Auction sale 'Liquidation L . . ., de Londres', Amsterdam, W. M. Mensing (F. Muller & Cie), 27 October, 1927, lot x (for the sculptured portrait); Sotheby sale (of the former Sharp collection), 14 March 1966, part lot 152 (for a second specimen of the medal).

NICOLAS BRIOT
(b. 1579/80; d. 1646)

Born 1579/80, settled in Paris 1601/2, graver to the mint 1605, settled in London 1625, died 1646. See Forrer, 1, pp. 285–294; Alvin, in Thieme-Becker, 5 (1911) pp. 27–8.

555. LOUIS XIII, King of France (1601–10–43).

Obv. Bust to right, wearing crown, ermine mantle, ruff and collars of St. Michael and the Holy Ghost. Around, LVDOVICVS XIII D(ei) G(ratia) FRANCORVM ET NAV(arae) REX CHRISTIANISSIMVS

Rev. A hand issuing from clouds, holding the sacred *ampulla*, over the city of Rheims; below, RHEMIS; around, FRANCIS DATA MVNERA COELI XVII OCTOB. 1610 NB

Silver, 48 mm. Struck. A1294–555A

Commemorates the coronation at Rheims.

Literature: Cp. Mazerolle, no. 556; Cott p. 197.

GUILLAUME DUPRÉ
(b. *ca.* 1576; d. 1643)

The most brilliant exponent of the French medal in its High Renaissance stage, and the greatest French medallic portraitist. Dupré was also a sculptor and gem-engraver. Controller-general of the French Mint 1604–39. This artist is strongly represented here. See Forrer, 1, pp. 654–660; 7, p. 239; Alvin in Thieme-Becker, 10 (1914), pp. 173–4 (with a chronological list of medals); Babelon, La *médaille en France*, Paris, 1948, pp. 39–43; Mazerolle, 1, pp. cxxix–cxxxix; 2, pp. 125–142, with references to the pieces reproduced in *Trésor de Numismatique, médailles francaises*, part 2, Paris, 1834. The artist still lacks a monograph.

556. HENRY IV (1553–89–1610) and MARIE DE MÉDICIS, 1603.

Obv. Busts to right, jugate. Around, HENR(icus) IIII R(ex) CHRIST(ianissimus) MARIA AVGVSTA and, below G DVPRE F Engraved on truncation, 1603

Rev. Henry as Mars joining hands with Marie as Pallas; between them, the future Louis XIII, his foot on a dolphin, putting on his father's helmet; above, an eagle flying down with a crown. Around, PROPAGO IMPERI and, below, 1603

68 mm. Bronze gilt, with loop. A1295–556A

Henry and Marie de Médicis were married on 10 Dec. 1600, and Louis was born on 27 Sept. 1601. Maumené suggests that the portraits of Henry IV on Dupré's medals, and the reverse composition of this medal, were used by Rubens in his decorations of the gallery of the Luxembourg for Marie de' Médicis, 1622–5. The composition of the medal reverse appears in the scene of Henry IV departing for war in Germany.

Literature: Cp. Mazerolle, no. 639; Cott p. 197; Alvarez-Ossorio, p. 137, no. 316 (recording a specimen in gold, now lost, diam. 73 mm, wt. 147·3 gms.); C. Maumené, 'Le visage royale d'Henri IV, des médailles de Guillaume Dupré aux peintures de Rubens', in *Demareteion*, Paris, 1, no. 1 (1935) pp. 28–39.

557. JEAN-LOUIS DE NOGARET DE LAVALETTE (1554–1642) Duc d'Épernon, colonel général de l'infanterie.

Obv. Bust to right, in cuirass and scarf. Around, I(ean) L(ouis) A LAVALETA D(ux) ESPERN(onis) P(rovinciae) ET TOT(ius) GAL(liae) PEDIT(atus) PRAEF(ectus) and, in inner arc behind, G DVPRE F 1607

Rev. A lion seated, watched by a fox from his den, looks up at a Fury who holds two torches. Above, INTACTVS VTRINQVE

55 mm. A1296–557A

Literature: Cp. Mazerolle, no. 656; Cott p. 197.

558. HENRY IV, King of France.

Obv. Bust three-quarters to right, in doublet, ruff, and mantle, wearing collar of the Saint Esprit. Around, HANRICVS IIII D(ei) G(ratia) FRANCOROM ET NAVAR(rae) REX

Without reverse.

102 mm. Cast hollow. A1297–558A

The form *Francorom* is found on another medal by Dupré, of 1606.

Literature: Cp. Mazerolle, no. 660; Cott p. 197.

559. LOUIS XIII, King of France (1601–10–43).

Obv. Bust to right, young, laureate, wearing cuirass and ruff; around, LVDOVIC(us) XIII D(ei) G(ratia) REX CHR(istianissimus) GALL(iae) ET NAVAR(ae) HENR(ici) MAGNI FIL(ius) P(ius) F(elix) AVG(ustus). Below, G DVPRE F 1610

Rev. The young Louis, nude, instructed by Minerva, who holds olive-branch and thunderbolt; around, ORIENS AVGVSTI TVTRICE MINERVA Below, ANN(o) NAT(i) CHR(isti) MDCX

Oval, with loop, 56 × 42 mm. A1298–559A

Literature: Cp. Mazerolle, no. 663; Cott p. 198.

560. HENRI DE BOURBON (1588–1646), Prince de Condé, first Prince of the Blood, and his wife Charlotte-Marie de Montmorency (married 1609, died 1650).

Obv. Bust to right, in lace collar, cuirass, and scarf. Around, H(enricus) BORBON(ius) CONDAEVS PRIM(us) REGIAE FRANC(iae) DOMVS PRINCEPS, and, on truncation, 1611

Rev. Bust of his wife to right in court dress. Around, CAR(lotta) MARIA MOMMORANTIA PRINCIP(is) CONDAEI VXOR and, behind shoulder, DVPRE; incised on truncation, 1611

56 mm. A1299–560A

Literature: Cp. Mazerolle, no. 666; Cott p. 198.

J. B. KELLER (1638–1702) After GUILLAUME DUPRÉ

561. FRANCESCO IV GONZAGA, Duke of Mantua (1586–1612–1612).

Obv. Bust to right, in cuirass, large ruff, and scarf. Around, FRAN(ciscus) IIII D(ei) G(ratia) DVX MANTV(ae) MONT(is) FER(rati) III AN(no) I AET(atis) XXVI, and, below, G DVPRE F 1612

Without reverse.

163 mm. Cast hollow. A1300–561A

The reverse of this is signed J. B. KELLER, 1654, in large raised letters. Keller and his brother Johann Jakob were celebrated bronze founders in Paris.

Literature: Cp. Mazerolle, no. 668; Cott p. 198; For the Keller brothers see H. Lüer, *Technik der Bronzeplastik* (Monographien des Kunstgewerbers, ed. J. L. Sponsel) Leipzig, n.d., pp. 71 ff.; Forrer, 3, p. 137; Thieme-Becker, 20 (1927) pp. 95–6. Another specimen of Keller's reproduction is recorded in auction catalogue Schulman, Amsterdam, 23–4 March 1953, lot 923.

GUILLAUME DUPRÉ (continued)

562. MARIA MAGDALENA, Grand-Duchess of Tuscany (wife of Cosimo II 1589, died 1636).

Obv. Bust to left, in court dress. Around, MAR(iae) MAGDALENAE ARCH(iducissae) AVSTR(iae) MAG(nae) D(ucissae) ETR(uriae) and, below, G D P 1613

Without reverse.

93 mm. Cast hollow. A1301–562A

Literature: Cp. Mazerolle, nos. 671–2; Cott p. 198.

563. NICOLAS BRULART DE SILLERY (d. 1624), Chancellor of Navarre 1603, of France 1607.

Obv. Bust to right, in furred gown. Around, NI(colaus) BRVLARTVS A SILLERY FRANC(iae) ET NAVAR(ae) CANCEL(larius); below, G DVPRE F and, incised on truncation, 1613

Rev. Apollo driving the Sun's car across the sphere of the heavens; above, LABOR ACTVS IN ORBEM

73 mm. A1302–563A

Literature: Cp. Mazerolle, no. 679; Cott p. 198.

564. PIERRE JEANNIN (1540–1622) Councillor of the King, surintendant des finances.

Obv. Bust to right, in gown. Around, PETRVS IEANNIN REG(is) CHRIST(ianissimi) A SECR(etis) CONS(iliarius) ET SAC(ri) AERA(rii) PRAEF(ectus), and, below, G DVPRE F 1618

Without reverse.

190 mm. Thick hollow cast. A1303–564A

This piece is also known as a thin hollow casting, finely finished. Such specimens are in the British Museum, and at Cambridge.

Literature: Cp. Mazerolle, no. 683; Cott p. 198.

565. LOUIS XIII and ANNE D'AUTRICHE (1601–1615–66), 1620 and 1623.

Obv. Bust of Louis to right, in cuirass, ruff, and cloak. Around, LVDOVIC(us) XIII D(ei) G(ratia) FRANCOR(um) ET NAVARAE REX and, below, G DVPRE; engraved on truncation, 1623

Rev. Bust of Anne to right in court dress, with large ruff. Around, ANNA AVGVS(ta) GALLIAE ET NAVARAE REGINA; below, G DVPRE F 1620

66 mm. A1304–565A

Literature: Cp. Mazerolle, no. 685; Cott p. 198.

566. LOUIS XIII, 1623.

Obv. Bust to right, in large ruff, cuirass, and scarf. Around, LVDOVIC(us) XIII D(ei) G(ratia) FRANCOR(um) ET NAVARAE REX Below, G DVPRE

Rev. Justice seated with sword and scales. Around, VT GENTES TOLLATQVE PREMAT QVE and, below, 1623

60 mm. A1305–566A

The date 1623 was engraved on the truncation of the arm, but is barely legible.

Literature: Cp. Mazerolle, no. 689; Cott p. 198.

567. MARIE DE MÉDICIS, Queen of France (1573–1600–42).

Obv. Bust to right, in court dress. Around, retrograde, MARIA AVG(usta) GALL(iae) ET NAVAR(ae) REGIN(a) and, below, G DVPRE F Engraved on truncation, 1624

Rev. The Queen as Mother of the Gods, with orb and sceptre, lion beside her; around her, five other deities; in the clouds, car drawn by two lions; below, LAETA DEVM PARTV

54 mm. A1306–567A

Literature: Cp. Mazerolle, no. 693; Cott p. 198.

568. MARIE DE MÉDICIS, 1624.

Obv. Bust to right, in court dress. Around, retrograde, MARIA AVGVSTA GALLIAE ET NAVARAE REGINA and, below, G DVPRE F 1624

Without reverse.

103 mm. Cast hollow, with loop. A1307–568A

Collection: J. Fau (sale, Paris, 3 March 1884, lot 542).

Literature: Cp. Mazerolle, no. 696; Cott p. 198.

569. ANTOINE RUZÉ (1581–1632), Marquis d'Effiat et de Longjumeau, surintendant des finances in 1626.

Obv. Bust to right, in cuirass, falling lace collar, and scarf. Around, A(ntoine) RVZE M(arquis) DEFFIAT ET D(e) LONIVMEAV SVR(intendan)T DES FINANCES

Rev. Hercules helping Atlas to bear the globe; around, QVIDQVID EST IVSSVM LEVE EST; below, engraved, 1629

65 mm. A1308–569A

Unsigned, but generally accepted as the work of Dupré.

Literature: Cp. Mazerolle, no. 702; Cott p. 198. For a note on the other medals with the reverse type see Middeldorf, *Morgenroth*, no. 287.

570. JEAN DE CAYLAR DE SAINT-BONNET (1585–1636), Marquis de Toyras, Maréchal de France in 1630.

Obv. Bust to right, in cuirass, with falling lace collar. Around, LE MARESCHAL DE TOYRAS; below, GVIL DVPRE F 1634

Rev. Radiant sun in clouds above landscape; inscription: ADVERSA CORONANT

59 mm. A1309–570A

Literature: Cp. Mazerolle, no. 705; Cott p. 198.

571. CHRISTINE DE FRANCE, Duchess of Savoy (wife of Victor Amadeus 1619, regent 1637–48, died 1663), 1635.

Obv. Bust to right, in court dress, wearing small crown. Around, CHRISTIA(na) A F[RAN]CIA DVCISSA SAB(audiae) REG(ina) CY(pri) and G DVPRE F 1635.

Without reverse.

55 mm. Cast hollow, with loop. A1310–571A

The reverse should depict a diamond mounted in a pin and the motto PLVS DE FERMETE QVE DECLAT

Literature: Cp. Mazerolle, no. 706; Cott, p. 198; Turin exhibition catalogue, *Mostra del Barocco Piemontese*, 1963, vol 3, section *Monete e medaglie* p. 26, no. 20, pl. xiii (complete medal).

ABRAHAM DUPRÉ

(b. 1604; d. 1647)

Abraham Dupré, son and pupil of Guillaume, worked in Savoy as cannon-founder 1626–39, when he succeeded his father at the Paris Mint. See Forrer I, pp. 646–7; Alvin in Thieme-Becker, 10 (1914), p. 168 (bibliography ends with Forrer).

572. JACQUES BOICEAU, Seigneur de la Barauderie, intendant des jardins du Roi, 1624.

Obv. Bust to right, in doublet and ruff. Around, IACQVES BOICEAV S(eigneu)R DE LA BARRAVDERIE and, below, AB DVPRE F 1624

Rev. Landscape; caterpillars crawling on the ground; in the air, butterflies. Inscription: NATVS HVMI POST OPVS ASTRA PETO

72 mm. A1311–572A

Literature: Cp. Mazerolle, no. 712; Cott p. 198.

NICOLAS GABRIEL JACQUET

Known as the maker of some thirty medals between 1601 and 1630. Mazerolle supposed the medallist to be connected with the family of sculptors of the same name at Grenoble. See Thieme-Becker, 18 (1925) p. 316.

573. POMPONNE DE BELLIÈVRE (1529–1607) Chancellor of France 1599.

Obv. Bust to left, aged, in ruff and gown. Around, POMPONIVS DE BELIEVRE FRANCIAE CANCEL(larius) AET(atis) 71 and, below, N G I F 1601

Rev. Justice and Piety at an altar. Around, COLIT HANC RIGIDE MODERATVR ET ISTAM Below, PIE(tas) AEQ(uitas) PVB(lica).

55 mm. A1312–573A

Literature: Cp. Mazerolle, no. 720; Tricou, no. 33; Cott p. 198.

PHILIPPE LALIAME

Philippe Laliame (or Philibert Lalyame), sculptor, architect, and medallist, recorded in Lyon from 1600 to 1628.
See Thieme-Becker, 22 (1928) pp. 240–1.

574. NICOLAS DE LANGES (1525–1606), président de la sénéchaussée et siège présidial de Lyon; 1603.

Obv. Bust to left, in brocaded gown. Around, NICOLAVS LANGAEVS LVGD(unensis) and, in front, *æt.* 78.

Rev. Apollo, leaning on an olive-tree trunk and holding lyre; on each side of him, obverse and reverse of a coin of Augustus; below, AN(no) 1603; around, VETERVM VOLVIT MONVMENTA VIRORVM

51 mm. A1313–574A

The inscription on the reverse is from Virgil, *Aeneid*, 3.102.

Literature: Cp. Mazerolle, no. 732; Tricou, no. 37; Cott p. 198.

JEAN DARMAND, called LORFELIN (b. *ca.* 1600; d. 1669)

Born about 1600, died 1669, graver to the Paris Mint 1630–46, is succession to Briot. See Forrer 1, pp. 509–510; Alvin in Thieme-Becker, 8 (1913), p. 407.

575. ANNE D'AUTRICHE (1601–66); 1642.

Obv. Bust to right, dress embroidered with fleurs-de-lis and trimmed with lace. Around, ANNA AVSTRIACA FRANC(iae) ET NAVAR(ae) REGINA; on truncation, LORFELIN F(ecit).

Rev. Crown surrounded by stars in clouds; below, flowers growing; around, NON EST MORTALE QVOD OPTO

51 mm. With loop for suspension. A1314–575A

Specimens in silver and bronze are at Paris. An unsigned specimen has the date 1642 on the truncation of the arm.

Literature: Cp. Mazerolle, no. 780; Cott p. 199.

JEAN VARIN (b. *ca.* 1604; d. 1672)

Varin was born at Liège and died in Paris. He worked in Rochefort in *ca.* 1615, in Liège and Sedan, *ca.* 1623, and in about 1627 went to Paris to practice as a sculptor and engraver. He succeeded René Olivier at the mint in 1629. He produced both excellent struck medals, and cast portrait pieces.

See F. Mazerolle, *Jean Varin*, 2 vols., Paris, 1932; V. Tourneur, 'Les origines de Jean Varin', in *Rev. belge de Num.*, 84 (1932), pp. 65–76; Thieme-Becker 35 (1942) p. 161.

575*a*. ARMAND-JEAN DUPLESSIS (1585–1642) Cardinal de Richelieu in 1622.

Obv. Bust to right; around, ARMANDVS IOANNES CARDINALIS DE RICHELIEV.

Rev. The figure of France seated in a chariot drawn by four horses, Fortune chained to the chariot, and Fame standing on the chariot, guiding the horses and trumpeting. Around, TANDEM VICTA SEQVOR Below, I WARIN 1630

78 mm. A1672

Literature: Mazerolle, *Jean Varin*, 1, p. 86, no. 5 (variety).

576. ARMAND-JEAN DUPLESSIS (1585–1642), Cardinal de Richelieu.

Obv. Bust to right; around, ARMANVS IOAN(nes) CARD(inalis) DE RICHELIEV; below, I WARIN

Rev. The globe within the circle of the planets which is turned by a little winged genius. Around, MENS SIDERA VOLVIT Below, 1631

51 mm. A modern strike. A1315–576A

Literature: Cp. *Médailles françaises dont les coins sont conservés au Musée monétaire*, Paris, 1892, no. 83; Mazerolle, *Jean Varin*, 1, p. 87, no. 13; Cott p. 199.

UNIDENTIFIED MEDALLISTS

577. NICOLAS DE BAILLEUL, Prévôt des Marchands of Paris 1622–8, died 1662.

Obv. Bust to right, in gown. Around, NICO(lao) DE BAILLEVL PROPRAET(ore) VRB(is) ET PRAEF(ecto) AEDIL(ium) CVRANTE Below, 1623

Rev. The Nymph of the Seine seated in a landscape, resting on an urn from which water flows. Around, AETERNOS PRAEBET LVTETIA FONTES

52 mm. A1316–577A

Literature: Cp. Mazerolle, no. 842; Cott p. 199.

578. NOËL BRULART DE SILLERY, Knight of St John 1632.

Obv. Bust to right, in skull-cap, doublet, falling ruff, and cross of order. Around, F(rère) NOEL BRVLART DE SILLERI CHEVALIER DE L'ORDRE DE S(aint) JEAN DE HIERVSAL(em). Below, 1632

Rev. Achievement of Brulart, the shield placed on a Cross of Malta and surrounded by collar of the Order. Around, INCLVSVS MVNDO SECLVSIT GAVDIA MVNDI

Silver, 51 mm. A1317–578A

Literature: Cp. Mazerolle, no. 856; Cott p. 199.

579. JOACHIM DE CHÂTEAUVIEUX, Comte de Confolens, died 1615.

Obv. Bust to left, in cuirass, scarf, and ruff. Around, IOACH(im) A CASTROVETERI COM(es) CONFLVENTIS

Without reverse.

45 mm. A1318–579A

Another specimen in the Cabinet des Médailles, Paris.

Literature: Cp. Mazerolle, no. 857; Cott p. 199.

580. ANTOINE DE LOMENIE (1560–1638), councillor and Secretary of State.

Obv. Bust to right, in skull-cap, wearing gown with falling collar. Around, ANT(oine) DE LOMENIE CONSELLIER ET SECRETAIRE DESTAT Below, MDCXXX

Rev. Above a landscape, the Sun in car driving along the Zodiac, accompanied by Mercury. Above, SIC TE REX MAGNE SEQVEBAR

48 mm. A1319–580A

Literature: Cp. Mazerolle, no. 874; Cott p. 199.

581. JEAN DE SAULX, Vicomte de Tavanes et de Lugny.

Obv. Bust to right, in cuirass and scarf. Around, IEAN DE SAVLX COMMANDENT EN BOVRGONGNE NORMANDIE MARESCHAL P FI DE CAMP

Rev. Rampant lion on a chain; above, SEMPER; to left a flame, to right a crown. Around, VICONTE DE TAVANES LIGNI MARQVIS DE MIREBET 1614

75 mm. A1320–581A

Apparently unpublished. It represents Jean, son of Gaspard de Saulx, who was chevalier de l'ordre du Roi and maréchal général des camps et armées catholiques in 1552. He made his will in 1629.

Literature: Cott p. 199.

582. See Appendix.

IV

GERMAN MEDALS

The medals of the sixteenth century, for the most part cast, are grouped according to Habich's Corpus of German medals, *Die deutschen Schaumünzen des XVI. Jahrhunderts*, 5 vols., Munich, 1929–1935. After these are placed a few medals, mostly the work of die-engravers, and a few pieces by later masters.

ALBRECHT DÜRER

(b. 1471; d. 1528)

583. CHARLES V, Emperor, 1521.

Obv. Bust of the Emperor to right, wearing crown, armour, and Order of the Fleece. Around, CAROLVS V RO(manorum) IMPER(ator). On a raised border, 14 coats of arms; above, the two pillars with PLVS VLTR(a) on scroll.

Rev. Imperial double-headed eagle, charged on the breast with shield of Austria-Burgundy. On raised border, 13 coats of arms; below in a wreath, N (for Nuremberg).

Lead, 72 mm. A1322–583A

Struck from dies made after designs by Albrecht Dürer, to the order of the Council of Nuremberg for presentation to the Emperor in 1521 to commemorate the Diet to be held in the city. There are other lead specimens in the Germanisches Museum, Nuremberg, and the Wallace collection, London. The silver specimen in the Victoria and Albert Museum, London, has the number 14 stamped on the edge.

Literature: Cp. Habich, *Deutsche Schaumünzen*, i, 1, no. 18; J. G. Mann, Wallace collection catalogue: *Sculpture, marbles, terra-cottas and bronzes*, London, 1931, p. 148, no. s. 400, pl. 88 (lead specimen); Alvarez-Ossorio, p. 116, no. 112 (silver specimen); Cott p. 199.

HANS SCHWARZ

(b. 1492; active 1512–1532)

Schwarz was born in Augsburg in 1492. He was active from 1512, was in Nuremberg 1519–1520, in the Palatinate, in Poland, 1527, at the Danish court, in Paris 1532, and also in the Netherlands. The place and date of death of the artist are unknown. His medals are all cast from models carved in wood. See Grotemeyer in Thieme-Becker, 30 (1936) pp. 362–3; A Suhle, *Die deutsche Renaissance-Medaille*, Leipzig, 1950, pp. 13–28.

584. KUNZ VON DER ROSEN, confidential Councillor of Maximilian I.

Obv. Bust three-quarters to right, hair in net, flat cap. On left, incised, monogram of H S

Without reverse.

64 mm. A1323–584A

Other specimens are in Berlin and Milan. Kunz died soon after his master in 1519.

Literature: Habich, *Deutsche Schaumünzen* i, 1, no. 120; Cott p. 199.

585. MELCHIOR PFINZING (1481–1535), Provost of St Sebald in Nuremberg.

Obv. Bust to left, in berretta and robe. Around, MCCCCCXIX AET(atis) XXXVII

Rev. XIX DEO VINDICTA ET IPSE RETRIBVET AN(no) MD in wreath.

44 mm. A1324–585A

Literature: Cp. Habich, *Deutsche Schaumünzen*, i, 1, no. 134 (the Berlin specimen); Cott, p. 199.

ALEXANDER VON BRUCHSAL

(d. 1545)

The artist was a goldsmith and die-engraver, working at Antwerp from 1505. He engraved dies for Henry VII of England, 1509, and was mentioned by Dürer after an encounter in 1521. See Hill and Tourneur, 'Alexander of Bruchsal', in *Num. Chron.*, 4 (1924) pp. 254–260.

586. ALEXANDER VON BRUCHSAL.

Obv. Bust to left, wearing cap and robe.

Without reverse.

45 mm. Thrice pierced. A1325–586A

There is an inscribed specimen of the medal in Brussels.

Literature: *Les Arts*, Aug. 1908, p. 13, no. xiv; cp. Habich,

Deutsche Schaumünzen, i. 1, p. 51, fig. 66 (Berlin specimen), pl. xli, 6 (Brussels specimen); Cott p. 200.

CHRISTOPH WEIDITZ
(b. *ca.* 1500; d. 1559)

Weiditz was active from 1523 to 1536 as medallist, wood-carver, gold and silver smith. He worked in Strassburg, Ulm, and Augsburg, and in Spain and the Netherlands. See Grotemeyer in Thieme-Becker, 35 (1942) pp. 267–8; Suhle, *Die deutsche Renaissance-Medaille*, Leipzig, 1950, pp. 29–35.

587. AMBROSIUS JUNG, physician, born at Ulm 1471, city-physician at Augsburg, died 1548.

Obv. Bust to right, in broad hat and robe. Around, AMBROSIVS IVNG ARTIVM ET MEDICINAE DOCTOR AN(no) AETATIS LVII

Rev. Arms. Around, IVSTICIA NOSTRA CHRISTVS M D XXVIII

70 mm. A1326–587A

Literature: Cp. Habich, *Deutsche Schaumünzen*, i, 1, no. 365; Cott p. 200.

588. FRANCISCO COVO (DELOSCOPOS), Chancellor of Charles V in Spain, in Augsburg in 1530, in Brussels in 1531.

Obv. Bust to front, wearing hat, gown, and chain with pendant. Around, FRANCISCO COVO MAGNO CO(m)ME(n)D(atori) LEGIONIS CAES(aris) CAROLI V A SECRET(is) CONS(iliario) A(nno) MDXXXI

Rev. Man riding towards a cliff; carries scroll inscribed FATA VIAM INVENIENT

Lead, 60 mm. A1327–588A

Literature: Cp. Habich, *Deutsche Schaumünzen*, i, 1, no. 396, (specimens at Berlin and Madrid); Cott p. 200.

FRIEDRICH HAGENAUER

Born in Strassburg; active from 1525 to after 1543; the dates of his birth and death are unknown. He worked chiefly in Munich, Augsburg, Strassburg, Baden, Cologne, and the Netherlands. Less vigorous than Schwarz, he is more pleasing as a portraitist.

See (besides the entry in Habich, *Deutsche Schaumünzen*), Suhle, *Die deutsche Renaissance-Medaille*, Leipzig, 1950, pp. 36–51; F. Baillion, 'Une médaille inédite de Frédéric Hagenauer', in *Rev. belge de Num.*, 96 (1950) pp. 195–6.

588*a*. CASPAR WINNTZRER, b. 1475 (or 1465), d. 1542.

Obv. Bust to left, in field, AET S LI H

Rev. DIVORVM MAXIMIL ET CAROLI EIVS NEPOT ROM IMPP TRIBVTVS MILIT CASPAR VVINNTZRER AVRATVS M D XXVI H

Lead, 69 mm. After-cast. A1450–710A

The reverse has been altered to read TRIBVTVS, it should read TRIBVNVS.

Literature: Cp. Habich, *Deutsche Schaumünzen*, i, 1, no. 449; Cott p. 200.

588*b*. AUGUSTIN LÖSCH (1471–1535), Chancellor of the Duchy of Bavaria, 1526.

Obv. Bust to right. Around, EFFIGIES AVGVSTINI LESCH DE HILKERS I V DOC BAIO DVCVM CANCELLA Across the field, M D XXVI

Without reverse.

Lead, 68 mm. A1457–717A

Literature: Cp. Habich, *Deutsche Schaumünzen*, i, 1, no. 457; Cott p. 200.

589. SEBASTIAN and URSULA LIEGSALZ, 1527.

Obv. Bust of Sebastian to right, hair in net, furred robe. Incised, around, SEBASTIANS LIGSALCZ GESTALT WAR IM XXXXIIII IAR ALT and, across field, MD XXVII

Rev. Bust of Ursula to left, in hat. Incised, around, VRSVLA SEBASTI(ans) LIGSALCZ HAVSFRAV WAS IM XXVIII IAR ALT and, across field, MDXXVII

126 mm. Separate old lead castings of obverse and reverse.
A1328–589A
A1329–589A

From the wooden models in Munich. Ursula Senffel was the second wife of Sebastian Liegsalz, a citizen of Munich.

Literature: Cp. Habich, *Deutsche Schaumünzen*, i, 1, no. 465; Cott p. 200.

590. GIOVANNI ALESSANDRO BALBIANI of Chiavenna, Captain in the army of Georg von Frundsberg, 1529.

Obv. Bust to left, in cap and gown. Around, IOANN(es) ALEXANDER BALBIANVS COMES CLAVENE ANNO SALVTIS MDXXIX In field to left, monogram of FH

Without reverse.

58 mm. A1330–590A

Literature: Cp. Habich, *Deutsche Schaumünzen*, i, 1, p. 81, no. 529 (the Munich specimen); Cott p. 200.

590*a*. MARGARET VON FIRMIAN (1509–36), wife of Caspar von Frundsberg, 1529.

Obv. Bust to left. Around, MARGARITA A FIRMIAN D CASPARIS A FRVNT SPERG VXOR ANNO ETATIS SVE XX and in field left, H

Without reverse.

Lead, 60 mm. Old after-cast. A1445–705A

Literature: Cp. Habich, *Deutsche Schaumünzen*, i, 1, no. 540; Suhle, pl. 16, 1; Cott p. 200.

591. UNKNOWN MAN.

Obv. Bust of young man to left, wearing small flat cap, doublet, and mantle.

Without reverse.

52 mm. Cast hollow. A1331–591A

Probably an after-cast. The wooden model is in the Cabinet des Médailles, Paris.

Literature: Cp. Habich, *Deutsche Schaumünzen*, i, 1, no. 603; Cott p. 200.

592. JOHANNES MULICUM.

Obv. Bust to left, wearing habit. Around, FRATER IOANNES MVLICVM DE NOVI(O)MAGIO ET INFIRMARIVS CAMPENSIS

Rev. AVGV(sta) I(n) EP(u)LA MELI(u)S EST ORARE CV(m) SILENTIO CORDIS QVA(m) SOLVM VERBVM SINE INTVITV MENTIS MDXXXX

47 mm. The only specimen known. A1332–592A

Mulicum of Nimwegen was infirmarer in the Cistercian monastery of Kamp near Neuss.

Literature: Habich, *Deutsche Schaumünzen*, i, 1, no. 637; Cott p. 200.

593. PHILIPP MELANCHTHON, Reformer (1497–1560).

Obv. Bust to left. Around, PHILIPPVS MELANTHON ANNO AETATIS SVAE XLVII and, in field left, monogram of FII

Rev. PSAL 36 SVBDITVS ESTO DEO ET ORA EVM ANNO M D XXXXIII

39 mm. A1333–593A

Literature: Habich, *Deutsche Schaumünzen*, i, 1, no. 651; Cott p. 200.

594. *Obv.* Bust to left, in flat cap and gown. Around, PHILIPPVS MELANTHON A(nn)O AETATIS SVAE XLVII

Rev. Inscription from Psalm xxxvi, as on no. 593, and date MDXLIII

47 mm. A1334–594A

Some specimens bear the monogram of Hagenauer on the obverse. The wooden portrait model is reproduced in Suhle.

Literature: Cp. Habich, *Deutsche Schaumünzen*, i, 1, no. 652; Suhle, pl. 17, 2 (wooden model); Cott p. 200.

595. KASPAR VON MÜHLHEIM, 1506–70/71, Councillor of Cologne, 1543.

Obv. Bust to right, wearing cap and fur robe. Around, CASPAR VAN MVLLEM SYNES ALDERS IM XXXVII IAER

Rev. Small shield with house-mark. Around, in two circles, O HYMLICHSCHER VATER DYN GENAED VND BARMHERTZICHKEIT SONST IST ALLES VERLOEREN ARBEYT MDXLIII

Lead, 46 mm. A1335–595A

Literature: Cp. Habich, *Deutsche Schaumünzen*, i, 1, no. 659; Cott p. 200.

596. HANS HAUSCHEL, born 1520.

Obv. Bust to right, in flat cap. Around, HANS HAVSCHEL SIENS ALTERS 24 IAR

Rev. ICH HABS GESTALT IN GOTS GEWALT M D XXXXIIII

39 mm. A1336–596A

The original box-wood model is in the British Museum; a cast at Munich.

Literature: Cp. Habich, *Deutsche Schaumünzen*, i, 1, no. 665; Cott p. 200.

HANS KELS THE YOUNGER

(b. *ca.* 1510; d. 1565/6)

Hans Kels the younger was active as a medallist in Augsburg, where he was born, from 1530 until his death. See Habich in *Deutsche Schaumünzen*; Simon in Thieme-Becker, 20 (1927) pp. 127–9.

596*a*. BARBARA REIHINGIN, wife of Georg Hermann (no. 597*b*). Dated 1538.

Obv. Bust to left. Around, BARBARA REIHINGIN VXOR AETATIS AN XXXXVII

Rev. Coat of Arms. Around, IN DOMINO CONFIDO ANNO MD XXXVIII

52 mm. A1461–721A

Literature: Cp. Habich, *Deutsche Schaumünzen*, i, 1, no. 777; Cott p. 201.

MATHES GEBEL

(b. *ca.* 1500; d. 1574)

Became a citizen of Nuremberg in 1523 and worked until 1554, but lived for another twenty years. A very large number of medals formerly ascribed to other artists, such as Ludwig Krug and especially Peter Flötner, are now given to Gebel. He is the most able representative of the Nuremberg school, whose work has the fine qualities derived from its origin in goldsmithery, as opposed to the Augsburg school, which is based on ordinary metal-casting. See (besides the entry in Habich, *Deutsche Schaumünzen*) Suhle, *Die deutsche Renaissance-Medaille*, Leipzig, 1950, pp. 52–62.

596*b*. CHRISTOPH KRESS VON KRESSENSTEIN (1484–1535), 'Kriegsrat' in Nuremberg, dated 1526.

Obv. Bust to right. Around, CRISTOF KRES XXXXII IAR ALT

Rev. A blazon of arms. Around, CRISTOFF KRES VOM KRESENSTAIN MD XXVI

Lead, 39 mm. A1447–707A

Literature: Cp. Habich, *Deutsche Schaumünzen*, i, 2, no. 957; Middeldorf, *Morgenroth*, no. 158; Cott p. 201 (attributed to Gebel).

596*c*. FREDERICK (1460–1532), Archduke of Brandenburg-Ansbach, 1528.

Obv. Bust to left. Around, DEI GRATIA INVICTA VIRTVS FRIDERICH ANN NAT LXX SVPERST

Rev. Blazon of arms. Around, MARCH BRAND DV STETI POME CASVB VAND BVRGR NVREN PRIN RVG MDXXVIII

Lead, 38 mm. A1455–715A

Literature: Cp. Habich, *Deutsche Schaumünzen*, i, 2, no. 979; Cott p. 201.

597. PHILIPP (1503–48), Count Palatine.

Obv. Bust to right, in cuirass. Around, PHILIPPVS CO(mes) PA(latinus) RHE(ni) DVX BAIO(ariae) ZC (etc.) NA(tus) AN(nos) XXV

Rev. Shield with two casques and crests. Around, ECIAM SI OCCIDERIT ME IN IPSO SPERABO MDXXVIII.

42 mm. A1337–597A

Literature: Cp. Habich, *Deutsche Schaumünzen*, i, 2, no. 985; Cott p. 201.

597*a*. HIERONYMUS HOLZSCHUHER (d. 1529), dated 1529, patrician of Nuremberg.

Obv. Bust to right. Around, HIERONYMVS HOITZSCHVER SENIOR AETATIS SVAE LX

Rev. Shield of arms, with crest and mantling. Around, MVNIFICENTIA AMICOS PATIENTIA INIMICOS VINCE M DXXIX

Silver (base) 40 mm. A1434–694A

Literature: Cp. Habich, *Deutsche Schaumünzen*, i, 2, no. 993; Cott p. 201.

597*b*. GEORG HERMANN (1491–1552), connected with the Fugger House, dated 1529.

Obv. Bust to right. Around, GIORGIVS HERMAN AETATIS SVAE AN XXXVIII

Rev. Shields and a helm. Across field, MD XXIX FVNGENDO CONSVMOR, all within a wreath.

Lead, 38 mm. A1440–700A

Literature: Cp. Habich, *Deutsche Schaumünzen*, i, 2, no. 1001; Cott p. 201.

598. MARX RECHLINGER (d. 1532).

Obv. Bust to right, with beard, in small flat cap. Around, MARX RECHLINGER GESTALT DO ICH WVRT XX IAR ALT

Without reverse.

Lead, 44 mm. A1338–598A

One of three specimens recorded by Habich, the others are at Wiesbaden and Augsburg. A cut-out of the portrait is at Munich.

Literature: Habich, *Deutsche Schaumünzen*, i, 2, no. 1041; Cott p. 201.

599. CHARLES V, 1530.

Obv. Bust to right, wearing small flat cap and jewel of the Fleece. Around, IMP(erator) CAES(ar) CAROLVS V P(ius) F(elix) AVGVST(us) AN(no) AET(atis) XXX

Rev. In wreath, FVNDATORI QVIETIS MDXXX

Silver (base), 37 mm. A1339–599A

Literature: Cp. Habich, *Deutsche Schaumünzen*, i, 2, no. 1010; Bernhart, *Bildnismedaillen Karls des Fünften*, Munich, 1919, no. 65; Cott p. 201.

599*a*. RAIMOND FUGGER (1489–1535) German scholar and patron of the arts, 1525.

Obv. Bust to right. Around, RAIMVNDVS FVGGER AVGVST VIND AETATIS XXXX

Rev. An allegory of Liberality. Around, PVDEAT AMICI DIEM PERDIDISSE. LIBERALITAS.

42 mm. Silver (base) A1437–697A

The reverse reproduces a design by Hagenauer.

Literature: Cp. Habich, *Deutsche Schaumünzen*, i, 2, no. 1014; Suhle, pl. 15, no. 3 (the model for the reverse by Hagenauer); Cott p. 201 (Gebel ? or Floetner ?).

599*b*. LORENZ TRUCHSES VON POMERSFELDEN (1473–1543).

Obv. Bust to right. Around, LAVRENT TRVCHSES A BOMERSFELDEN DECANVS ECLIE MAGVNT MDXXX

Rev. A tablet, inscribed CONFVNDANTVR SVPERBI QVIA INIVSTE INIQVITATEM FECERVNT IN ME, on the tablet, an hour-glass. Around, PERICVLVM IN FALSIS FRATRIBVS MICHI HODIE CRAS TIBI

Lead, 41 mm. A1438–698A

Literature: Cp. Habich, *Deutsche Schaumünzen*, i, 2, no. 1025; Cott p. 201.

599*c*. JOHANN FRIEDRICH, b. 1503, Elector of Saxony (1532–54), *ca*. 1532.

Obv. Bust to right. Around, IO FR I IO I RO IMP ELECT PRIMOG D SAX

Rev. Blazon of arms. Around, SPES MEA IN DEO EST

Silver (base), 46 mm. A1435–695A

Literature: Cp. Habich, *Deutsche Schaumünzen*, i, 2, no. 1080; Middeldorf, *Morgenroth*, no. 163; Cott p. 202.

599*d*. LORENZ STAIBER (1485/6–1539), and his wife, dated 1535.

Obv. Bust to right of Lorenz Staiber. Around, LAVREN STAVBERVS EQ AVR AC ANGL ET FRANC REGIS ORATOR

Rev. Bust of Frau Staiber to left. Around, ICH ANYM GOT ZV HILFF M D XXXV

Lead, 38 mm. A1439–699A

Staiber was a writer and orator.

Only two specimens are recorded by Habich (Chemnitz, Vögel collection, and this piece).

Literature: Cp. Habich, *Deutsche Schaumünzen*, i, 2, no. 1120; Cott p. 202 (as 'Master L'); Rosenheim and Hill, 'A medal of Lorenz Staiber', in *Num. Chron.*, 21 (1919) pp. 244–252 (for Staiber's career in England).

600. LUDWIG X, Duke of Bavaria-Landshut, etc. (1495–1516–1545), dated 1535.

Obv. Bust to right, with long beard, wearing flat cap and fur robe. Around, LVDVIG VON GOTS GNADEN PFALCZGRAF BEI RHEIN SEINS ALTERS IM XXXVIII IAR

Rev. Shield with two crests. Around, HERCZOG IN OBERN VND NIDERN BAIRN ZC ANN(o) DOM(ini) MDXXXV

Lead, 43 mm. A1340–600A

There is another medal by Gebel of the elector of the same year, with lion and three shields on the reverse.

Literature: Cp. Habich, *Deutsche Schaumünzen*, i, 2, no. 1123; Middeldorf, *Morgenroth*, no. 164; Cott p. 201.

601. WILHELM LÖFFELHOLZ VON KOLBERG (1501–1554).

Obv. Bust to right, in flat cap. Around, WILHELM LOFFLHOLCZ ZV KOLBERG ETATIS XXXX

Rev. Shield, cuirass, casque, and crest. Around, VNVERSVCHT VNERFARN ANNO MDXXXXI

Silver, 37 mm. With ring. A1341–601A

Literature: Cp. Habich, *Deutsche Schaumünzen*, i, 2, no. 1191; Cott p. 201.

MASTER OF THE PISTORIUS MEDAL

Author of a series of Saxon, especially Leipzig, medals, from 1535 to 1544.

602. EMILIA, MARGRAVINE OF BRANDENBURG (1516–1591).

Obv. Bust to left, in flat hat with plume, hair in net. Around, GOT VORMAGK AL[LE] DINGK 1540

Without reverse.

33 mm. After-cast. A1342–602A

There are other specimens at Vienna, Paris (École de Beaux-Arts), Victoria and Albert Museum, London (uniface) and Görlitz (uniface). The motto is 'God can do all things'. Emilia married George, Margrave of Brandenburg, in 1532, and was widowed in 1546.

Literature: Cp. Habich, *Deutsche Schaumünzen*, ii, 1, no. 1877; Cott p. 201.

M. P.

603. WENZESLAUS BEYER, physician (1488–1526). State physician in Bohemia, 1526.

Obv. Bust to left. Around, WENCES(laus) BEYER MAEDI(cus) NATIO(n)E BOEMVS AETATIS SVE 38

Rev. Rider on a rearing horse (?) in landscape; in foreground a book, skull and bones. Around, IAM PORTVM INVENI SPES ET FORTVNA VALETE

57 mm. Iron casting, late ? A1343–603A

By a medallist who signs MP on another medal of the same man. Beyer, the first to write on the Carlsbad waters, died in 1526; some specimens of this medal bear that date stamped on them.

Literature: Cp. Habich, *Deutsche Schaumünzen*, i, 2, no. 1467; Cott p. 201.

LUDWIG NEUFAHRER
(d. 1563)

Neufahrer was active as medallist, die-cutter, and goldsmith from about 1530 to 1562, principally in Nuremberg, Vienna, and Prague. His medals bear dates between 1530 and 1557. He died in Prague, 1563. See (besides the entry in Habich, *Deutsche Schaumünzen*) Grotemeyer, in Thieme-Becker, 25 (1931) p. 406; G. Probszt, *Ludwig Neufahrer*, Vienna, 1960.

604. CHARLES V.

Obv. Bust to right, bearded, wearing flat cap and jewel of the Fleece. Around, CAROLVS HESPERY REX ET MODERATOR IBERI(ae) IN(victissimus ?) and, below, LVD NEIFA

Rev. Double-headed crowned eagle standing on the two pillars of Hercules with scroll inscribed PLVS VLTRA Around, TVLIT AVRIFERO ROMVLA SCEPTRA TAGO ANNO 1542 LV NE

Pewter, 41 mm. Struck? A1344–604A

Literature: Cp. Habich, *Deutsche Schaumünzen*, i, 2, no. 1404; Bernhart, *Bildnismedaillen Karls des Fünften*, Munich, 1919, no. 84; Probszt, no. 63, pls. 4 and 5 (struck); Cott p. 202.

604*a*. FRANCIS I, King of France (1515–1547), 1537.

Obv. Bust three-quarters to left, wearing cap with plume, and robes. Around, FRANCISCVS I FRANCORVM REX C° 43

Rev. In a wreath, salamander in flames; below it, L N; around, DISCVTIT HA(n)C FLA(m)MA(m) FRA(n)CISC(us) ROBORE ME(n)TIS O(m)NIA P(er)VI(n)CIT RERV(m) I(m)MERSABILIS V(n)D(a).

Silver, 43 mm. A1275–536A

Thieme-Becker ascribes the medal to an unknown French medallist of the first half of the sixteenth century, which Probszt thinks unsatisfactory and includes the medal in his monograph on Neufahrer.

Literature: Cp. Forrer, 4, p. 249; Habich, *Deutsche Schaumünzen*, i, 2, no. 1397 (as Neufahrer); Thieme-Becker, 37 (1950) p. 429 (artist signing L.N); Probszt, no. 25, pl. 37; Cott p. 196; Tervarent, cols. 333–4 (for the salamander device).

HANS REINHART THE ELDER
(d. 1581)

Reinhart was medallist and goldsmith. His medals date between 1535 and 1574, and his patrons included Cardinal Albrecht of Brandenburg and the Elector Johann Friedrich of Saxony. See (besides the entry in Habich, *Deutsche Schaumünzen*) Grotemeyer, in Thieme-Becker, 28 (1934) pp. 123–4. For a double plaquette in the Kress collection, see Pope-Hennessy, *Kress Bronzes*, no. 434.

605. JOHANN FRIEDRICH, Elector of Saxony (1503–32–54) dated 1535.

Obv. Half-figure three-quarters to right, with sword and hat. Around, IOANN(e)S FRIDERICVS ELECTOR DVX SAXONIE FIERI FECIT ETATIS SVAE 32 On his collar, traces of motto *Alles in Ehren kann Niemand wehren.*

Rev. Shield with three helms and crests. Around, SPES MEA IN DEO EST ANNO NOSTRI SALVATORIS MDXXXV

Silver, 65 mm. A1345–605A

Literature: Cp. Domanig, *Deutsche Medaille*, no. 154; cp. Habich, *Deutsche Schaumünzen*, ii, 1, no. 1995; Cott p. 202.

606. CHARLES V, 1537.

Obv. Bust to right, wearing small flat cap, robes and jewel of the Fleece, holding orb and sceptre. Around, CAROLVS V DEI GRATIA ROMAN(orum) IMPERATOR SEMPER AVGVSTVS REX HIS(paniarum) ANNO SAL(utis) MDXXXVII AETATIS SVAE XXXVII Incised across field, G G

Rev. Double-headed eagle, crowned, charged with shield and collar of the Fleece; at sides the two pillars of Hercules and PLVS OVLTRE; below, H R

Silver, 64 mm. With loop. A1346–606A

Literature: Cp. Habich, *Deutsche Schaumünzen*, ii, 1, no. 1926; Bernhart, *Bildnismedaillen Karls des Fünften*, Munich, 1919, no. 93; Cott p. 202.

HANS BOLSTERER
(d. 1573)

Worked chiefly at Nuremberg from 1540 to 1567.

607. JOHANN FICHARD (1512–1581) and his wife ELISABETH, 1547.

Obv. Bust of Johann to right, in flat cap and gown. Around, IOANNES FICHARDVS V(triusque) I(urius) D(octor) ZC AETATIS SVAE XXXVI A(nn)O MDXLVII

Rev. Bust of Elisabeth to left, in cap. Around, ELISABET FICHARDIN GE(borene) GRVNBERGERIN AE(tatis) 29 A(nn)O 1547

47 mm. A1347–607A

Johann Fichard was a Syndic of Frankfurt a. Main in 1532, and married in 1539 Elizabeth Grünenberger (b. 1518).

Literature: Habich, *Deutsche Schaumünzen*, i, 2, no. 1779 (this specimen cited); Cott p. 202; Middeldorf, *Morgenroth*, no. 171 (obverse only).

JOACHIM DESCHLER
(Active 1532–1571)

Born about 1500, became a citizen of Nuremberg in 1537; living there or in Austria he worked from 1548 for the courts of Austria, Saxony, and the Palatinate, dying in 1571 or 1572.

608. HIERONYMUS PAUMGARTNER of Nuremberg (1497–1565).

Obv. Bust facing, in gown. Around, HIERONYMVS PAVMGARTNER ANNO AETATIS 56 and, on truncation, 1553 Narrow wreath.

Rev. Arms of Paumgartner. Around, IN VMBRA ALARVM TVARVM SPERABO DONEC TRANSEAT INIQVITAS Narrow wreath.

65 mm. A1348–608A

Literature: Cp. Habich, *Deutsche Schaumünzen*, i, 2, no. 1611; Löbbecke sale, lots 297–8; Cott p. 202.

609. MARGARETHE BALBUS, née Ganzhorn, 1565.

Obv. Bust to left, wearing cap. MARGARETA DOCTOR WILLELM GANCZHORNS LLEIBLICHE DOCHT(er). Arabesqued field. All in narrow wreath.

Rev. Two shields. Above, ANNO 65 DOCTOR IOA(nnes) BALBVS VICECAN(cellarius) ELICHE HAVSFRAV IRES ALTERS XXV

Silver, 39 mm. With ring. A1349–609A

Literature: Cp. Habich, *Deutsche Schaumünzen*, i, 2, no. 1680; Cott p. 202.

JAKOB HOFMANN
(b. 1512; d. 1564)

The following medal is attributed to this Nuremberg goldsmith, as is also a portrait of Peter Zeitler dated 1555.

610. ANNA HOFMANN, wife of the medallist.

Obv. Bust to left, in small flat cap, hair in queue. Around, ANNA I HOEFMENNE

Rev. Venus kneeling; towards her runs a Cupid escaping from bees that issue from a tree-trunk; above, in the air, another Cupid, while a third hides behind Venus. Below, AMOR

34 mm. A1350–610A

Literature: Cp. Habich, *Deutsche Schaumünzen*, ii, 1, no. 2399; i, 1, no. 834; Cott p. 202.

VALENTIN MALER
(Active 1563–1593)

An extremely prolific medallist, and a brilliant wax-modeller, but considerably influenced from time to time by different foreign masters, was working at Nuremberg as early as 1563, and was active until 1593, producing portraits of Nuremberg dignitaries, clerics and members of the court of Saxony.

611. JAKOB MUFFEL of Nuremberg, 1509–69.

Obv. Bust three-quarters to right, with long beard. Around, IACOB MVFFEL V(on) EKENHAID AETA(tis) LIX ANNO MDLXIX On truncation, trace of VM incised.

Without reverse.

Lead, 55 mm. Cast hollow. A1351–611A

Literature: Cp. Domanig, *Deutsche Medaille*, no. 279; Habich, *Deutsche Schaumünzen*, ii, 1, no. 2421; Cott p. 202.

612. MATTHÄUS SCHYRER, secretary to Nuremberg Council.

Obv. Bust to right, in doublet and ruff. Around, MATTHAEVS SCHYRER AETAT 34 and, below, 1584

Rev. Fortune, nude, with veil, on globe on the sea. Around, FINGITVR FORTVNA MORIBVS

33 mm. A1352–612A

Literature: Cp. Habich, *Deutsche Schaumünzen*, ii, 1, no. 2562 (as South German, or by Maler); Cott p. 202.

613. JAKOB FUGGER the Elder (1459–1525).

Obv. Bust three-quarters to right, in large cap; low relief, in imitation of Dürer. Around, IACOB FVGGR DER ELTER

Without reverse.

Lead, oval, 47 × 42 mm. A1353–613A

Literature: Cp. Habich, *Deutsche Schaumünzen*, ii, 1, no. 2559 (as South German, or by Maler); Cott p. 202.

MATTHÄUS CARL

Working 1584–1608 or 1609, influenced by Antonio Abondio and the Netherlanders.

614. HANS SCHEL (1518–1592).

Obv. Bust three-quarters to right, wearing cap, ruff, and gown. Around, in two circles, HANS SCHEL AETA(tis) LXXIIII VERSCHIDT DEN XXIX SEPTEMBER A(nn)O MDXCII

Rev. Arms, surrounded by SOLI DEO GLORIA; around, BEATI QVI IN DOMINO MORIVNTVR

Lead, 43 mm. A1354–614A

Literature: Cp. Habich, *Deutsche Schaumünzen*, ii, 1, no. 2674; Cott p. 202.

JOHANN PHILIPP VON DER PÜTT (d. 1619)

The artist came from Dordrecht to Nuremberg in 1586, becoming a Burger in 1589 and a Master in 1593. He practised as goldsmith, wax-modeller, and medallist, and died in Nuremberg. See Thieme-Becker, 27 (1933) p. 449.

615. JULIUS GEUDER (1531–1594), Nuremberg patrician, 1591.

Obv. Bust facing, with long beard, in ruff and fur-trimmed robe. Around, IVLIVS GEVDER V(on) HEROLTZBERG AE(tatis) 60.

Without reverse.

Silver, 44 mm. A1355–615A

Literature: Cp. Habich, *Deutsche Schaumünzen*, ii, 1, no. 2740; Cott p. 202 (as Nuremberg master of 1591/3).

CONCZ WELCZ (d. *ca.* 1554)

A goldsmith and medallist active at Joachimstal, Bohemia, by whom there are works dating between 1532 and 1551. See Thieme-Becker, 35 (1942) p. 354, and V. Katz, *Die Erzgebirgische Prägemedaille des XVI. Jahrhunderts*, Prague, 1931, pp. 113–19 (for Welcz and his school).

615*a*. LUNA.

Obv. Bust to right of young woman, draped, crescent before her forehead; in front, LVNA 1543

Rev. Diana to right, holding horn and staff; across field, C W

Silver, 19 mm. Struck. A1362–622A

One of a small group of similar allegorical pieces which are ascribed to Welcz.

Literature: Arm. II, 178, 6; Katz (cited above) p. 128, no. 228, pl. xxvii, 9; Cott p. 203.

VARIOUS MEDALS OF THE XVI CENTURY BY GERMAN OR AUSTRIAN MASTERS

616. MAXIMILIAN I as Archduke of Austria, and MARIA OF BURGUNDY.

Obv. Bust of Maximilian to right, with long hair, wreathed. Around, MAXIMILIAN(us) MAGNANIM(us) ARCHIDVX AVSTRIE BVRGVND(ie) and, across field, ETATIS 19 1479

Rev. Bust of Maria to right, wearing hennin and veil. Around, MARIA KAROLI FILIA HERES BVRGVND(ie) BRAB(antie) CONIVGES and, across field, ETATIS 20

Silver, 42 mm. Struck. A1356–616A

One of the restored Schautaler, with the mistaken date 1479 instead of 1477, made at the mint of Hall in Tyrol after 1500. The portraits derive from the medal by Candida (no. 225).

Literature: M. Herrgott, *Nummotheca Principum Austriae. II, Monumentorum Augustae Domus Austriacae*, Freiburg im Br., 1752–3, pl. xi, 12; Lanna sale, lot 581; Cott p. 203; P. Grotemeyer, 'Falschungen nach habsburgischen Medaillen', in *Schweizer Münzblätter*, Jahrgang 10, Heft 37 (Mai 1960) pp. 10–13 (for a forgery of this type).

617. JOHN HUSS CENTENARY.

Obv. Bust of Huss to right, in cap. Across field, IO A(nnes) HVS Around, CREDO VNAM ESSE ECCLESIAM SANCTAM CATOLICAM

Rev. Huss at the stake; around, in two circles, CENTVM REVOLVTIS ANNIS DEO RESPONDEBITIS ET MIHI and ANNO A CHRIST(o) NATO 1415 IO(annes) HVS; across field, CONDEMNATVR

Silver, 43 mm. Struck. A1357–617A

Related to the Huss pieces by the monogrammist HM, Hieronymus Magdeburger.

Literature: Cp. E. Fiala, *Beschreibung der Sammlung böhmischer Münzen und Medaillen des Max Donebauer*, Prague, 1888–9, no. 3443; cp. Habich, *Deutsche Schaumünzen*, ii, 1, no. 1896; cp. V. Katz, *Die Erzgebirgische Prägemedaille des XVI. Jahrhunderts*, Prague, 1931, no. 71, pl. xi, 5; Cott p. 203.

618. FRIEDRICH THE WISE OF SAXONY (1463–86–1525) dated 1522.

Obv. Bust to right, in cap and fur robe. Around, FR(i)D(ericus) DVX SAXON(ie) S(acri) RO(mani) IMP(erii) ELECT(or) and four small shields.

Rev. C(rux) C(hristi) N(ostra) S(alus) in angles of a cross, within a circle, round which MDXXII Around, VERBVM DOMINI MANET IN AETERNVM

Silver, 42 mm. Struck, Schautaler. A1358–618A

Attributed to Hans Krafft the Younger, Nuremberg goldsmith, engraver to the Nuremberg Mint from 1513 to 1527.

Literature: Cp. W. E. Tentzel, *Sächsisches Medaillen-Kabinet, Ernestin Lin.*, 1, Frankfort, Leipzig, Gotha, 1714, p. 32, pl. 4, 1; Lanna catalogue, no. 851; Cott p. 201 (as Krafft ?).

619. FERDINAND I, Archduke of Austria, and his wife ANNA, 1524.

Obv. Bust of Ferdinand to left, in broad hat; around, EFFIG(ies) FERDIN(andi) PRINCIP(is) ET INFANT(is) HISPAN(iae) ARCH(iducis) AVSTR(iae) &C RO(mani) IMP(erii) VICAR(ius) and, across field, AN(n)O ETAT(is) SVE XXI

Rev. Bust of Anne to left, in broad hat; around, EFFIGIES SER(enissimae) ANNE HV(n)GA(riae) REGINE ARCH(iducissae) AVSTR(iae) DVCISS(ae) BVRGV(ndiae) & COM(itissae) TYRO(lis) and, across field, AN(n)O AETA(tis) SVE XX

60 mm. After-cast. A1359–619A

Literature: Cp. K. Domanig, *Porträtmedaillen des Erzhauses Österreich,* Vienna, 1896, no. 80; Lanna, no. 681; Cott p. 203.

620. LUDWIG II OF HUNGARY and his wife MARIA, 1526.

Obv. Bust to left, wearing broad hat and collar of the Fleece. Around, [LV]DOVIC(us) VNGA(riae) EC REX CONTRA TVRCA(s) PVGNANDO OCCVBVIT and, across field, 1526 ETATIS SVE 30

Rev. Bust of Maria to right, wearing hat, hair in net. Around, MARIA REGINA EC QVOS DEVS CONIVNXIT HOMO NO(n) SE(paret).

Silver, 41 mm. Struck. Remains of loop formerly soldered on. A1360–620A

Literature: Cp. E. Fiala, *Beschreibung der Sammlung böhmischer Münzen und Medaillen des Max Donebauer*, Prague, 1888–9, no. 981; Löbbecke, no. 424; Lanna, no. 657; Cott p. 203.

621. FERDINAND I, Archduke of Austria (afterwards Emperor 1556–64) 1541.

Obv. The Archduke in tourney-armour riding to left. Around, FERDINANDVS D. G. ROM HVNG BOEM DALMA CROA REX. Below, 1541.

Rev. Eagle displayed, charged with shield. Around, INFANS HISPANIEN ARCHIDVX AVSTRIE DVX BVRGVNDIE

Silver, 53 mm. A1361–621A

Cast after a struck original.

Literature: Cp. Lanna catalogue, no. 671 (and no. 670, pl. 35 for the struck version); Cott p. 203.

622. (See no. 615*a*).

GEORG HOLDERMANN
(b. 1585; d. 1629)

A wax modeller and medallist of Nuremberg, active from *ca.* 1610 to 1629. See Thieme-Becker, 17 (1924) pp. 361–2.

623. WILLIBALD PIRKHEIMER and ALBRECHT DÜRER.

Obv. Busts of Pirkheimer three-quarters to right and of Dürer three-quarters to left, the latter at an easel drawing the former. Above, H BILIBALDI BIRKEYM ALBER DVRER

Without reverse.

Silver, oval, 44 × 53 mm. A1363–623A

Literature: Cp. A. Erman, 'Deutsche Medailleure des sechzehnten und siebzehnten Jahrhunderts', in *Zeitschrift für Numismatik*, 12 (1885) pp. 14–102 (at p. 88); Lanna catalogue, no. 1113; H. J. Erlanger, 'The medallic portraits of Albrecht Dürer', in *Museum Notes X* (American Numismatic Society) 1962, pp. 145–172 (no. 21, pl. xxxi); Cott p. 203.

GEORG SCHWEIGGER
(b. 1613; d. 1690)

Sculptor, bronze-founder, and armourer, born and died at Nuremberg. See Klapsia in Thieme-Becker, 30 (1936) pp. 374–5.

624. FREDERICK III, Emperor 1463–93.

Obv. Bust to left, in high relief, wearing fur cap and gown. Around, incised, FRIDERICVS III RO(manorum) IMPERATOR *etc.* 1493 AET(atis) 78

Without reverse.

48 mm. A1364–624A

Literature: M. Herrgott, *Nummotheca Principum Austriae. II, Monumentorum Augustae Domus Austriacae*, Freiburg im Br., 1752–3, pl. viii, 4; Riechmann auction catalogue xviii, Halle, 5 July 1921, no. 248; Cott p. 203.

625. MAXIMILIAN I.

Obv. Bust three-quarters to right in very high relief, wearing flat hat with feathered edge, ermine robe, and collar of the Golden Fleece.

Without reverse.

84 mm. Cast hollow. A1365–625A

One of a series representing also Luther, Paracelsus, Erasmus, Witman, Dürer, Pirkheimer and Melanchthon.

Literature: L. Planiscig, *Die Bronzeplastiken* (Kunsthistorisches Museum in Wien), Vienna, 1924, p. 272, no. 486; Cott p. 203.

JOHANN BARTHOLOMÄUS BRAUN (d. 1684)

Working at Nuremberg as wax modeller and medallist between 1636 and 1674. See Hampe in Thieme-Becker, 4 (1910) pp. 547–8.

626. SIGMUND GABRIEL HOLTZSCHUHER of Nuremberg 1575–1642.

Obv. Bust three-quarters to right, in ruff and robe. Around, SIGM(und) GABRIEL HOLZSCHVHER AE(tatis) 67.

Without reverse.

Lead, 49 mm. A1366–626A

Literature: Cp. Erman, p. 91; Lanna catalogue, no. 1123, pl. 48 (with heraldic reverse, dated 1642); Cott p. 203.

627. CHRISTOPH FÜRER VON HAIMENDORF, Nuremberg Patrician, 1645.

Obv. Bust three-quarters to right, in ruff and fur robe. Around, incised, CHRISTOF FVRER.

Rev. Shields of Fürer and his two wives (Gruder and Poemer). Inscriptions all incised: around, AB HAIMENDORF IN WOLCRERSDORF REIP(ublicae) NORIB(ergensis) DVVMVIR; across field, AET(atis) 67; below, 1645

39 mm. A1367–627A

Literature: Cp. Imhof, *Sammlung eines Nürnbergischen Münz-Cabinets*, Nuremberg, 1780/2, p. 326, 14; Erman p. 92; Löbbecke catalogue, lot no. 626, pl. xxxiv (inscription slightly varied); Cott p. 203.

628. See Appendix.

V

MEDALS BY ARTISTS OF THE LOW COUNTRIES

The medallists represented in this section are chiefly the Italianate artists of the second half of the sixteenth century. General accounts of these medals are Simonis, *L'Art du Médailleur en Belgique,* 2 vols., Brussels/Jemeppe, 1900, 1904; J. W. Frederiks, *Nederlandsche Penningen,* Amsterdam, 1947.

UNIDENTIFIED MEDALLIST

629. ADRIAN VI, Pope 1522–3.

Obv. Bust of the Pope to left, wearing tiara and cope, between two shields with the arms of the Pope and of the City of Utrecht; around, M(eester) ADRIAEN VAN GOD GHEKOREN PAVS VA(n) ROMEN TVTRECHT GEBOREN

Without reverse.

86 mm. A1369–629A

Enno van Gelder argues that because no print or drawing is known from which the medal could derive, it could be the only portrait of the pope from his Netherlands period. Hill observed that the style of the medal suggests a seal-engraver as the medallist. There is a specimen in the Victoria and Albert Museum, and another was in the Lanna collection.

Literature: V. Tourneur, 'Les médailles du pape Adrien VI', in *Rev. belge de Num.*, 77 (1925) pp. 102–4; H. Enno van Gelder, 'Het penningportret van Paus Adrianus VI', in *De Geuzenpenning Munt- en Penningkundig Nieuws*, 10 (1960) pp. 1–3; Cott p. 204. Lanna collection lot 497.

QUENTIN MASSYS

(b. *ca.* 1466; d. 1530)

The painter was born at Louvain, became a master in the Antwerp guild, 1491, and died in that city. On the medals see V. Tourneur, 'Quentin Metsys, médailleur', in *Rev. belge de Num.*, 72 (1920) pp. 139–160; G. Habich, 'Die Erasmus-Medaille' in *Archiv für Medaillen- und Plakettenkunde*, 4 (1923–4), pp. 119–122; Friedländer in Thieme-Becker, 24 (1930), pp. 227–8.

629*a*. DESIDERIUS ERASMUS (1465/6–1530).

Obv. Bust left, around ΤΗΝ ΚΡΕΙΤΤΩ ΤΑ ΣΥΓΓΡΑΜΜΑΤΑ ΔΕΙΞΕΙ IMAGO AD VIVA(m) EFFIGIE(m) EXPRESSA 1519. Across the field, ER ROT

Without reverse.

Lead 100 mm. Late cast. A1408–668A

The specimen of the medal in bell metal sent to Erasmus by the artist was included in the materials bequeathed by Erasmus to his friend Amerbach at Basel, and is now preserved in the Historical Museum at Basel. The medal has a reverse depicting Terminus. The Greek inscription also appears in Dürer's engraved portrait of 1526.

Literature: Tourneur (cited above) pp. 141–153 (including quotations from the letters of Erasmus concerning the medal and the dissemination of the medal amongst admirers); E. Treu, *Die Bildnisse des Erasmus von Rotterdam*, Basel, 1959, pp. 26–8, fig. 9 (discussing the medal and reproducing the Basle specimen). E. Wind, 'Aenigma Termini', in Warburg *Journal*, 1 (1937/8) pp. 66–9 (for Erasmus and the device of Terminus); Cott p. 203. W. Waetzoldt, *Dürer and his times*, London, 1950, pl. 51 (for the Dürer engraving).

JACOB ZAGAR

(Active 1554–1584)

Zagar was an amateur medallist, being by profession a lawyer. In 1557 and 1567 he held high office in the municipality of Middelburg. His medals are dated from 1554 to 1584. See Thieme-Becker, 36 (1947) p. 383 (listing seven medals).

630. FRÉDÉRIC PERRENOT, Sieur de Champagney, Governor of Antwerp.

Obv. Bust to right, in cuirass, scarf, and small ruff. Around,

FREDERICVS PERRENOT N(icolai) F(ilius) and, below, I(acobus) ZAGAR F(ecit) 1574

Rev. Stern view of a ship sailing through a strait between high rocks; over it, a putto hovers, holding scales; above, NI CA NI LA

62 mm. A1370–630A

Frédéric Perrenot was named governor of Antwerp in 1571. In 1576 he helped to organise the defence of the city against the Spaniards. The motto 'ni çà ni là' (with a balance) was the personal device of Perrenot.

Literature: C. Picque, 'Iconographie de la furie espagnole', in *Rev. belge de Num.*, 35 (1879) pp. 288–303 (at p. 293, pl. xv); Cott p. 204.

JACOB JONGHELINCK
(b. 1530; d. 1606)

The artist was born in Antwerp, and died in the same city. His many medals reflect the influence of the Italian artists who worked in the Netherlands. Jonghelinck made a journey to Italy, 1552, and may have worked under Leone Leoni. In the Netherlands he also practised as a sculptor and seal engraver. See Thieme-Becker, 19 (1926) pp. 135–7; V. Tourneur, 'La médaille d'Antoine Morillon par Jacques Jongheling', in *Rev. belge de Num.*, 92 (1940–6) pp. 77–81; Marcel Hoc, 'L'oeuvre de Jacques Jongheling, médailleur anversois (1530–1606)', in exhibition catalogue, Paris, Cabinet des Médailles- *Concours de Numismatique*, April-May 1949, pp. 127–30 (materials from the collection of the Cabinet des Médailles, Bibliothèque Royale de Belgique); L. Wellens-De Donder, 'Documents inédits relatifs à J. Jonghelinck', in *Rev. belge de Num.*, 106 (1960) pp. 295–305; L. Wellens-De Donder, *Médailleurs en Numismaten van de Renaissance in de Nederlanden*, Brussels (Koninklijke Bibliotheek) 1959, pp. 95–117. G. Probszt, 'Unbekannte Renaissance-Medaillen', in *Numismatische Zeitschrift*, 74 (1951), pp. 86–95, nos. 23, 25 (attributing two medals to Jonghelinck)

631. ANTOINE PERRENOT, Cardinal Granvelle (born 1517; Bishop of Arras 1540; cardinal 1561; died 1586).

Obv. Bust to right, wearing cape with hood. Around, ANT(onius) S(acrae) R(omanae) E(cclesiae) P(res)B(yte)R CARD(inalis) GRANVEL(l)ANVS

Without reverse.

74 mm. Cast hollow. A1371–631A

The medal is recorded with a reverse of the Crucifixion which does not seem to have been made for it.

Literature: Cp. Arm. I, 170, 37 (as Leone Leoni); Simonis, 2, pl. ix, 4; M. Bernhart, 'Die Granvella Medaillen des XVI Jahrhunderts', in *Archiv für Medaillen- und Plakettenkunde*, 2 (1920–1), pp. 101–119 (at p. 117, no. 18, pl. vi); V. Tourneur, 'La Médailleur Jacques Jongheling et le cardinal Granvelle, 1564–1578', in *Rev. belge de Num.*, 79 (1927) pp. 79–93. Another Granvelle medal, with reverse Neptune and the legend DVRATE is studied by R. van Luttervelt, 'Bij een penning van J. Jonghelinck', in *Jaarboek voor Munt- en Penningkunde*, 42 (1955) pp. 99–102. Alvarez-Ossorio, p. 206, no. 165; Cott p. 204.

632. VIGLIUS VAN ZUICHEM (1507–77), lawyer, then (1565) Provost of Saint-Bavon, Chancellor of the Order of the Fleece, President of the Privy Council, etc.

Obv. Bust to left, in robe with fur collar. Around, VIGLIVS ZVICHEMVS PRAESES SEC(reti) CON(cilii) CAES(aris) Z (et) REG(iae) MA(iestatis); incised on truncation, AET(atis) XLIX

Without reverse.

Lead, 54 mm. A1372–632A

This medal should have a reverse similar to the following.

Literature: Cp. Simonis, 2, p. 84; Cott p. 204.

633. *Obv.* Bust to right, in flat berretta and robe with fur collar. Around, VIGLIVS PRAEP(ositus) S(ancti) BAV(onis) PRAES(es) SECR(eti) CON(cilii) R(egiae) MA(iestatis) ET CANC(ellarius) ORD(inis) AV(rei) VEL(leris); incised on truncation, AET(atis) LXII

Rev. On a table, candle burning, hour-glass and open book on which, incised, DEVS OP(timus) MA(ximus); below, incised on a tablet, 1568; around, VITA MORTALIVM VIGILIA

51 mm. A1373–633A

The motto, punning on the man's name, is from the preface to Pliny's *Natural History*.

Literature: Cp. Simonis, 2, p. 85; Cott p. 204.

634. *Obv.* Bust to right, wearing gown. Around, VIGLIVS ZVICHEMVS PRAESES

Rev. Similar type and motto to preceding, but without date.

Lead, 24 mm. A1374–634A

Literature: Cp. Simonis, 2, p. 84; L. Wellens-De Donder, *Medailleurs en Numismaten*, no. 112, pl. xvi; Cott p. 204.

GIOVANNI V. MELON

A medallist of Cremona (?), working especially in the Netherlands from 1571 to 1579. See Hill in Thieme-Becker, 24 (1930), p. 368.

635. ANTOINE PERRENOT, Cardinal Granvelle. (See no. 631.)

Obv. Bust to left, wearing cape with hood. Around, same

inscription as on no. 631. Incised on the truncation, IO(annes) MELON F(ecit).

Rev. A ship at sea, blown upon by winds. Above, DVRATE

Silver, 43 mm. A1375–635A

This would appear to be among the latest of the medallic portraits of the Cardinal.

Literature: Cp. Arm. I, 265, 13; Bernhart, 'Die Granvella Medaillen des XVI Jahrhunderts', in *Archiv für Medaillen- und Plakettenkunde*, 2 (1920–1) pp. 101–119 (at p. 117, no. 20); Cott p. 204. On the reverse legend and Granvelle, see bibliography to no. 631.

STEVEN VAN HERWIJCK
(b. *ca.* 1530; d. 1565/67)

Steven van Herwijck was born in Utrecht. He worked in Italy, 1557, in Antwerp, 1558, briefly in Utrecht, and again in Antwerp, 1559–1561. He went to the court of the king of Poland, 1561–2, and to London, 1562–3. He was again in Utrecht and Antwerp, 1564–5, returned to London, 29 March 1565, and died there sometime before Easter 1567. The classic account of van Herwijck is V. Tourneur, 'Steven van Herwijck, médailleur anversois (1557–1565)', in *Num. Chron.*, 2 (1922) pp. 91–132 (including full descriptions of medals); Thieme-Becker, 16 (1923) pp. 565–6 (including list of medals); to which may be added, Hill, 'Two Netherlandish artists in England. Steven van Herwijck and Steven van der Meulen', in *Transactions of the Walpole Society*, 11 (1923), pp. 29–32; E. Majkowski, 'Steven van Herwijck's serie der Jagellonen-Medaillons en zijn vermeend verblijf in Polen, 1551–1562', in *Jaarboek van het Koninklijk Nederlandsch Genootschap voor Munt- en Penningkunde*, 24 (1937) pp. 1–37; V. Tourneur, 'Steven van Herwijck et les baillis de l'ordre de Malte à Utrecht', in *Rev. belge de Num.*, 93 (1947) pp. 59–66; V. Tourneur, 'La médaille Guilielmus Fabius de Steven van Herwyck', in *Rev. belge de Num.*, 94 (1948) pp. 101–4; L. Wellens-De Donder, 'La médaille "Venus et l'Amour" de Steven van Herwijck' in *Rev. belge de Num.*, 105 (1959) pp. 165–70; L. Wellens-De Donder, *Medailleurs en Numismaten van de Renaissance in de Nederlanden*, Brussels (Koninklijke Bibliotheek), 1959, pp. 83–95; *National Portrait Gallery, Annual Report* (London), 1962–3, pp. 9–10, no. 4294 (attributing a lead portrait medal of Queen Elizabeth I to Herwijck).

636. SIGISMUND AUGUSTUS, KING OF POLAND (1520–30–72).

Obv. Bust to right, in cuirass. Around, SIGISMVND(us) AVGVSTVS D(ei) G(ratia) REX POLONIAE Signed on truncation STE H F

Rev. The king, in armour, on horseback, wielding sword. Around, DA MIHI VIRTVTEM CONTRA HOSTES TVOS

42 mm. A1376–636A

The Vienna specimen also shows the signature STE. H. F. under the bust, and the date 1562 engraved on the truncation.

Literature: K. Domanig, *Porträtmedaillen des Erzhauses Österreich,* Vienna, 1896, no. 91; Tourneur (in Num. Chron., 1922) p. 119, no. 19; Cott p. 204.

637. ANTONIS MOR, the painter (1512–75).

Obv. Bust to right, in doublet and gown. Around, ANTONIVS MOR TRA(iectensis) PICTOR

Without reverse.

63 mm. A1377–637A

Hill attributed this piece to Steven van Herwijck, Tourneur did not accept the attribution, and was followed by Thieme-Becker in this opinion.

Literature: Simonis, 2, p. 104, pl. xii, 1 (as Jongheling, with reverse an allegory of Painting); Hill, 'Stephen H., medallist and painter', in *Burl. Mag.*, 12 (1908) pp. 355–363 (at p. 362, pl. 1, 3, 4, this medal recorded by Tourneur as no. 32); Tourneur (in *Num. Chron.*, 1922), p. 127; Cott p. 204 (as Herwijck ?).

CONRAD BLOC
(b. *ca.* 1550)

Bloc worked in the Netherlands, Germany, and France, his medals dating between 1575 and 1602. See C. Picqué, 'Medailles d'art flamandes inédites du XVIe siècle', in *Mémoires, Congrès international de Numismatique*, Brussels, 1891, pp. 661–678 (on Bloc, Corneille Cort, Frans and Corneille Floris); Alvin in Thieme-Becker, 4 (1910) p. 119; V. Tourneur, 'Conrad Bloc, médailleur anversois', in *Rev. belge de Num.*, 77 (1925) pp. 199–211; F. Mazerolle, 'Coins de médailles de Conrad Bloc', in *Rev. belge de Num.*, 79 (1927) pp. 95–8; L. Wellens-De Donder, *Medailleurs en Numismaten van de Renaissance in de Nederlanden*, Brussels (Koninklijke Bibliotheek) 1959, pp. 117–127.

638. WILLIAM I OF ORANGE (1533–84) and CHARLOTTE DE BOURBON.

Obv. Bust of William to right, in cuirass, scarf, and ruff. Around, GVILEL(mus) D(ei) G(ratia) PR(inceps) AVRAICAE CO(mes) NASSAVIAE 1577 and, below, COEN BLOC F Incised on truncation, AET(atis) 44

Rev. Bust of Charlotte to left, in ruff. Around, CHARLOTTE DE BOVRBON PR(incesse) DAVRENGE A(nno) 1577

Silver, 44 mm. With loop. Made from two separate pieces. A1378–638A

Literature: Cp. G. Van Loon, *Histoire métallique des XVII provinces des Pays-Bas*, vol. I (The Hague, 1732) p. 236; Tourneur (Rev. belge., 1925) no. 2; Cott p. 204.

GIULIANO GIANNINI

Giannini was possibly a Florentine, who settled in Brussels, *ca.* 1580, and was working until *ca.* 1599. His earliest medal is dated 1560. See Thieme-Becker, 13 (1920) p. 585.

639. FERNANDO ALVAREZ DE TOLEDO, Duke of Alba (1508–82).

Obv. Bust to right, in cuirass, cloak, and ruff. Around, FERDINANDVS ALVAREZ A TOLETO DVX ALVAE

Rev. Pallas in car drawn by two owls; a little Victory crowns her; below, MDLXVIII; around, RELIGIONEM ET OBEDIENTIAM REDINTEGRAVIT

37 mm. A1379–639A

The medal is attributed to Giuliano Giannini on the authority of Pinchart, who describes a specimen with the signature IVLIAN G. F. The year on the reverse is that of Alba's first victories, but the medal dates from 1580 or thereabouts.

Literature: Cp. Arm. III, 140, A; Pinchart, *Histoire de la Gravure des Médailles en Belgique*, Brussels, 1870, pp. 30–1; Cott p. 204.

BERNARDO RANTVIC

(d. *ca.* 1596)

Rantvic was a Flemish painter, miniaturist, goldsmith, and medallist, who is recorded at Siena as a painter. See Thieme-Becker, 28 (1934) pp. 11–12. Forrer, 5, pp. 28–9 (where a medal of Cardinal Cesi is wrongly ascribed to the artist).

640. SIR RICHARD SHELLEY (b. *ca.* 1513–d. *ca.* 1589), Prior of the English Nation of the Knights of Malta.

Obv. Bust to right in armour, Maltese cross on breast. Around, RICARDVS SCELLEIVS PRIOR ANGLIAE and, below, BERN(ardus) RANTWIC F(ecit).

Rev. Griffin, ducally gorged, in a landscape. Around, PATRIARVM EXCVBITOR OPVM

70 mm. A1380–640A

This medal was copied by Rantvic from a medal of Shelley made in Italy, probably at Venice, in 1577. Shelley's crest was a griffin's head, and the reverse alludes to this, and to his successful negotiations for Queen Elizabeth concerning the Levant trade. Rantvic has slightly modified the portrait, and provided a new reverse for his version of the medal.

Literature: Cp. Franks and Grueber, *Medallic Illustrations of the History of Great Britain and Ireland*, London, 1885, I, p. 127, no. 75; Plates nos. ix, 1 (Rantvic's medal), viii, 18, 19 (the original medals); Cott p. 204.

VI

COINS

All struck, unless otherwise described.

HOUSE OF SAVOY

641. FILIBERTO II, eighth Duke, 1497–1504.

Obv. Bust to right, wearing cap. Around, PHILIBERTVS D SABAVDIE VIII

Rev. Shield of Savoy, inclined, casque, crest and lambrequins, two Savoy-knots in the field. Around, IN TE D(omi)NE CONFIDO T CAS

Silver half-testoon, 27 mm. Wt. 4 grm. 55. A1381–641A

Literature: Cp. *C.N.I.*, I, 131, 38; Cott p. 205.

642. CARLO II, 1504–53.

Obv. Bust to right, bearded, in flat cap and cuirass. Around, CAROLVS II DVX SABAVDIE IX

Rev. Crowned shield, across field, FE RT Around, MARCHIO IN ITALIA PR B HP

Silver testoon, 29 mm. Wt. 9 grm. 28. A1382–642A

Literature: Cp. *C.N.I.*, I, 147, 98; Cott p. 205.

CARMAGNOLA

643. LODOVICO II, Marquess of Saluzzo, 1475–1504.

Obv. Bust to left, in cap and cuirass. Around, LV M SALVTIARVM

Rev. Crowned shield inclined, with eagle crest, between L M Around, SANCT CONSTANTIVS

Gold ducat, 24 mm. Wt. 3 grm. 47. A1383–643A

Literature: Les Arts, Aug. 1908, p. 12, no. xvi; cp. *C.N.I.*, II, 57, 21; Bernareggi, p. 129, no. 28 *b*; Cott p. 205.

MANTUA

644. FRANCESCO II GONZAGA, fourth Marquess, 1484–1519.

Obv. Bust to left. Around, FRANCISCVS MAR MANT IIII

Rev. Pyxis of the Blood of Christ. Around, XPI IHESV SANGVINIS

Silver testoon, 25 mm. Wt. 7 grm. 09. A1384–644A

Literature: Les Arts, Aug. 1908, p. 12, no. xxiv; cp. *C.N.I.*, IV, 239, 37; Cott p. 205.

645. *Obv.* Bust to left, in cap. Around, FRANCISCVS MARCHIO MANTVE IIII

Rev. Pyxis of the Blood of Christ. Around, XPI SANGVINIS TABERNACVLVM

Silver half-testoon, 25 mm. Wt. 3 grm. 62. A1385–645A

Literature: Cp. *C.N.I.*, IV, 243, 74; Cott p. 205.

646. FRANCESCO III GONZAGA, second Duke of Mantua and second Marquess of Monferrat, 1540–50.

Obv. Youthful bust to left. Around, FRAN DVX MAN II ET MAR MON F

Rev. Tobias conducted by the angel. Around, VIAS TVAS DOMINE DEMOSTRA MIHI

Silver testoon, 30 mm. Wt. 6 grm. 09. A1386–646A

Literature: Cp. *C.N.I.*, IV, 293, 13; Cott p. 205.

MILAN

647. FRANCESCO I SFORZA, fourth Duke 1450–66.

Obv. Bust to right, in cuirass. Around, FRANCISCHVS SFORTIA [VIC](ecomes).

Rev. The Duke in armour on horseback, wielding sword. Around, DVX MEDIOL[ANI AC IAN]VE D(ominus).

Gold ducat, 22 mm. Wt. 3 grm. 51. A1387–647A

The end of the legend confused by restriking.

Literature: Cp. *C.N.I.*, V, 147, 22; Bernareggi, p. 142, no. 69 type; Cott p. 205.

648. GALEAZZO MARIA SFORZA, fifth Duke.

Obv. Bust to right, in cuirass; behind, an annulet. Around, GALEAZ M SF VICECOS DVX MLI QIT (mint-mark, head of St Ambrose).

Rev. Shield, inclined, casque and crest, flanked by G3 M and brands with buckets. Around, PP ANGLE Q3 CO AC IANVE D

Silver testoon, 28 mm. Wt. 9 grm. 60. A1388–648A

Literature: Cp. *C.N.I.*, V, 162, 2; Cott p. 205.

649. GIANGALEAZZO MARIA SFORZA, sixth Duke, Count of Pavia and Anghiera, alone 1481.

Obv. Bust to right, in round cap. Around, IO G3 M SF VICECO DVX MLI SX (mint-mark, head of St Ambrose).

Rev. Shield with two crests. Around, PP ANGLEQ3 COS 7 C

Gold double testoon, 29 mm. Wt. 6 grm. 92.

A1389–649A

Literature: Cp. *C.N.I.*, v, 186, 14; Bernareggi, p. 149, no. 100; Cott p. 205.

650–1. THE SAME, with his uncle LODOVICO MARIA, il Moro, 1481–94.

Obv. Bust of Giangaleazzo to right, in cuirass. Around, IO GZ M SF VICECOMES DVX MLI SX (mint-mark, head of St Ambrose).

Rev. Shield with two crests. Around, LV PATRVO GVB(er)NANTE (same mint-mark).

Silver testoon, 29 mm. Two specimens.
Wt. 9 gms. 67 (not illustrated). A1390–650A.
Wt. 9 gms. 56. A1391–651A.

Literature: Cp. *C.N.I.*, v, 190, 32; Cott p. 205.

652. *Obv.* Same as preceding obverse. Around, IO GZ M SF VICECO DVX MLI SX

Rev. Bust of Lodovico to right, in cuirass. Around, LVDOVICVS PATRVVS GVB(er)NANS (same mint-mark).

Silver testoon, 29 mm. Wt. 9 grm. 71. A1392–652A

Literature: Cp. *C.N.I.*, v, 190, 31; Cott p. 205.

653. LODOVICO MARIA SFORZA, il Moro, 7th Duke, 1494–1500.

Obv. Similar bust to preceding reverse. Around, LVDOVICVS M SF ANGLVS DVX MLI (mint-mark, head of St Ambrose).

Rev. Crowned shield; on either side, brand with buckets. Around, PP ANGLEQ3 CO AC IANVE D 7C (same mint-mark).

Silver testoon, 27 mm. Wt. 9 grm. 70. A1393–653A

Literature: Cp. *C.N.I.*, v, 199, 19; Cott p. 205.

654. THE SAME with BEATRICE D'ESTE, 1497.

Obv. Bust of the Duke to right, in cuirass. Around, LVDOVIC M SF ANGLV DVX M (mint-mark, head of St Ambrose); below bust, 1497

Rev. Bust of Beatrice to left. Around, BEATRIX SF ANGLA EST(en)SIS DVCISA MLI

Copper, 27 mm. A1394–654A

An impression in copper from the dies for a testoon.

Literature: Les Arts, Aug. 1908, p. 12, no. xx; cp. *C.N.I.*, v, 202, 5 (variety); Cott p. 205.

655. LOUIS XII OF FRANCE as Duke 1500–12.

Obv. Bust to right, in cap encircled by crown; on breast, fleur-de-lis. Around, LVDOVICVS D G FRANCORVM REX

Rev. St Ambrose on horseback, wielding scourge; below, crowned shield of France modern. Around, MEDIOLANI DVX

Silver testoon, 28 mm. Wt. 9 grm. 63. A1395–655A

Literature: Cp. *C.N.I.*, v, 207, 35; Cott p. 205.

FERRARA

656. ERCOLE I D'ESTE, second Duke, 1471–1505.

Obv. Bust to left, in cuirass. Around, HERCVLES DVX FERRARIE

Rev. Christ rising from the tomb, holding banner. Around, SVREXIT XPS REX GL(ori)E

Gold ducat, 24 mm. Wt. 3 grm. 43. A1396–656A

Nussbaum suggests that the reverse design derives from an anonymous fresco of the same subject in S. Apollinare, Ferrara.

Literature: Cp. *C.N.I.*, x, 435, 9; Cott p. 205; H. Nussbaum, 'Fürstenporträte auf italienischen Münzen des Quattrocento' in *Zeitschrift für Numismatik*, 35 (1925), pp. 145–92 (at pp. 178–9, 181); Bernareggi, p. 135, no. 41.

657. *Obv.* Head to left. Around, HERCVLES DVX FERRARIAE

Rev. Nude man on horseback to right.

Copper, 28 mm. A1397–657A

Quarto.

Grierson has shown that the reverse design preserves an image of the clay model by Leonardo da Vinci for the monument to Francesco Sforza, which had been moved to Ferrara in 1502 at the request of the Duke Ercole d'Este. The detail of the rider and cloak was added by the engraver, Giannantonio da Foligno.

Literature: Cp. *C.N.I.*, x, 436, 22; Cott p. 205; P. Grierson, 'Ercole d'Este and Leonardo da Vinci's equestrian statue of Francesco Sforza', in *Italian Studies*, 14 (1959) pp. 40–48.

658. ALFONSO I, third Duke, 1505–34.

Obv. Bust to left, bearded, in cuirass. Around, ALFONSVS DVX FER III S(acri) R(omani) E(cclesiae) CONF(alonerius).

Rev. Helmeted nude figure seated, holding lion's head from which issue bees. Around, DE FORTI DVLCEDO

Cast of a silver testoon, 28 mm. Wt. 8 grm. 27.

A1398–658A

On the reverse, a tree-trunk encircled by a serpent has been tooled away.

Literature: Cp. *C.N.I.*, x, 446, 34; Cott p. 205.

BOLOGNA

659. GIOVANNI II BENTIVOGLIO, Lord of Bologna, 1494–1509.

Obv. Bust to right, in cap. Around, IOANNES BEN T[IV]OLVS II BONONIEN(sis).

Rev. Shield surmounted by eagle. Around, MAXIMILIANI MVNVS

Gold ducat, 23 mm. Wt. 3 grm. 47. A1399–659A

Weiss has shown that this issue, formerly ascribed to the mint of Antignate, was really struck in Bologna.

Literature: Cp. *C.N.I.*, IV, 4, 25; Bernareggi, p. 122, no. 4; Cott p. 205; R. Weiss, 'La leggenda di Antignate', in *Italia Numismatica*, 14, no. 9 (Sept. 1963) pp. 137–141. See also no. 184.

660. JULIUS II, Pope 1503–13.

Obv. Bust to right, beardless, in cope. Around, IVLIVS II PONTIFEX MAXIMVS

Rev. San Petronio seated, holding model of city and crozier; below, arms of Cardinal Alidosi. Around, S(anctus) P(etronius) BONONIA DOCET

Silver giulio, 28 mm. Wt. 4 grm. 41. A1400–660A

Literature: Cp. *C.N.I.*, x, 65, 64; Cott p. 205.

661. LEO X, Pope 1513–21.

Obv. Bust to right, in cope. Around, LEO X PONTIFEX MAXIMVS

Rev. Lion rampant, holding banner; above, on left, arms of Cardinal Giulio de' Medici. Around, BONONIA MATER STVDIORVM

Silver bianco, 27 mm. Wt. 3 grm. 78. A1401–661A

Literature: Cp. *C.N.I.*, x, 74, 42; Cott p. 206.

PESARO

662. GIOVANNI SFORZA, 1489–1510.

Obv. Bust to right, bearded, in cuirass. Around, IOANNS SFORTIA PISAVRI P(rinceps).

Rev. PVBLICAE COMMODITATI

Copper denaro, 19 mm. A1402–662A

Literature: Cp. *C.N.I.*, XIII, 455, 98; Cott p. 206.

FLORENCE

663. ALESSANDRO I DE' MEDICI, first Duke 1532–7.

Obv. Bust to left. Around, ALEXANDER M(edices) R(ei) P(ublicae) FLOREN(tinae) DVX

Rev. SS. Cosmas and Damian. Around, S COSMVS S DAMIANVS

Silver testoon, 28 mm. Wt. 8 grm. 26. A1403–663A

By Benvenuto Cellini, 1535. The making of the coin is mentioned in the artist's autobiography.

Literature: Cp. *C.N.I.*, XII, 244, 17; Cott p. 206. *The Life of Benvenuto Cellini* (ed. Pope-Hennessy), London, 1949, p. 148.

ROME

664. SIXTUS IV, Pope 1471–84.

Obv. Bust to left, in cope. Around, SIXTVS IIII PONT MAX VRBE REST(aurata).

Rev. Shield of della Rovere, surmounted by crossed-keys and tiara. Around, PVBLICAE VTILITATI

Silver grosso, 24 mm. Wt. 4 grm. 41. A1404–664A

Literature: Cp. *C.N.I.*, XV, 294, 69; Cott p. 206.

NAPLES

665. FERDINANDO I, 1458–94.

Obv. Bust to right, crowned. Behind, C Around, FERRAND(u)S ARAGO(nensis) REX SI(ciliae) HIE(rusalem).

Rev. St Michael spearing the Dragon. Around, IVSTA TVENDA

Silver coronato, 27 mm. Wt. 3 grm. 93. A1405–665A

Literature: Cp. *C.N.I.*, XIX, 137, 476; Cott p. 206.

LORRAINE

666. ANTOINE, Duke 1508–44.

Obv. Bust to left, crowned, in cuirass. Around, ANTHON(ius) D G LOTHO(ringiae) ET BA(ri) DVX

Rev. Crowned shield. Around, MONETA NANCEII CVSA. Below, 1523

Silver testoon of Nancy, 30 mm. Wt. 9 grm. 53. A1406–666A

Literature: Cp. F. de Saulcy, *Recherches sur les Monnaies des ducs héréditaires de Lorraine,* Metz, 1841, pl. XV, 16; Cott p. 206.

SPAIN

667. FERDINAND V of Castile (1452–1504–16) and ISABELLA, married 1469, d. 1504.

Obv. Crowned busts of Ferdinand and Isabella confronted. Around, FERNANDUS ET ELISABET D G REX ET R

Rev. Eagle displayed charged with crowned shield of Leon and Castile quartering Aragon and Sicily; in field to right, T; to left, five pellets. Around, SUB UMBRA ALARVM TVARVM PROTEG(e).

Gold excelente, 29 mm. Wt. 7 grm. 02. A1407–667A

Literature: Cp. A. Heiss, *Descripcion General de las Monedas Hispano-Cristianas* (Reprint, Zaragoza) 1962, I, pl. 20, 63 (var); Cott p. 206. H. Rosenau, 'The portrait of Isabella of Castille on coins', in Warburg *Journal*, 3 (1939–1940) p. 155.

APPENDIX

ITALIAN MEDALS

PISANELLO

21. ALFONSO V of Aragon, King of Naples and Sicily, born 1394, established in Naples, 1442, died 1458.

Obv. Bust of Alfonso to right, above a crown. Inscription: DIVVS ALPHONSVS &C. (titles of King of Aragon, the two Sicilies, Valencia, Jerusalem, Hungary, Majorca, Sardinia, Corsica, Count of Barcelona, Duke of Athens and Neopatras, Count of Roussillon, etc.).

Rev. An angel with drawn sword in a car drawn by four horses led by two young men. Above, FORTITVDO MEA ET LAVS MEA DOMINVS ET FACTVS EST MICHI IN SALVTEM; below, OPVS PISANI PICTORIS

110 mm. Late cast. A757–21A

The signature does not appear on the earliest specimens of this medal, which appears to have been left unfinished in this respect by the artist about 1449.

Literature: Les Arts, Aug. 1908, pp. 4–5, no. iv; cp. Arm. I, 7, 19; *Corpus*, no. 43; Cott p. 162.

ESTE MEDALS I

41. ALFONSO I D'ESTE, afterwards 3rd Duke of Ferrara (1476–1505–34).

Obv. Bust to left as an infant. Around, ALFONSVS MARCHIO ESTENSIS

Rev. Alfonso as infant Hercules, nude, grasping two snakes, lying in a cradle inscribed MCCCCLXXVII; above, fantastic inscription.

66 mm. Late cast. A777–41A

Companion piece, in very low relief, to a medal of Alfonso's parents Ercole I and Eleonora (*Corpus*, no. 117). The way in which the ground is cut away suggests that these pieces were meant for enamelling.

Literature: Cp. Arm. II, 89, 1; *Corpus*, no. 118; Cott p. 163.

GIANCRISTOFORO ROMANO

77. ISABELLA OF ARAGON, wife of Giangaleazzo Sforza, Duke of Milan, born 1470, married 1489, died 1524.

Obv. Bust to right, veiled. Around, ISABELLA ARAGONIA DVX M(edio)L(an)I

Rev. Nearly nude female figure seated before a palm-tree, holding palm-branch and snake-encircled wand. Around, CASTITATI VIRTVTIQ(ue) INVICTAE

46 mm. Late cast. A814–77A

Jacopo d'Atri wrote that Giancristoforo was making a medal of Isabella at Naples on 24 Oct. 1507, but the veil was not quite finished.

Literature: Cp. Arm. III, 49, B; *Corpus*, no. 223; Cott p. 165.

IN THE NEIGHBOURHOOD OF GIANCRISTOFORO ROMANO

81. MADDALENA ROSSI, unknown.

Obv. Bust to left. Around, MAGDALENA RVBEA MORIB(us) ET FORMA INCOMPARABIL(is).

Rev. Captive Love, and inscriptions, all as on no. 80.

50 mm. Late cast. A818–81A

Literature: Cp. Arm. I, 118, 2; *Corpus*, no. 235; Cott p. 166. Tervarent, cols. 19 v; 40–41; Panofsky, pp. 95–128 (Blind Cupid).

SPERANDIO

121. PELLEGRINO PRISCIANO of Ferrara, man of letters and agent of the Estensi (died 1518).

Obv. Bust to left, in flat cap and gown. Around, PRISCIANVS FERRARIENSIS EQVESTRI DECORATVS AVRO DVCIBVS SVIS AC MERCVRIO GRATISSIMVS and, across field, SVPER(is) GRAT(us) ET IMIS

Rev. A man wearing cap covering ears and neck, long coat with fluttering skirts, and scarf floating out from shoulders, standing on body of an eagle or vulture; he holds in right hand a long arrow, in left a flame; leafless bushes on either side. Around, SPERANDEVS MANTVANVS DEDIT ANNO LEGIS GRATIAE MCCCCLXXIII INPERFECTO

Lead, 97 mm. Late cast. A858–121A

Prisciano was counsellor to the Dukes Borso and Ercole. The formula of dating ('in the uncompleted year of the law of grace') is as extravagant as the allegory, one of Sperandio's most fantastic.

Literature: Cp. Arm. I, 72, 35; *Corpus*, no. 374; Cott p. 168.

122. PARUPUS, an unknown poet.

Obv. Bust to left, wearing laureate cap. Around, INGENIVM MORES FORMAM TIBI PVLCHER APOLLO

Rev. Winged unicorn-pegasus; above, below clouds, FATVM; around, ARGVTAMQVE CHELVM DOCTE PARVPE DEDIT

53 mm. Late cast. A859–122A

Only late casts of this medal seem to be known.

Literature: Cp. Arm. I, 71, 31; *Corpus*, no. 378; Cott p. 168.

129. GUIDO PEPOLI, noble of Bologna (1449–1505).

Obv. Bust to left, in cap. Around, GVIDO PEPVLVS BONONIENSIS COMES

Rev. King Evilmerodach and a philosopher playing chess; around, SIC DOCVI REGNARE TYRANNVM; below, OPVS SPERANDEI

83 mm. Late cast. A866–129A

About 1485–6. According to the story in the *Game and Playe of the Chesse*, the philosopher (Xerxes or Philometor) taught Evilmerodach the moral significance of the game for rulers. The Pepoli arms, of chessboard pattern, suggested the device. The reverse type and legend are known as a ceramic decoration.

Literature: Cp. Arm. I, 72, 34; II, 288; *Corpus*, no. 393; Cott p. 169; G. B(allardini), 'Nuovi Acquisti del Museo' in *Faenza*, 28 (1940) at p. 105, pl. 27, fig. *a*; and G. Cora, 'Opus. Sperandei', in *Faenza*, 36 (1950) pp. 108–110 (for the reverse type as a decoration on maiolica).

130. CAMILLA (COVELLA) SFORZA; married Costanzo Sforza 1475, widowed 1483, retired from Pesaro 1489.

Obv. Bust three-quarters to left, in widow's veil. Around, CAMILLA SFOR(tia) DE ARAGONIA MATRONAR(um) PVDICISSIMA PISAVRI DOMINA

Rev. Female figure to front on a seat composed of foreparts of unicorn and hound; she holds an arrow in her right hand; her left arm is entwined with a dragon-headed serpent that threatens her. Above, SIC ITVR AD ASTRA; below, OPVS SPERANDEI

84 mm. A rough, not contemporary casting. A867–130A

Probably 1490–5, made during the lady's retirement at Torricella. The unicorn for innocence, the hound for fidelity.

Literature: Cp. Arm. I, 74, 43; *Corpus*, no. 399; Cott p. 169. Tervarent, 237 (Unicorn).

132. AGOSTINO BARBADIGO, Doge of Venice 1486–1501.

Obv. Bust three-quarters to right, wearing ducal cap and robes. Around, AVGVSTINVS BARBADICVS VENETORVM DVX

Rev. The Doge, holding banner of St Mark, kneeling before the winged lion. Below, OPVS SPERANDEI

87 mm. Late cast. A869–132A

Doubtless commemorating the battle of Fornovo in 1495.

Literature: Cp. Arm. I, 75, 46; *Corpus*, no. 401; Cott p. 169.

133. LODOVICO BROGNOLO, of the Observant Friars, patrician of Mantua.

Obv. Bust left, in habit, with hood over head. Around, LODOVICVS BROGNOLO PATRICIVS MANTVANVS

Rev. Two forearms in sleeves, joined in prayer, a rosary hanging from them; above, cloud; around, SPES MEA IN DEO EST and, below, OPVS SPERANDEI

84 mm. Late cast. A870–133A

Probably from Sperandio's second Mantuan period (1495–1496).

Literature: Cp. Arm. I, 65, 10; III, 17, *a*; *Corpus*, no. 402; Cott p. 169.

134. ANTONIO VINCIGUERRA, poet, Secretary to the Republic of Venice (died 1502).

Obv. Bust to left in tall cap. Around, ANT(onius) VINCIGVERRA REI P(ublicae) VENET(ae) A SECRETIS INTEGERIMVS

Rev. Apollo seated under a laurel on a low car drawn by swans, playing violin. Above, CELO MVSA BEAT and, below, OPVS SPERANDEI

81 mm. Late cast. A871–134A

No contemporary castings seem to have been preserved. The original was probably made in the artist's last period, 1496–1504.

Literature: Cp. Arm. I, 76, 47; *Corpus*, no. 403; Cott p. 169. Tervarent, cols. 81, ii, 405, iii.

ANTONELLO DELLA MONETA

Goldsmith, printer, and engraver to the Venetian mint from 1454 or earlier to 1484.

137. CRISTOFORO MORO, Doge of Venice (1462–1471).

Obv. Bust to left in ducal cap and robe. Around, CRISTOFORVS MAVRO DVX

Rev. Venetia, as on the medal of Foscari (no. 136); inscription: VENETIA MAGNA; below, A N

40 mm. Late cast. A874–137A

This is a hybrid, the obverse being taken from Antonello's portrait, the reverse, signature and all, from that of Antonio Gambello's medal of Foscari (no. 136).

Literature: Cp. Arm. I, 46, 2; *Corpus*, no. 411 note; Cott p. 170.

SAVOY, Early XVI Century

200. FILIPPO, son of Filippo II, seventh Duke of Savoy (about 1490–1533).

Obv. Bust to left, in cap with back-flap, and furred gown. Around, PH(ilipp)VS DE SABAVDIA COMES GEBENARV(m).

Without reverse.

47 mm. Late cast. A937–200A

The medal was made after 1514, when Philip became Count of Genevois, and before 22 Dec. 1528, when he was made Duke of Nemours.

Literature: Cp. Arm. II, 122, 11; *Corpus*, no. 724; Cott p. 174.

MEDALLIST OF THE ROMAN EMPERORS

205 *bis*. MARCUS CROTO.

Obv. A reworked version of no. 205, the portrait profile lost, and only . . . CVS CROT in the legend being legible.

Rev. Man in armour riding to left, carrying a standard; below, helmet and shield; around, VICTORIAE AGVSTE and, below, S(enatus) C(onsultus).

63 mm. A943–205 *bis* A

On the name Croto, see no. 205.

Literature: Molinier, no. 38; cp. Arm. II, 129, 7; *Corpus*, no. 736; Cott p. 174; Middeldorf, *Morgenroth*, no. 72.

NICCOLÒ DI FORZORE SPINELLI (Niccolò Fiorentino)

257. LORENZO DE' MEDICI, il Magnifico (1448–1492).

Obv. Bust to left, with long hair. Around, MAGNVS LAVRENTIVS MEDICES

Without reverse.

90 mm. Late casting, hollow. A995–257A

A late cast of the obverse of the signed medal by Niccolò Fiorentino.

Literature: Cp. Arm. I, 85, 4; III, 20, D; *Corpus*, no. 926; Middeldorf, *Morgenroth*, 97 (*Corpus* no. 926 *h*); Cott p. 178.

IN THE MANNER OF NICCOLÒ SPINELLI

274. GIOVANNI PAOLO ORSINI, Count of Atripaldi 1486, died 1502.

Obv. Bust to left, with long hair in cap and armour. Around, IO(annes) PAVLVS VRSINVS ATRIPALDE COMES

Rev. Orsini on horseback. Above, TE SEQVOR and, below, AN(no) XXXV

Lead, 35 mm. Recent cast. A1012–274A

The original probably dated from about 1485–90.

Literature: Cp. Arm. II, 65, 19; *Corpus*, no. 995; Middeldorf, *Morgenroth*, no. 102 (*Corpus*, no. 995 *h*); Cott p. 179.

275. GIULIANO PARTICINI.

Obv. Bust to left, with long hair. Around, GIVLIANO PARTICINI MCCCCLXXXXII

Rev. Hope gazing up at the Sun in prayer; around, ISPERO IN DEO and, across field, AN(no) XXII

62 mm. Not a contemporary casting. A1013–275A

There were two men of this name, both born in 1470. either of whom may be represented.

Literature: Cp. Arm. I, 95, 9; *Corpus*, no. 996; Cott p. 179.

283. CATERINA SFORZA-RIARIO, Countess of Forlì and Imola, born 1463, died 1509.

Obv. Bust to left, wearing widow's veil. Around, CATHARINA SF(ortia) DE RIARIO FORLIVII IMOLAE Q(ue) C(omitissa).

Rev. Winged Victory, holding palm-branch, in car drawn to right by two horses; on the side of the car, Sforza shield. Above, on right, VICTORIAM FAMA SEQVETVR

72 mm. Late cast. A1021–283A

This medal of the famous virago was probably made soon after the murder of Girolamo Riario in April 1488. Two years later she married Giacomo Feo. The portrait was subsequently modified by removing the widow's veil.

Literature: Cp. Arm. I, 87, 15; *Corpus*, no. 1014; Cott p. 180.

293. FRANCESCO LANCILOTTI, painter. (b. 1472).

Obv. Bust to left, bearded, with long hair, wearing cap. Around, FRANCISCHVS LANCILOTTIS FLORENTINVS

Without reverse.

70 mm. Late, rough cast. A1031–293A

Lancilotti was born in 1472, travelled much, and wrote a poem on painting, printed in 1509. The medal, sometimes attributed to Niccolò Fiorentino, may date from the beginning of the sixteenth century. It should have a reverse of Lancilotti on horseback.

Literature: Corpus, no. 1049 *f*; cp. Arm. II, 50, 10; Cott p. 181.

297. LODOVICA, daughter of Giovanni Tornabuoni.

Obv. Bust to left, hair in sling-shaped band and long queue. Around, LVCDOVICA DE TORNABONIS IO(annis) FI(lia).

Rev. Unicorn lying to left before a tree on which is perched a dove. Above, a blank scroll.

75 mm. Late cast. A1035–297A

The original was a pendant to the medal of Lodovica's brother Lorenzo (no. 296). The Berlin specimen has the curious spelling LVCDOVIIC

Literature: Cp. Arm. I, 88, 18; *Corpus*, no. 1069; Cott p. 181.

GIAMPAOLO POGGINI

338. PHILIP II, King of Spain (1527–56–98).

Obv. Bust to left in cuirass, with scarf. Around, PHILIPPVS D(ei) G(ratia) ET CAR(oli) V AVG(usti) PAT(ris) BENIGNIT-(ate) HISP(aniae) (REX) 1557 Below, I(oannes) PAVL(us) POG(inus) F(ecit).

Rev. Hercules bearing the Globe. Around, VT QVIESCAT ATLAS

Silver, 42 mm. Electrotype. A1075–338A

The edge of this piece is stamped RR R, the initials of R C. Ready (1811–1901) and his son Augustus P. Ready, who were employed as electrotypists at the British Museum. These official productions are also known stamped MB on the edges. The original medal was occasioned by Philip's relieving Charles of the burden of sovereignty in 1556.

Literature: Cp. Arm. I, 238, 1; Cott p. 183. For the Readys, see Forrer, 5, pp. 53–4.

VALERIO BELLI

385*a*. VALERIO BELLI.

Obv. Bust to left, bearded, wearing gown. Around, VALERIUS BELLVS VICENTINVS

Without reverse.

Lead, 48 mm (reproduction). A1456–716A

The portrait profile of the sitter appears in a drawing once the property of Vasari. Mr. A. E. Popham (private communication) has kindly provided the following information on this portrait drawing, which was subsequently in the collections of the grand duke of Weimar, of F. Koenigs, and is now in the Boymans- van Beuningen Museum at Rotterdam (inv. no. I. 392). The drawing is probably the model from which the medal was taken. It was certainly the original of the woodcut portrait in the second edition of Vasari's *Lives*. The drawing has been variously attributed, to Michaelangelo, to the school of Parmigianino, to Luini, and to Valerio Belli himself (by Kurz). The last attribution is improbable as Vasari particularly insists on Belli's incompetence as a draughtsman and his constant reliance on the drawings of other artists. A self-portrait moreover is unlikely to be in profile. The drawing seems to be by Parmigianino, as was first tentatively suggested by Weigel, and would date between 1524 and 1541, perhaps to 1527–30.

A painted roundel by Raphael, in the collection of Sir Kenneth Clark, shows a very similar profile to that of the drawing but the two portraits are probably independent. There is evidence that the roundel was painted in 1517, when Valerio Belli acted as godfather to Raphael's daughter. A relief profile portrait ascribed to Ammanati, is in the Victoria and Albert Museum.

Literature: for the medal—Cp. Arm. I, 135, 1; Habich, pl. lxxvi, 8; Kris, I, pp. 56–7; fig. 217; Hill, P.M.I.A., pp. 48–9, no. 24; Middeldorf, *Morgenroth*, no. 119; Cott p. 187. For the drawing—Weigel, *Die Werke der Maler in ihren Handzeichnungen*, Leipzig, 1865, p. 412, no. 4939; Kris, I, pp. 56–7; fig. 218; Otto Kurz, 'Giorgio Vasari's "Libro de'disegni" ', in *Old Master Drawings*, 12 (1937–8) no. 47, pp. 32–44 (at p. 38, pl. 34). For the Raphael roundel—Lord Balniel and Kenneth Clark (editors), *A Commemorative Catalogue of the Exhibition of Italian Art held in the . . . Royal Academy . . . London, 1930*, Oxford, 1931, Text p. 134, no. 388; O. Fischel, *Raphael*, Berlin, 1962, p. 91, pl. 152. J. Pope-Hennessy, *Catalogue of Italian Sculpture in the Victoria and Albert Museum*, London, 1964, no. 517, fig. 513 (for the sculptured portrait).

ATTRIBUTED TO LEONE LEONI

433. IPPOLITA DI FERDINANDO GONZAGA (1535–63).

Obv. Bust to left; dress with high collar, necklace and scarf. Around, HIPPOLITA GONZAGA FERDINANDI FIL(ia) AET(atis) AN(no) XV

Rev. Ippolita, holding a book, looking up at a crown of seven stars; around her, musical and scientific instruments. Around, NEC TEMPVS NEC AETAS

61 mm. Late cast. A1170–433A

This has been attributed to Leone Leoni, but is not on the same level as the medal of the same girl, no. 432.

Literature: Cp. Arm. II, 213, 3; III, 257, *a*; Magnaguti, no. 136, pl. xxi; Cott p. 191.

UNATTRIBUTED ITALIAN MEDAL
XVI Century

503. MARGUERITE DE FRANCE, Duchess of Savoy. See no. 367.

Obv. Bust to left, in rich dress with high collar. Around, MARGARITA DE FRANTIA D(ucissa) SABAVDIAE

Rev. Same as obverse.

51 mm. Late cast. A1241–503A

Literature: Cp. Litta, *Savoia*, no. 139; Cott p. 194.

MISCELLANEOUS FICTITIOUS PORTRAITS

522. EUCLID.

Obv. Bust to right, head veiled.

Rev. EUCLIDES across field.

53 mm. A1261–522A

Except for its high relief, the style of this betrays the same hand as was responsible for a series of fictitious medals of Francia, Guercino, and others.

Literature: Cott p. 195; Hill, P.M.I.A., pp. 24–5, pl. xxxii (the forged medals of Francia, Primaticcio, and Guercino).

523. NICOLÒ GANDER.

Obv. Bust to left, in cap. Around, NICOLO GANDER

Without reverse.

115 mm. Cast hollow. A1262–523A

In some specimens, as in that illustrated by Habich, the cap is continued beyond the edge of the medal. Habich regards this as a Florentine portrait of a German, and mentions it among works attributable to Niccolò Fiorentino.

Literature: Cp. Habich, pl. l, 2; Berlin, *Simon collection*, no. 298; *Corpus*, no. 1274; Cott p. 178.

JACOPO PRIMAVERA

Italian medallist working in France from about 1568 to 1585. See Hill in Thieme-Becker, 27 (1931) p. 403; Babelon, *La Médaille en France*, Paris, 1948, pp. 33–4.

543. MARY STUART, Queen of Scots, married Francis II 1558, executed 1587.

Obv. Bust of Mary to right, wearing coif and long veil. Around, MARIA STOVVAR REGI(na) SCOTI(ae) ANGLI(ae) and, in inner arc behind, IA(cobus) PRIMAVE(ra).

Without reverse.

Lead, 64 mm. A1282–543A

Reproduction of a good specimen of the medal.

Literature: Cp. Mazerolle, no. 299; Franks and Grueber, *Medallic Illustrations of the History of Great Britain and Ireland*, London, 1885, I, p. 118, no. 52; Hill, *Med. Ren.*, p. 146, pl. xxvi, 5; Cott p. 197.

JEAN-BAPTISTE NINI
(b. 1717; d. 1786)

Jean-Baptiste Nini of Urbino, engraver and maker of terracotta medallions, established at Paris 1758–72, then at Chaumont.

582. ALBERTINE DE NIVENHEIM, of a Gelders family, married (1) M. Pater, separated 1765, (2) Marquis de Champcenetz 1777.

Obv. Bust to right, décolletée, cloak over shoulders. Around, ALBERTINE NEE BARONNE DE NIVENHEIM 1768

Without reverse.

148 mm. With ring for suspension. A1321–582A

From the terracotta which in 1930 was in the possession of Prince A. de Broglie.

Literature: A. Storelli, *Jean-Baptiste Nini*, Tours, 1896, p. 73; Cott p. 199.

PSEUDO-DÜRER

(W. Sommer of Frankfurt, working 1880–1900).

628. SEBALD SCHREIER.

Obv. Bust to right, in cap and gown. Around, SEBALDVS SCHREIER Behind, 1512 and monogram of Albrecht Dürer.

Without reverse.

Lead, 95 mm. Cast hollow. A1368–628A

The stone-model for this interesting invention was in the possession of Freiherr Guido von Volkamer, of Munich. (Information from Dr. Max Bernhart to Hill.)

Literature: Cott p. 203.

ILLUSTRATIONS

All illustrations are in the size of the originals.

1 *obv*. John VIII Palaeologus, Emperor of Constantinople

1 *rev*. John VIII Palaeologus riding in a rocky landscape

2 *obv*. Gianfrancesco I Gonzaga, Marquess of Mantua

2 *rev*. Gianfrancesco I Gonzaga riding in a rocky landscape

3 *obv*. Filippo Maria Visconti, Duke of Milan

3 *rev*. Filippo Maria Visconti riding in a mountainous landscape

4 *obv*. Niccolò Piccinino, condottiere

4 *rev*. The she-griffin of Perusia suckling two infants

5 *obv*. Francesco Sforza, fourth Duke of Milan

5 *rev*. Charger, books and sword

PISANELLO

6 *obv*. Leonello d'Este, Marquess of Ferrara

6 *rev*. Head with three infantile faces

7 *obv*. Leonello d'Este, Marquess of Ferrara

7 *rev*. Two nude men carrying baskets
with olive-branches

8 *obv*. Leonello d'Este, Marquess of Ferrara

8 *rev*. Blindfolded lynx seated on a cushion

9 *obv*. Leonello d'Este, Marquess of Ferrara

9 *rev*. Nude youth lying before a rock

10 *obv*. Leonello d'Este, Marquess of Ferrara

10 *rev*. Lion being taught by Cupid to sing

12 *obv*. Sigismondo Pandolfo Malatesta,
Lord of Rimini and Fano

12 *rev*. Sigismondo armed and holding sword

13 *obv*. Sigismondo Pandolfo Malatesta,
Lord of Rimini and Fano

13 *rev*. Sigismondo on charger before a fortress

15 *obv*. Domenico Novello Malatesta, Lord of Cesena

15 *rev*. Malatesta in armour, kneeling before a Crucifix

16 *obv*. Lodovico III Gonzaga, second Marquess of Mantua

16 *rev*. The Marquess in armour, riding

17 *obv*. Cecilia Gonzaga, daughter of Gianfrancesco I of Mantua

17 *rev*. Innocence and unicorn in moonlit landscape

18 *obv*. Vittorino Rambaldoni da Feltre, humanist

18 *rev*. Pelican in her piety

22 *obv*. Don Inigo d'Avalos, Grand Chamberlain of Alfonso of Naples

22 *rev*. Sphere representing earth, sea and sky

PISANELLO

20 Alfonso V of Aragon,
King of Naples and Sicily

19 *obv*. Alfonso V of Aragon, King of Naples and Sicily

19 *rev*. Eagle and lesser birds of prey in rocky landscape

23 *obv*. Alfonso V of Aragon

23 *rev*. Female figure with purse and sceptre

24 *obv*. René d'Anjou and Jeanne de Laval

24 *rev*. Peace holding olive-branch and helmet

26 *obv*. Jean d'Anjou, Duke of Calabria and Lorraine

26 *rev*. Temple surmounted by figure of St. Michael

PAOLO DA RAGUSA (23) · FRANCESCO LAURANA (24, 26)

27 *obv*. Louis XI, King of France

27 *rev*. Concordia holding lily-sceptre and olive-branch

28 *obv*.
Borso, Marquess of Este

28 *rev*.
Marigold and door-knocker

29 *obv*. Niccolò III d'Este,
Marquess of Ferrara

29 *rev*. The Este shield

30 Pisanello

LAURANA (27) · AMADIO DA MILANO (28–29) · NICHOLAUS (30)

31 *obv*. Saint Bernardino of Siena, Minorite of the Observance

31 *rev*. The trigram in a flaming halo

32 *obv*. Pisanello the medallist

33 Giulio Cesare Varano, Lord of Camerino

32 *rev*. Initials of the Seven Virtues

34 Ginevra Sforza, wife of Giovanni II Bentivoglio

ANTONIO MARESCOTTI

35 *obv*. Borso d'Este, Duke of Modena and Reggio

35 *rev*. Unicorn dipping its horn into a stream

36 *obv*. Borso d'Este,
Duke of Modena and Reggio

36 *rev*. Hexagonal font
in a landscape

38 *obv*. Ercole d'Este,
Duke of Ferrara, Modena and Reggio

37 Ercole I d'Este, Duke of Ferrara,
Modena and Reggio

38 *rev*. Hercules,
and three columns in the sea

LIXIGNOLO (35) · PETRECINO (36) · BALDASSARE D'ESTE (37) · CORADINO (38)

40 *obv*. Borso d'Este,
Marquess of Este,
first Duke of Ferrara

40 *rev*. Shield of Este
on floriated ground

39 Acarino d'Este, legendary ancestor of the Estensi

44 Unknown man

42 *obv*. Ercole I d'Este, Duke of Ferrara, Modena and Reggio

42 *rev*. Putti receiving shower of Este diamond rings

45 Unknown man

43 Ercole I d'Este

47 Unknown boy

FERRARESE AND OTHER NORTH ITALIAN SCHOOLS

50 Unknown man

48 Unknown man

49 Unknown man

46 Unknown man

51 *obv*. Unknown man

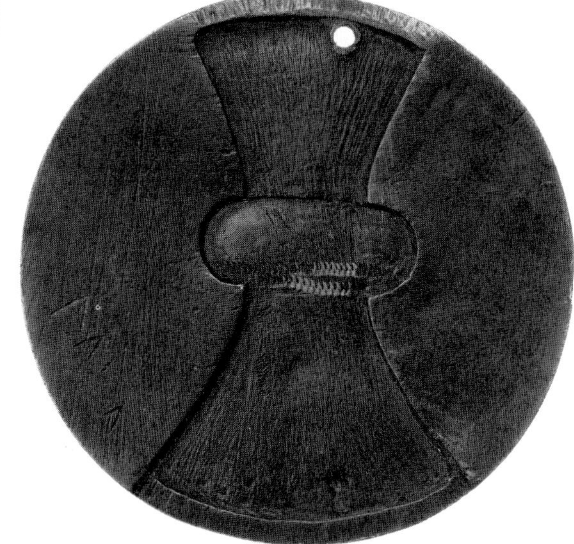

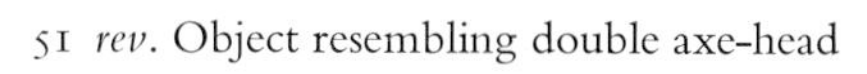

51 *rev*. Object resembling double axe-head

53 Unknown woman

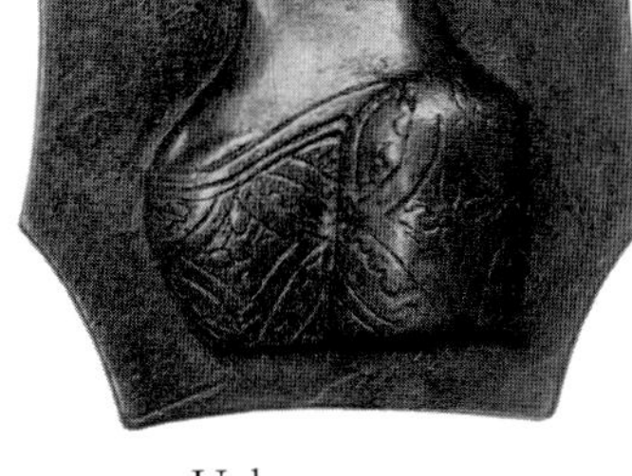

52 Unknown woman

54 Unknown woman

FERRARESE AND OTHER NORTH ITALIAN SCHOOLS

55 *obv*. Guarino da Verona, humanist

55 *rev*. Fountain surmounted by nude male figure

56 *obv*. Leone Battista Alberti, architect and writer

56 *rev*. Winged human eye

MATTEO DE' PASTI

57 *obv*. Jesus Christ

57 *rev*. Christ in the tomb

58 *obv*. Sigismondo Pandolfo Malatesta, Lord of Rimini and Fano

58 *rev*. Shield, helmet, elephant-crest, and mantling

61 *obv*. Sigismondo Pandolfo Malatesta, Lord of Rimini and Fano

61 *rev*. Fortitude holding broken column

MATTEO DE' PASTI

59 *obv*. Isotta degli Atti da Rimini, wife of Sigismondo Malatesta

59 *rev*. The Malatesta elephant in a meadow

60 *obv*. Sigismondo Pandolfo Malatesta, Lord of Rimini and Fano

60 *rev*. The Castle of Rimini

62 *obv*. Sigismondo Pandolfo Malatesta, Lord of Rimini and Fano

62 *rev*. The Castle of Rimini

MATTEO DE' PASTI

63 *obv*. Isotta degli Atti

63 *rev*. The Malatesta elephant

64 *obv*.
Isotta degli Atti

67 Sigismondo Malatesta, laureate, in armour

65 *obv*.
Isotta degli Atti

64 *rev*. A closed book

65 *rev*. A closed book

66 *obv*.
Sigismondo Malatesta,
Lord of Rimini and Fano

66 *rev*.
San Francesco at Rimini

68 *obv*. Lodovico III Gonzaga, second Marquess of Mantua

68 *rev*. The Marquess with Faith and Pallas

70 *obv*. Chiara Gonzaga,
wife of Gilbert de Bourbon

69 *obv*. Francesco II Gonzaga, fourth Marquess of Mantua

71 *obv*. Francesco II Gonzaga,
Marquess of Mantua

70 *rev*. Goldsmiths' ornaments

69 *rev*. Health standing between sea and fire

71 *rev*. Battle scene

BARTOLOMMEO MELIOLI (68–70) · GIANFRANCESCO RUBERTI (71)

71 *bis obv*. Gianfrancesco Gonzaga di Ròdigo, Lord of Sabbioneta

71 *bis rev*. Fortune, Mars and Minerva

72 *obv*. Antonia del Balzo, wife of Gianfrancesco Gonzaga di Ròdigo

72 *rev*. Hope on prow of broken-masted vessel

73 *obv*. Diva Julia

73a *obv*. Maddalena of Mantua

73a *rev*. Occasion in pursuit of Time

73 *rev*. Battle scene

74 *obv*. Luca de' Zuhari, provost of Pomponesco

75 *obv*. Giulia Astallia

76 *obv*. Isabella d'Este, wife of Francesco II Gonzaga

74 *rev*. Venus and Mars

75 *rev*. Phoenix on pyre looking at sun

76 *rev*. Astrology and sign of Sagittarius

ANTICO (71bis, 72, 73) · IN THE MANNER OF ANTICO (73a, 74, 75)
GIANCRISTOFORO ROMANO (76)

78 Lucrezia Borgia, wife of Alfonso I d'Este

79 Lucrezia Borgia, wife of Alfonso I d'Este

83 Beatrice of Aragon, wife of Matthias, King of Hungary

82 *obv*. Maddalena of Mantua

80 *obv*. Jacoba Correggia

80 *rev*. Captive Love bound to a tree

82 *rev*. Swan, standing on bow and quiver

84 *obv*. Francesco II Gonzaga

85 *obv*. Francesco II Gonzaga

85 *rev*. The Marquess giving alms

84 *rev*. The Marquess giving alms

87 *obv*. Battista Spagnoli of Mantua, Carmelite, poet

86 *obv*. Francesco Bonatti of Mantua, jurisconsult

86 *rev*. Truth escaping from book

88 *obv*. Giovanni Gonzag Marquess of Ariano

87 *rev*. Cherub, swan and eagle

IN THE NEIGHBOURHOOD
OF GIANCRISTOFORO ROMANO (78–80, 82, 83)
GIAN MARCO CAVALLI (84, 85) · MEA (86–88)

88 *rev*. Galley in full sai

89 *obv*. Ortensia Piccolomini

91 Corrado (of the Nobili Gonzaga)

89 *rev*. The Judgement of Paris

90 *obv*. Federigo II Gonzaga
first Duke of Mantua

90 *rev*. St. Catherine

92 *obv*. Francesco Sforza,
fourth Duke of Milan

93 *obv*. Francesco Sforza,
fourth Duke of Milan

93 *rev*. Galeazzo Maria Sforza,
fifth Duke of Milan

92 *rev*. Greyhound

94 *obv*. Taddeo di Guidacci Manfredi,
Count of Faenza and Lord of Imola

98 Francesco Sforza,
fourth Duke of Milan

94 *rev*.
Female figure and putto

99 *obv*. Costanzo Sforza,
Lord of Pesaro

99 *rev*.
The Castle of Pesaro

MANTUAN SCHOOL, Early Sixteenth Century (89–91) · GIANFRANCESCO ENZOLA (92–94, 98, 99)

95 *obv*. Costanzo Sforza, Lord of Pesaro

95 *rev*. Costanzo riding in the country

96 *obv*. Costanzo Sforza, Lord of Pesaro

96 *rev*. Alessandro Sforza, father of Costanzo

97 *obv*. Costanzo Sforza, Lord of Pesaro

97 *rev*. The Castle of Pesaro

GIANFRANCESCO ENZOLA

100 *obv*. Federigo da Montefeltro, Count of Urbino

100 *rev*. Eagle with spread wings supporting devices

101 *obv*. Borgese Borghesi, jurisconsult of Siena

101 *rev*. Minerva holding spear and shield

103 *obv*. Andrea Matteo III d'Acquaviva,
Duke of Atri and Teramo

103 *rev*.
Crowned shield of arms

CLEMENTE DA URBINO (100) · FRANCESCO DI GIORGIO MARTINI (101)
NEAPOLITAN SCHOOL, Late Fifteenth Century (103)

102 *obv*. Mohammad II, Sultan of the Turks

102 *rev*. The Sultan riding

COSTANZO DA FERRARA

104 *obv*. Ferdinand of Aragon,
Prince of Capua, afterwards King Ferdinand

104 *rev*. Felicitas seated,
holding ears of corn and waving cornucopiae

105 *obv*. Ferdinand II of Aragon,
King of Naples

105 *rev*. Janiform head
(bearded male to left, female to right)

106 *obv*. Giovanni Gioviano Pontano, poet

106 *rev*. Urania walking to right, holding globe and lyre

ADRIANO FIORENTINO

107 *obv*. Elisabetta Gonzaga, Duchess of Urbino

107 *rev*. Female figure holding bridle

108 Unknown boy

109 *obv*. Andrea Caraffa, Count of Santa Severina

109 *rev*. Prudence holding double-faced head

111 *obv*. Andrea Caraffa, Count of Santa Severina

110 *obv*. Andrea Caraffa, Count of Santa Severina

110 *rev*. Shield of Caraffa arms

111 *rev*. Shield of Caraffa arms

ADRIANO FIORENTINO (107–108) · GIROLAMO SANTACROCE (109)
NEAPOLITAN SCHOOL, Early Sixteenth Century (110–111)

112 *obv*. Bartolommeo Pendalia, merchant of Ferrara

112 *rev*. Figure seated on cuirass, holding globe and spear

113 *obv*. Antonio Sarzanella De' Manfredi of Faenza, diplomatist

113 *rev*. Prudence seated on two hounds holding Manfredi shield

114 *obv*. Lodovico Carbone of Ferrara, poet

114 *rev*. Carbone receiving a wreath from Calliope

SPERANDIO OF MANTUA

115 *obv*. Francesco Sforza, Duke of Milan

115 *rev*. Renaissance building with four cupolas

116 *obv*. Ercole I d'Este and his wife, Eleonora of Aragon

115a *obv*. Fra Cesario Contughi, a Servite of Ferrara

115a *rev*. Fra Cesario seated on rock, contemplating a skull

SPERANDIO OF MANTUA

117 *obv.* Sigismondo, son of Niccolò III d'Este

117 *rev.* Cupid holding palm-branch and balance

118 Sigismondo, son of Niccolò III d'Este

119 *obv.* Pietro Bono Avogario, physician and astrologer of Ferrara

119 *rev.* Aesculapius, standing on a dragon, and Urania on a globe

120 Agostino Buonfrancesco of Rimini, Councillor of Ercole I d'Este

SPERANDIO OF MANTUA

124 *obv.* Alessandro Tartagni, jurisconsult of Imola

124 *rev.* Mercury seated on a dragon

123 Carlo Manfredi, lord of Faenza

126 *obv.* Niccolò da Correggio, Count of Brescello

126 *rev.* Niccolò da Correggio and a friar

SPERANDIO OF MANTUA

125 *obv*. Andrea Barbazza of Messina, legist

127 *obv*. Niccolò Sanuti, noble of Bologna

125 *rev*. Fame holding a closed and an open book

127 *rev*. Pelican in her piety and inscription

128 *obv.* Giovanni II Bentivoglio, Lord of Bologna

128 *rev.* Giovanni II Bentivoglio and squire

131 *obv.* Francesco II Gonzaga, Marquess of Mantua

131 *rev.* Francesco II Gonzaga and soldiers

135 *obv*. Doge Pasquale Malipieri

135 *rev*. Dogaressa Giovanna Dandolo

136 *obv*. Doge Francesco Foscari

136 *rev*. Venetia and two Furies

138 *obv*. Bartolommeo Colleone of Bergamo, condottiere

138 *rev*. Laureate figure holding plummet line

PIETRO DA FANO (135) · ANTONIO GAMBELLO (136) · MARCO GUIDIZANI (138)

139 *obv*. Filipo Maserano, of Venice

139 *rev*. Arion riding on a dolphin

140 *obv*. Nicolaus Schlifer, German musician

140 *rev*. Apollo with lyre and long scroll

141 *obv*. Giovanni Boldù

141 *rev*. Boldù, between Faith and Penitence

GIOVANNI BOLDÙ (139–143) · GENTILE BELLINI (144)

142 *obv*. Giovanni Boldù
142 *rev*. The artist, with the genius of Death

143 *obv*. The Emperor Caracalla
143 *rev*. Boldù with the genius of Death

144 *obv*. Mohammad II, Sultan of the Turks
144 *rev*. Three crowns: Constantinople, Iconium and Trebizond

145 *obv*. Pope Sixtus IV

147 *obv*. Gentile Bellini, the painter

146 *obv*. Giovanni Bellini, the painter

145 *rev*. The Pope in audience

147 *rev*. Incised inscription

146 *rev*. An owl

148 *obv*. Camelio

148 *rev*. Sacrificial scene

150 *obv*. Camelio

150a *obv*. Male figure carrying stag

150a *rev*. Flaming tripod on altar

152 *obv*. Leonardo Loredano, Doge of Venice

150 *rev*. Male figure and winged caduceus

152 *rev*. Equity holding scales and sceptre

CAMELIO (145–150a) · MANNER OF CAMELIO (151-155) · FALIER (156) · ANTONIO DA BRESCIA (157

153 *obv*. Andrea Gritti, Doge of Venice

151 *obv*. Marco Barbadigo, Doge of Venice

154 *obv*. Giuliano II de' Medici

153 *rev*. Venetia holding scales and cornucopiae

151 *rev*. Inscription in wreath of ivy

154 *rev*. Virtue and Fortune

156 *obv*. Andrea Gritti, Procurator of St. Mark's

155 *obv*. Agostino Barbadigo, Doge of Venice

155 *rev*. Venetia on throne

156 *rev*. Gritti before breached city wall

157 *obv*. Niccolò Tempestà

157 *rev*. Winged dragon with balance

158 *obv*. Francesco di Andrea Malipieri

159 *obv*. Vincenzo di Andrea Malipieri

162 *obv*. Sebastiano Montagnacco

158 *rev*. Pelican in her piety

159 *rev*. Crowned eagle on a mound

162 *rev*. Fortress with tall tree

160 *obv*. Augusto da Udine
160 *rev*. Urania

161 *obv*. Altobello Averoldo, Bishop of Pola

161 *rev*. Truth unveiled by two men

MAFFEO OLIVIERI

164 *obv*. Antonio Grimani, Doge of Venice

163 Beato Lorenzo Giustinian

165 *obv*. Giovanni Fasiol

164 *rev*. Justice and Peace

165 *rev*. Figure holding Victory and branch

167 *obv*. Tommaso Mocenigo

166 Simone Michiel, Protonotary

169 Paolo Diedo

168 *obv*. Fra Giovanni Cornaro

167 *rev*. Toilet of Venus (?)

170 Giovanni Mannelli

168 *rev*. Shepherd and flock

172 *obv*. Antonio Roselli, jurist

171 *obv*. Alvise da Noale, jurist

171 *rev*. Inscription

172 *rev*. Roselli seated on bracket

VENETIAN SCHOOL (163–171) · BELLANO (172)

173 *obv*. Girolamo di Benedetto Pesaro, Captain of Padua

174 *obv*. Girolamo di Benedetto Pesaro

174 *rev*. Inscription

173 *rev*. Inscription

175 *obv*. Stefano di Andrea Magno

176 *obv*. Giovanni Emo, Podestà of Padua

177 *obv*. Tommaso Moro, Captain of Verona

175 *rev*. Neptune spearing a lobster

176 *rev*. Pallas and Mars

177 *rev*. Phoenix on pyre gazing at sun

179 *obv*. Francis I of France

178 *obv*. Emperor Charles V

178 *rev*. Genius writing on shield

179 *rev*. Salamander in flames

PADUAN SCHOOL (173–174) · POMEDELLI (175–179)

180 *obv*. Unknown lady

180 *rev*. Man holding fruit, and Cupid

181 *obv*. Federigo II Gonzaga

181 *rev*. Altar of Fides

182 *obv*. Isabella Sesso

182 *rev*. Occasion holding bridle

183 *obv*. Francis I of France

183 *rev*. Diomede seated on cippus

6 *obv*. Francesco degli Alidosi, Cardinal of Pavia

184 *obv*. Giovanni II Bentivoglio

184 *rev*. Inscription

187 *obv*. Bernardo de' Rossi, Bishop of Treviso

185 *obv*. Giovanni II Bentivoglio

185 *rev*. Shield of Bentivoglio

186 *rev*. Jupiter in car drawn by eagles

187 *rev*. Figure in car drawn by dragon and eagle

POMEDELLI (180–183) · FRANCIA (184–185) · BOLOGNESE SCHOOL (186–187)

188 Giangaleazzo Visconti, first Duke of Milan

190 *obv*. Francesco I Sforza

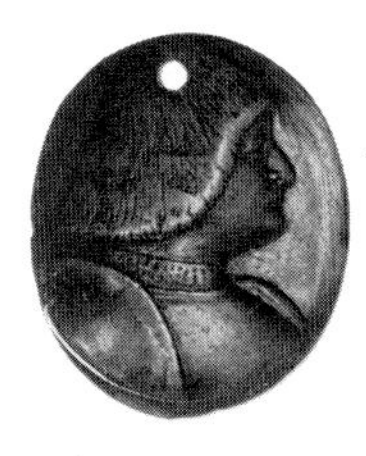

189 Lodovico Maria Sforza,
Duke of Milan

191 *obv*.
Lodovico Maria Sforza

190 *rev*.
Francesco approaching city

191 *rev*. The Doge of Genoa

MILANESE SCHOOL, Late Fifteenth Century (188–189) · CARADOSSO (190–191)

192 *obv*. Giangiacomo Trivulzio

192 *rev*. Inscription

193 *obv*. Donato di Angelo Bramante, architect

193 *rev*. Architecture, holding compasses and square

197 Simone Taverna of Milan

194 *obv*. Pope Julius II

195 *obv*. Pope Julius II

196 *obv*. Niccolò Orsini

194 *rev*. View of St. Peter's

195 *rev*. View of St. Peter's

196 *rev*. Orsini riding

CARADOSSO (192–196) · MILANESE SCHOOL, Early Sixteenth Century (197)

198 *obv*. Cardinal Scaramuccia di Gianfermo Trivulzio

199 *obv*. Giangiacomo Trivulzio

198 *rev*. Prudence holding mirror and compasses

201 *obv*. Battista II di Campofregoso, Doge of Genoa

199 *rev*. Giangiacomo Trivulzio

201 *rev*. Crocodile and trochilus

205 *obv*. Marcus Croto

205 *rev*. Marcus Croto riding

206 *obv*. Cardinal Pier Barbò

206 *rev*. Barbò shield

MILANESE SCHOOL, Early Sixteenth Century (198–199) · BATTISTA ELIA (201)
THE MEDALLIST OF THE ROMAN EMPERORS (205) · ROMAN SCHOOL (206)

202 *obv*. Nero, laureate, wearing cuirass and mantle

202 *rev*. Nero, laureate, seated under palm tree

203 *obv*. Hadrian in crested helmet, cuirass and mantle

203 *rev*. Hadrian, riding and carrying standard

204 *obv*. Faustina I

204 *rev*. Antonius Pius and Faustina joining hands

207 *obv*. Niccolò Palmieri, Bishop of Orte

208 *obv*. Pope Calixtus III

209 *obv*. Pope Sixtus IV

207 *rev*. Male figure holding hourglass

208 *rev*.
Borgia arms with tiara

209 *rev*. Constancy with Turkish captives

210 *obv*. Alfonso V of Aragon, King of Naples and Sicily

212 *obv*.
Lodovico Scarampi

212 *rev*.
Triumphal procession

210 *rev*.
Alfonso crowned by Mars and Bellona

211 *obv*. Constantine the Great

213 *obv*. Cardinal Guillaume d'Estouteville

214 *obv*. Paolo Dotti of Padua

211 *rev*. Constantine and the Church

213 *rev*. Shield of arms of Estouteville

214 *rev*. Constancy resting on staff and column

215 *obv*. Pope Paul II in public consistory

216 *obv*. Pope Paul II

216 *rev*. Palazzo di Venezia

215 *rev*. Christ in Glory, and the Resurrection

CRISTOFORO DI GEREMIA (211, 213–214) · ROMAN SCHOOL UNDER PAUL II (215–216)

217 *obv*.
Bartolommeo Parthenio
of Brescia

217 *rev*.
Lily and inscription

218 *obv*. Giovanni Francesco
de' Rangoni

218 *rev*.
Armed figure standing
on prostrate wolf

219 *obv*. Pope Sixtus IV

219 *rev*. Sixtus IV
being crowned

220 *obv*. Giovanni Alvise Toscani

220 *rev*. Neptune in sea-car

221 *obv*. Giovanni Alvise Toscani

222 Self-portrait of Candida

221 *rev*. Inscription in wreath

223 *obv*. Charles the Bold,
Duke of Burgundy

223 *rev*. A ram
between two briquets

224 *obv*. Antoine,
Grand Bastard of Burgundy

224 *rev*. Barbacane

LYSIPPUS JUNIOR (217–221) · ATTRIBUTED TO GIOVANNI CANDIDA (222–230)

225 *obv*. Maximilian of Austria

225 *rev*. Maria of Burgundy

226 *obv*. Jean Carondelet

226 *rev*. Marguerite de Chassey

227 *obv*. Raimondo Lavagnoli

228 *obv*. Robert Briçonnet

230 *obv*. Giuliano della Rovere

227 *rev*. Arms of Lavagnoli

228 *rev*. Inscription

230 *rev*. Clemente della Rovere

229 *obv*. Nicolas Maugras, Bishop of Uzès

229 *rev*. Arms of Maugras over a crozier

231 *obv*. Thomas Bohier

233 *obv*. Don Rodrigo de Bivar y Mendoza

232 *obv*. François de Valois

233 *rev*. Mars and Venus

231 *rev*. Arms of Thomas Bohier

234 *obv*. Marcello Capodiferro

232 *rev*. Salamander in flames

234 *rev*. Ox

235 *obv*. Cardinal Bernardino Carvajal

235 *rev*. Philosophy with manuscript and sceptre

236 *obv*. Cardinal Domenico Grimani

236 *rev*. Theology and Philosophy

SCHOOL OF GIOVANNI CANDIDA (231–232) · ROMAN SCHOOL UNDER INNOCENT VIII, ALEXANDER VI, AND JULIUS II (233–236)

237 *obv*. Guillaume de Poitiers

238 *obv*. Pope Julius II

238 *rev*. Shield of Rovere

237 *rev*. Mercury with female figure

239 *obv*. Pope Leo X

241 *obv*.
Giuliano II de' Medici

241 *rev*.
Roma holding Victory

239 *rev*. Medici arms

240 *obv*. Giuliano II de' Medici, Duc de Nemours

240 *rev*. Florence leaning on Medici shield

ROMAN SCHOOL UNDER INNOCENT VIII, ALEXANDER VI, JULIUS II AND LEO X

242 *obv*. Girolamo Arsago, Bishop of Nice

242 *rev*. Inscription

243 *obv*. Jesus Christ

243 *rev*. Inscription in wreath

244 *obv*. St. Paul

244 *rev*. Inscription in wreath

245 *obv*. Cosimo de' Medici, Pater Patriae

245 *rev*. Florence holding orb and triple olive-branch

246 *obv*. Cosimo de' Medici, Pater Patriae

246 *rev*. Florence holding orb and triple olive-branch

247 *obv*.
Cosimo de' Medici

247 *rev*. Florence

249 *obv*. Emperor Frederick III

249 *rev*. Emperor, Pope and Cardinals on Ponte S. Angelo

FLORENTINE SCHOOL (245–247) · BERTOLDO DI GIOVANNI (249)

248 *obv*. Mohammad II, Sultan of Turkey

248 *rev*. Triumphal car with Greece, Trebizond and Asia

250 *obv*. Antonio Gratiadei, Imperial envoy

250 *rev*. Triumphal car with Mercury and the Muses

253 *obv*.
Lorenzo de' Medici

251 *obv*. Filippo de' Medici, Archbishop of Pisa

253 *rev*.
Figure in antique armour

251 *rev*. The Last Judgement

252 *obv*. Lorenzo de' Medici
and the Pazzi conspiracy

252 *rev*. Giuliano de' Medici
and the Pazzi conspiracy

254 *obv*. Francesco Diedo, wearing cap and robe

254 *rev*. Hercules pursuing Nessus and Deianira

256 *obv*. Alfonso I d'Este, Duke of Ferrara

256 *rev*. Alfonso (?) in triumphal car

BERTOLDO DI GIOVANNI (252, 254 *rev*.) · NICCOLÒ SPINELLI, called NICCOLÒ FIORENTINO (256)

258 *obv*. Pope Innocent VIII

259 *obv*. Guglielmo Batonatti

258 *rev*. Justice, Peace, and Abundance

259 *rev*. Unicorn, and tau-cross

260 *obv*.
Bernardino Gamberia,
chamberlain of Innocent VIII

260 *rev*.
God the Father in clouds

262 King Charles VIII of France

261 *obv*. Rinaldo Orsini,
Archbishop of Florence

261 *rev*. Fortune, holding rudder
and cornucopiae

ATTRIBUTED TO NICCOLÒ FIORENTINO

263 *obv.* Jean Du Mas de l'Isle, Councillor of Charles VIII

263 *rev.* Jean Du Mas on a horse wearing chanfron and bardings

264 Lionora Altoviti

266 Antonio di Dante Castiglione

265 *obv.* Fra Alberto Belli

265 *rev.* Faith holding chalice with wafer and cross

ATTRIBUTED TO NICCOLÒ FIORENTINO (263) · IN THE MANNER OF NICCOLÒ (264–266)

269 *obv*. Pietro Machiavelli

269 *rev*. Eagle and Machiavelli shield

270 *obv*. Roberto di Ruggiero de Macinghi

267 *obv*. Ercole I d'Este, Duke of Ferrara and Modena

267 *rev*. Minerva resting on spear and shield

270 *rev*. Figure holding shield and peacock

268 *obv*. Marsilio Ficino, humanist

271 Lorenzo de' Medici, il Magnifico

268 *rev*. Inscription

IN THE MANNER OF NICCOLÒ FIORENTINO

272 *obv*. Maria de' Mucini

272 *rev*. Eagle on an armillary sphere

273 *obv*. Ruberto di Bernardo Nasi

276 *obv*. Costanza Bentivoglio, Countess of Concordia

278 *obv*. Antonio Pizzamani, Venetian scholar

273 *rev*. Virginity tying Love to a tree

276 *rev*. Constancy leaning on tall staff

278 *rev*. Felicity, Fame and Virtus

IN THE MANNER OF NICCOLÒ FIORENTINO

277 *obv*. Giovanni Pico della Mirandola, philosopher and poet

277 *rev*. The tree Graces

279 *obv*. Angelo Poliziano, humanist

280 *obv*. Maria Poliziana

281 *obv*. Costanza Rucellai

279 *rev*. Maria Poliziana

280 *rev*. Constancy leaning on a bundle of arrows

281 *rev*. Virginity tying Love to a tree

IN THE MANNER OF NICCOLÒ FIORENTINO

282 *obv*. Girolamo Savonarola, Dominican preacher

282 *rev*. Italy threatened by the hand of God

284 *obv*. Ottaviano Sforza-Riario, Count of Forlì and Imola

284 *rev*. Ottaviano riding with drawn sword

285 *obv*. Giovanni di Andrea da Stia

285 *rev*. Hope, gazing at the Sun

IN THE MANNER OF NICCOLÒ FIORENTINO

286 *obv*. Filippo Strozzi, Florentine merchant-prince

286 *rev*. Eagle and Strozzi shield in a meadow

289 *obv*. Giovanni di Francesco Tornabuoni

289 *rev*. Hope praying

287 Achille Tiberti of Cesena

288 *obv*. Giovanna Albizzi, wife of Lorenzo Tornabuoni

288 *rev*. The three Graces

IN THE MANNER OF NICCOLÒ FIORENTINO

292 Ippolito d'Este

290 *obv*. Alessandro di Gino Vecchietti

290 *rev*. Fortune with sail, on a dolphin

295 *obv*.
Michelangelo di Guglielmino Tanaglia

295 *rev*.
Youth wearing animal's skin

291 Unknown man

294 *obv*. Gianozzo di Bernardo Salviati

294 *rev*. Fortune with sail, on a dolphin

IN THE MANNER OF NICCOLÒ FIORENTINO

296 *obv*. Lorenzo di Giovanni Tornabuoni

296 *rev*. Mercury carrying caduceus

297a *obv*. Mathias Corvinus, King of Hungary

297a *rev*. Battle between Hungarians and Turks

298 Aristotle

299 *obv*. Dante Alighieri, Florentine poet

299 *rev*. Dante before the Mountain of Purgatory

IN THE MANNER OF NICCOLÒ FIORENTINO (296) · FLORENTINE SCHOOL, Late XV Century (297a, 298–2

300 *obv*. Giovanni Boccaccio, Florentine writer

302 Gianfrancesco Pallavicini

300 *rev*. Wisdom gazing at serpent

301 *obv*. Francesco Petrarca

301 *rev*. Poetry walking in a wood

304 *obv*. A Carrara (?)

305 *obv*. Baldassarre di Cristoforo Castiglione

304 *rev*. The heraldic *carro*

305 *rev*. Aurora stepping from car

303 Laura de Noves, friend of Petrarch

FLORENTINE SCHOOL, Late XV Century (300–302) · UNATTRIBUTED ITALIAN (before about 1530) (303–305)

306 *obv*. Louis XII, King of France

307 *obv*. Louis XII, King of France

307 *rev*. Incision

306 *rev*. Mars pursuing other figures

308 *obv*. Francis I, King of France

310 *obv*. Mattia Ugoni, Bishop of Famagusta

309 *obv*. Bernardino Francesconi of Siena

308 *rev*. Trophy of arms

310 *rev*. Ludovico Ugoni

309 *rev*. Arms of Francesconi

311 Unknown man

312 Castruccio Castracane degli Antelminelli

UNATTRIBUTED ITALIAN MEDALS (before about 1530)

314 *obv*. Giovanni de' Medici delle Bande Nere

314 *rev*. Winged thunderbolt

315 *obv*.
Cosimo I de' Medici

315 *rev*.
Capricorn and stars

316 *obv*. Alessandro de' Medici,
first Duke of Florence

316 *rev*. Cosimo I de' Medici,
first Grand Duke

317 *obv*. Alessandro de' Medici,
first Duke of Florence

318 Alfonso II d'Avalos, Marquess of Vasto

317 *rev*. Peace setting fire
to a pile of arms

FRANCESCO DA SANGALLO (314) · DOMENICO DE' VETRI (315–316) FRANCESCO DAL PRATO (317)
CESARE DA BAGNO (318)

319 *obv*. Beatrice da Siena

319 *rev*. Wheat-sheaf

322 *obv*.
Cornelia Siciliana

322 *rev*.
Truth unveiling herself

320 Costanza Buti

323 Ercole II d'Este,
fourth Duke of Ferrara

324 Francesco d'Este, son of
Alfonso I, Marquess of Massa

321 Camillo Castiglione,
son of Baldassarre di Cristoforo Castiglione

325 Lucrezia de' Medici, daughter of Cosimo I

327 Isabella Trotti Negrisoli

326 Eleonora d'Austria, Duchess of Mantua

328 Isabella Manfro de' Pepoli

PASTORINO DE' PASTORINI

329 Lodovica Felicina Rossi

330 Girolama Sacrata of Ferrara

331 Girolama Sacrata of Ferrara

332 Girolama, daughter of Galeazzo Farnese

333 Ginevra Trotti

334 Nicolosa Bacci, wife of Giorgio Vasari

335 *obv*. Francesco Visdomini of Ferrara, humanist

336 Unidentified man

335 *rev*. A hand, issuing from a cloud, holding a flaming sword

337 Unknown lady

PASTORINO DE' PASTORINI

338a Alessandro Farnese, third Duke of Parma and Piacenza

339 Lodovico Ariosto, poet

340 *obv*. Alfonso II d'Este, fifth Duke of Ferrara

340 *rev*. Lucrezia de' Medici, wife of Alfonso II d'Este

341 *obv*. Cosimo de' Medici, Duke of Florence

341 *rev*. The Uffizi and the Palazzo Vecchio

342 *obv*. Eleonora de Toledo, first wife of Cosimo I de' Medici

342 *rev*. Pea-hen with six young

343 *obv*. Giulio Nobili, Florentine Senator

343 *rev*. Figure holding scales, and swan

344 *obv*. Camilla Peretti, sister of Sixtus V

344 *rev*. S. Lucia at Grottamare

345 *obv*. Niccolò Todini of Ancona, Captain of Castel Sant'Angelo

345 *rev*. Castel Sant'Angelo

346 *obv*. Benedetto Varchi, Florentine man of letters

346 *rev*. A man lying at the foot of a laurel-tree

GIAMPAOLO POGGINI (338a) · DOMENICO POGGINI (339–346)

347 *obv*. Camilla Albizzi

347 *rev*. Apollo pursuing Daphne

347a *obv*. Barbara Borromeo, wife of Camillo Gonzaga

347a *rev*. Two summits of Pindus, on each a flaming vase

347b *obv*. Alessandro Caimo, jurist of Milan

347b *rev*. Fortune holding sail, and helmeted woman

348 *obv*. Antonio Calmone, Secretary of Philip II

348 *rev*. Flowering shrub growing through thorns

350 *obv*. Girolamo Figino, Milanese painter

350 *rev*. Minerva armed

349 *obv*. Bianca Pansana Carcania

349 *rev*. Island with high wall and rock

352 *obv*. Cardinal Cristoforo Madruzzo

352 *rev*. Figure beside a river

351 *obv*. Franco Lercari

351 *rev*. Figure carrying cornucopiae

353 *obv*.
Cardinal Cristoforo Madruzzo

353 *rev*.
Neptune on a dolphin, before a harbour

354 *obv*. Tommaso Marini, Duke of Terranuova

354 *rev*. Sun shining on sea

355 Jacopo de' Medici, Marquess of Marignan

356 *obv*. Cassandra Marinoni, wife of Deifobo II Melilupi

356 *rev*. Circular temple with city in background

359 *obv*. Chiara Taverna

360 *obv*. Francesco Taverna, Milanese jurisconsult

360a *obv*. Gianfrancesco Trivulzio, Marquess of Vigevano

359 *rev*. Cybele in car drawn by lions

360 *rev*. Hound looking at constellation of the Goat

360a *rev*. Fortune on a dolphin

PIER PAOLO GALEOTTI

357 *obv*. Giampaolo Melilupi, son of Deifobo II

357 *rev*. Child addressing Deifobo II

358 *obv*. Elisabetta Scotti, wife of Giov. Alvise Gonfalonieri

358 *rev*. Type obliterated

361 *obv*. Pietro Vettori the Younger

361 *rev*. Olive-branch

362 *obv*. Pietro Vettori the Younger, Florentine scholar

362 *rev*. Minerva holding olive-branch and spear

363 *obv*. Vincenzo Gonzaga, fourth Duke of Mantua

363 *rev*. St. George and the Dragon

365 *obv*. Pope Clement VII

365 *rev*. Joseph revealing himself to his brethren

366 *obv*. Pope Paul III

366 *rev*. Ganymede watering the Farnese lilies

367 *obv*. Emanuele Filiberto, tenth Duke of Savoy

367 *rev*. Marguerite de France

368 *obv*. Dido, Queen of Carthage

368 *rev*. Carthage with galleys in harbour

369 *obv*. Priam, King of Troy

369 *rev*. Troy with galleys in harbour

GALEOTTI (357–358) · ROMANELLI (361–362) · MOLA (363) · BERNARDI (365) · CESATI (366–369)

369a Pope Julius III

370a Pope Pius IV

370 *obv.* Pope Marcellus II

370 *rev.* The Church reading the Gospels

371 *obv.* Vincenzo Bovio of Bologna

371 *rev.* Religion and an ox

372 *obv*. Pope Pius IV

372 *rev*. The Porta Pia

373 *obv*. Pope Pius V

373 *rev*. Battle of Lepanto

374 *obv*. Ippolito II d'Este

374 *rev*. Incuse of obverse

375 *obv*. Pierluigi Farnese, Duke of Parma and Piacenza

375 *rev*. Citadel of Parma

376 *obv*. Jean Parisot de la Vallette

378 *obv*. Pope Sixtus V

378 *rev*. Securitas near altar

376 *rev*. David and Goliath

377 *obv*. Prospero Publicola Santacroce

379 *obv*. Pope Leo X

379 *rev*. Liberality

377 *rev*. Villa at Gericomio

GIAN FEDERIGO BONZAGNI (372–375) · FEDERIGO COC... (376–377) · LORENZO FRAGNI (378)
GIOVANNI PALADINO (379)

380 Pope Clement VII

381 *obv*. Pope Paul III

381 *rev*. Griffin and serpent fighting

385 *obv*. Andrea Briosco, Paduan bronze sculptor

382 Pope Paul III

385 *rev*. Broken laurel tree with leafy branch

386 *obv*. Cardinal Pietro Bembo

387 *obv*. Helen of Troy

387 *rev*. Concord holding cornucopiae

388 *obv*. Alfonso II d'Avalos, Marquess of Vasto

386 *rev*. Bembo beside a stream

389 *obv*. Alessandro Bassiano and Giovanni dal Cavino

389 *rev*. Genius, sacrificing

388 *rev*. Man with arms, and Africa mourning

390 *obv*.
Giampietro Mantova Benavides

390 *rev*.
Temple with goddess

391 *obv*.
Girolamo Cornaro

391 *rev*.
Cornaro distributing alms

392 *obv*.
Giovanni Antonio Vincenzo Dolce

392 *rev*.
Genius holding dolphin, sacrificing

393 *obv*.
Giovanni Mels, jurist

393 *rev*.
Mels as Genius, sacrificing

394 *obv*. Balduino del Monte,
brother of Pope Julius III

394 *rev*.
Combat between two horsemen

395 *obv*.
Girolamo and Pompeo Ludovisi

395 *rev*.
Genius holding dolphin, sacrificing

396 *obv*. Francesco Quirini,
Venetian patrician

396 *rev*. Wolf and Twins

397 *obv*. Luca Salvioni

397 *rev*. Ceres
with book and cornucopiae

398 *obv*. Cosimo Scapti

398 *rev*. Salus and serpent

399 *obv*. Homer

399 *rev*.
Armed man with other figures

GIOVANNI DAL CAVINO

400 *obv*. Chariot on pedestal

400 *rev*. Head of Arethusa

401 *obv*. Agrippina Senior

401 *rev*. Funeral car

402 *obv*. Antonia,
daughter of M. Anthony

402 *rev*.
Claudius Caesar

403 *obv*.
Emperor Nero

403 *rev*.
Ceres and Annona

404 *obv*.
Sabina, wife of Hadrian

404 *rev*. Ceres holding
ears of corn and torch

406 *obv*.
Emperor Antoninus Pius

406 *rev*.
Roma, the Emperor and Victory

405 *bis obv*.
Antinous, favourite of Hadrian

405 *obv*. Antinous,
favourite of Hadrian

405 *rev*.
Mercury taming Pegasus

405 *bis rev*.
Mercury taming Pegasus

407 *obv*. Faustina,
wife of Marcus Aurelius

407 *rev*. Empress and five
women sacrificing

408 *obv*.
Emperor Lucius Verus

408 *rev*.
Roma, the Emperor and Victory

GIOVANNI DAL CAVINO

409 *obv*.
Emperor Commodus

409 *rev*.
Salus feeding serpent

410 *obv*.
Emperor Septimius Severus

410 *rev*. Mars resting
on spear and shield

412 *obv*. Sigismund Augustus, King of Poland

412 *rev*. Lion

411 *obv*.
Head of Hercules

411 *rev*. A messenger brings
Hercules the shirt of Nessus

413 *obv*. Andrea Gritti,
Doge of Venice

413 *rev*. Church of
S. Francesco della Vigna

414 *obv*. Antonio Mula,
Duke of Crete

414 *rev*. Mula and
another man joining hands

415 *obv*. Girolamo Zane,
Venetian Senator

415 *rev*.
St. Jerome in landscape

GIOVANNI DAL CAVINO (409–10) · MONOGRAMMIST H B (411) · GIOVANNI MARIA MOSCA (412)
ANDREA SPINELLI (413–15)

416 *obv*. Doge Pietro Lando and senators before Christ

416 *rev*. Venice crowned holding cornucopiae and scales, galley and arms

416a *obv*. Eternity veiled holding globe with phoenix on pyre

416a *rev*. Fame seated on celestial globe, blowing trumpets

417 *obv*. Pietro Lauro, poet and scholar

417b *obv*. Tommaso Rangone of Ravenna

417a *obv*. Tommaso Rangone of Ravenna

417 *rev*. Inscription within a wreath

417b *rev*. Jupiter as eagle brings infant Hercules to Juno

417a *rev*. Female figure places wreath on ox's horns

419 *obv*. Elisabetta Quirini, daughter of Francesco Quirini

419a *obv*. Giovanni de' Medici delle Bande Nere, father of Cosimo I

419 *rev*. The three Graces

419a *rev*. Thunderbolt issuing from a cloud

ANDREA SPINELLI (416, 416a) · I.A.V.F. (417) · JACOPO TATTI, called SANSOVINO (417a, b)
DANESE CATTANEO (419, 419a)

420 Gaspare Borgia, Bishop of Segorbe

420a *obv*. Tommaso Rangone of Ravenna

420a *rev*. Apollo placing wreath on lion

421 Caterina Sandella, wife of Pietro Aretino

423 *obv*. Pietro Piantanida of Milan

424 *obv*. Cardinal Jean de Lorraine

425 *obv*. Gianfrancesco Martinioni, Milanese physician

423 *rev*. Faith pointing to heaven

424 *rev*. Prudence with a dragon at her feet

425 *rev*. Hippocrates (?)

428 *obv*. Baccio Bandinelli, Florentine sculptor

426 *obv*. Emperor Charles V

428 *rev*. Inscription within laurel-wreath

426 *rev*. Jupiter thundering against the Giants

ALESSANDRO VITTORIA (420, 420a, 421) · MILANESE SCHOOL (423–425) · LEONE LEONI (426, 428)

429 *obv*. Michelangelo Buonarroti

431 *obv*. Andrea Doria, Genoese admiral

430 *obv*. Andrea Doria, Genoese admiral

429 *rev*. Blind man with staff and water-flask, led by dog

430 *rev*. Self-portrait of Leone Leoni

434 *obv*. Pope Paul III

431 *rev*.
Galley and small boat

432 Ippolita di Ferdinando Gonzaga

434 *rev*. Roma with Wolf and Twins, above River Tiber

436 Philippina Welser, wife of Archduke Ferdinand

436a *obv*. Girolamo Cardano of Pavia, physicist and philospher

436a *rev*. Vision of people approaching a vine

438 *obv*. Ippolita di Ferdinando Gonzaga

438 *rev*. Aurora riding through the heavens

439 *obv*. Isabella Capua, Princess of Malfetto

439 *rev*. Isabella at burning altar

440 *obv*. Juan de Herrera, architect of the Escorial

437 Philip II, King of Spain

440 *rev*. Architecture holding compasses and square

JACOPO NIZOLLA DA TREZZO

441a *obv*. Gianello della Torre of Cremona

441a *rev*. Fountain of the Sciences

441 *obv*. Ascanio Padula

442 *obv*. Fernando Francesco II d'Avalos

443 *obv*. Giov. Paolo Lomazzo, painter and writer

441 *rev*. Apollo holding bow and lyre

443 *rev*. Lomazzo presented by Mercury to Fortune

442 *rev*. Fernando as Hercules plucking the apples of the Hesperides

JACOPO NIZOLLA DA TREZZO (441, 441a) · ANNIBALE FONTANA (442–443)

445 *obv*. Gonsalvo de Córdoba, the Great Captain

444 *obv*. Giambattista Castaldi, Count of Piadena

445 *rev*. Battle under city walls

444 *rev*. Castaldi in armour and other figures

446 *obv*. Ercole II d'Este, fourth Duke of Ferrara

446 *rev*. Figure chained to a rock

449 Unknown lady

448 Self-portrait of Ruspagiari

450 Unknown lady

447 Camilla Ruggieri

452 Gabriele Lippi of Reggio d'Emilia

451 Costanza Bocchi

453 Giulia Pratonieri of Reggio d'Emilia

454 Leonora, wife of the artist

455 Isabella Mariani,
wife of Gianfrancesco Carcass…

459 Violante, wife of Giambattista Pigna

460 Unknown lady

ALFONSO RUSPAGIARI (447) · GIAN ANTONIO SIGNORETTI (451–453)
BOMBARDA (454–455, 459–460)

456 Anna Maurella Oldofredi d'Iseo

457 *rev.* The Judgement of Paris

457 *obv.* Anna Maurella Oldofredi d'Iseo

458 Anna Maurella Oldofredi d'Iseo

461 Unknown lady

463 Unknown lady

462 Unknown lady

467 Caterina Riva holding lap-dog

BOMBARDA (456–458) · EMILIAN SCHOOL (461–463) · ANTONIO ABONDIO (467)

464 *obv*. Emperor Maximilian II

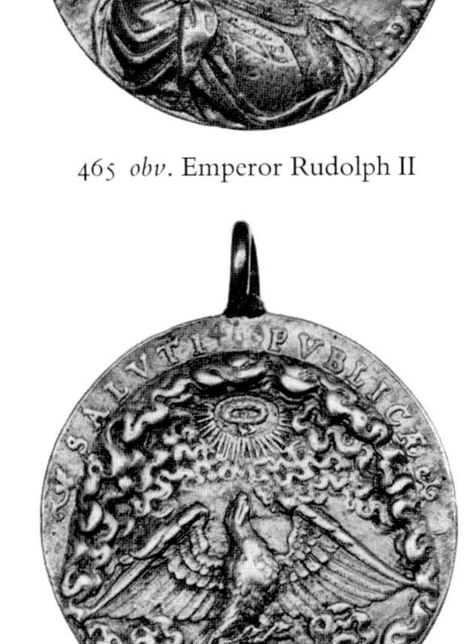

465 *obv*. Emperor Rudolph II

465 *rev*. Eagle and radiant wreath

464 *rev*. Empress Maria

466 *obv*. Johann Baron von Khevenhüller

466 *rev*. Minerva, Hercules, and Vice

469a *obv*. Faustina Romana (?)

468 *obv*. Jacopo Antonio Sorra

468 *rev*. Sorra shooting at a mark

469a *rev*. Leda and the swan

469 *obv*. Sebastian Zäh

469 *rev*. Susanna Schlecht

ANTONIO ABONDIO

470 *obv*. Altobello Averoldo, Bishop of Pola

470 *rev*. A prince receiving man with bridle

471 *obv*. Guido Rangoni,
Lord of Spilimberto

471 *rev*. Angel adorning a female figure
riding on bull

472 Argentina Pallavicini, poetess and botanist

473 *obv*. Giulia Orsini,
wife of Baldassare Rangoni

473 *rev*. Vase in a landscape

474 *obv*. Benedetto
Lomellini of Genoa

474 *rev*. Gentleness
standing on serpent

ANTONIO VICENTINO (470–472) · IAC. URB. (473) · T.R. (474)

477 *obv.* Lavinia Fontana, Bolognese painter

475 Giovanni Pico della Mirandola

477 *rev.* Lavinia Fontana painting

476 *obv.* Dionisio Ratta of Bologna

480 Ercole Teodoro Trivulzio

476 *rev.* Inscription

478 *obv.* Aulus Caecina Alienus

479 Paula Carlina and a Cupid

478 *rev.* Inscription

T.R. (475) · FELICE ANTONIO CASONI (476–477) · CAMILLO MARIANI (478)
MONOGRAMMIST A. G. (479) · M. A. S. (480)

482 Cardinal Francesco Maria Brancacci

483 Giovanna d'Austria, first wife of Francesco I de' Medici

481 Francesco Morosini, Venetian admiral

484 *obv*. Maria of Aragon, wife of Alfonso II d'Avalos

484 *rev*. Assembly of the Gods

484b *obv*. Cardinal Pietro Bembo

484a *obv*. Pietro Aretino, the satirist

484a *rev*. Truth crowned by Victory

484b *rev*. Pegasus on the fountain Hippocrene

ORMANO (481–482) · ANTON FRANCESCO SELVI (483) · UNATTRIBUTED, XVI Century (484, 484a, 484b)

484c Emperor Charles V

492 Mathias Corvinus, King of Hungary

485 Vittoria Colonna

486 *obv*. Lucia Bertani, Bolognese poetess

486 *rev*. The three Graces

497 Giulia Orsini

499 *obv*. Beatrice Roverella, wife of Ercole Rangoni

499 *rev*. Three-masted ship, without sails, in stormy sea

UNATTRIBUTED ITALIAN MEDALS OF THE XVI CENTURY

495 *obv*. Cornelio Musso, Bishop of Bitonto

495 *rev*. Unicorn in landscape

493 *obv*. Lorenzino de'Medici, son of Pierfrancesco II

495 *bis* Giovanni de Nores, Count of Tripoli

493 *rev*. Cap of Liberty between daggers

496 *obv*. Enrico Orsini

496 *rev*. Bees round a hive

498 *obv*. Girolamo Priuli, Doge of Venice

498 *rev*. Alvise Diedo

UNATTRIBUTED ITALIAN MEDALS OF THE XVI CENTURY

504 *obv*. Marcantonio Trevisan, Doge of Venice

504 *rev*. Inscription in wreath

506 *obv*. Laura Gonzaga Trivulzio

506 *rev*. River-god Mincio

507 *obv*.
Cardinal Andrea della Valle

507 *rev*.
Faith pointing to heaven

507 *bis obv*. Pierio Valeriano Bolzanio, scholar

507 *bis rev*. Mercury and broken obelisk

508 *obv*. Don Nicola Vicentino

509 *obv*. Calidonia Visconti

509 *rev*. Eagle looking at sun

508 *rev*. Organ and cymbalum

UNATTRIBUTED ITALIAN MEDALS OF THE XVI CENTURY

510 *obv*. Carlo Visconti

510 *rev*. Stalk of branching coral

512 Unknown lady

511 Unknown lady

514 Unknown lady

515 A Turk

513 Unknown lady

UNATTRIBUTED ITALIAN MEDALS OF THE XVI CENTURY

516 *obv.* Antinous

516 *rev.* Antinous on a griffin

518 Enrico Ambanelli

519 *obv.* Caterina Capalla

519 *rev.* Branch of coral

521 *obv.* Elvira, daughter of Gonsalvo de Côrdoba

520 *obv.* Filippo Casoli

521 *rev.* Time carrying scythe

520 *rev.* Man walking on town walls

UNATTRIBUTED ITALIAN MEDALS OF THE XVI CENTURY (516)
MISCELLANEOUS FICTITIOUS PORTRAITS (518–521)

524 *obv*. Emperor Constantine the Great

524 *rev*. The Church and Paganism beside the Fountain of Life

525 *obv*. Emperor Heraclius I

525 *rev*. The Emperor in a car drawn by three horses

526 *obv*. Charles VIII

526 *rev*. Anne de Bretagne

PARISIAN SCHOOL (524–525) · LOUIS LEPÈRE, NICOLAS DE FLORENCE, JEAN LEPÈRE (526)

527 *obv*. Louis XII, King of France

527 *rev*. Anne de Bretagne, Queen of France

NICOLAS LECLERC and JEAN DE SAINT-PRIEST

528 *obv*. Philibert II Le Beau, Duke of Savoy, and Margaret of Austria

529 Louis XII, King of France

530 Jean de Talaru, Canon of Fourrière

528 *rev*. Arms of Philibert impaling those of Margaret

531 *obv*. Jacques de Vitry-La Lière, Canon of Lyon

532 *obv*. Antonio Gonzalo de Toledo

531 *rev*. Putto holding arms of Vitry

532 *rev*. Woman sitting on saddle

JEAN MARENDE (528) · UNIDENTIFIED FRENCH (529) · MEDALLIST OF 1518 (530–532)

534 *obv*. Tommaso Guadagni, Florentine consul at Lyon

534 *rev*. Arms of Guadagni

533 *obv*. Bartolommeo Panciatichi

533 *rev*. Arms of Panciatichi

537 *obv*. Francis I, King of France

537 *rev*. Unicorn before a high rock

535 Francis I, King of France

538 Francis, Dauphin, son of Francis I

539 *obv*. Antoine, Duc de Lorraine

539 *rev*. Renée de Bourbon, wife of Antoine

JACQUES GAUVIN (533) · MATTEO DAL NASSARO (535) · UNATTRIBUTED FRENCH (537–539)

542 *obv*. Henry II, King of France

540 *obv*. Unknown man

540 *rev*. Unknown woman

541 *obv*. Henry II of France

541 *rev*. Victory

542 *rev*. Fame, Abundance, and Victory

546 Francis I, Henry II, and Francis II of France

545 *obv*. Henry II of France

545 *rev*. Perseus rescuing Andromeda

544 Simon Costière of Lyon

547 Catherine de Médicis, wife of Henry II

548 Isabelle de Valois, wife of Philip II of Spain

REGNAULT DANET (540) · ÉTIENNE DE LAUNE (541–542) · PIERRE II WOEIROT DE BOUZET (544)
UNIDENTIFIED FRENCH (545–548)

550 *obv*. Charles III de Lorraine, Duc de Guise

549 'Charles IX', King of France

551 *obv*. Diane de Poitiers, Duchess of Valentinois

550 *rev*. A man ploughing

551 *rev*. Diane trampling on Cupid

554 Jean Viret, scholar and mathematician

553 *obv*. Anne de Montmorency, Constable of France

553 *rev*. Prudence, Courage and Fortune

552 *obv*. Michel de l'Hôpital, Chancellor of France

555 *obv*. Louis XIII, King of France

555 *rev*. Hand holding sacred ampulla over Rheims

552 *rev*. Lightning striking a tower in the sea

UNIDENTIFIED FRENCH MEDALLISTS (549–554) · NICOLAS BRIOT (555)

556 *obv*. Henry IV and Marie de Médicis

556 *rev*. Louis XIII as Dauphin between Henry IV as Mars and Marie as Pallas

557 *obv*. Jean-Louis de Nogaret de Lavalette

557 *rev*. Lion and Fury with torches

558 Henry IV, King of France

559 *obv*. Louis XIII, King of France

559 *rev*. Young Louis, and Minerva

560 *obv*. Henri de Bourbon, Prince de Condé

560 *rev*. Charlotte-Marie de Montmorency, wife of Henri

GUILLAUME DUPRÉ (556–560)

561 Francesco IV Gonzaga, Duke of Mantua

562 Maria Magdalena, Grand-Duchess of Tuscany

J. B. KELLER after GUILLAUME DUPRÉ (561) · GUILLAUME DUPRÉ (562)

564 Pierre Jeannin, Councillor of the King

563 *obv*. Nicolas Brulart de Sillery

563 *rev*. Apollo driving the Sun's car

GUILLAUME DUPRÉ

565 *obv*. Louis XIII, King of France

566 *obv*. Louis XIII, King of France

567 *obv*. Marie de Médicis, Queen of France

565 *rev*. Anne d'Autriche

566 *rev*. Justice with sword and scales

567 *rev*. The Queen as Mother of the Gods

569 *obv*. Antoine Ruzé, Marquis d'Effiat et de Longjumeau

569 *rev*. Hercules helping Atlas to bear the globe

571 Christine de France, Duchess of Savoy

GUILLAUME DUPRÉ

568 Marie de Médicis, Queen of France

570 *obv.* Jean de Caylar de Saint-Bonnet

570 *rev.* Radiant sun over landscape

572 *obv.* Jacques Boiceau, Seigneur de la Barauderie

572 *rev.* Landscape with caterpillars and butterflies

GUILLAUME DUPRÉ (568, 570) · ABRAHAM DUPRÉ (572)

573 *obv*. Pomponne de Bellièvre, Chancellor of France

573 *rev*. Justice and Piety at an altar

574 *obv*. Nicolas de Langes

574 *rev*. Apollo, and coins of Augustus

575 *obv*. Anne d'Autriche

575 *rev*. Stars and clouds encircling crown

576 *obv*. Cardinal de Richelieu

576 *rev*. The globe and the planets

575a *obv*. Armand-Jean Duplessis, Cardinal de Richelieu

575a *rev*. Fortune chained to chariot carrying Fame and France

NICOLAS GABRIEL JACQUET (573) · PHILIPPE LALIAME (574)
JEAN DARMAND CALLED LORFELIN (575) · JEAN VARIN (575a, 576)

577 *obv*. Nicolas de Bailleul

577 *rev*. Nymph of the Seine

578 *obv*. Noël Brulart de Sillery

579 Joachim de Châteauvieux

578 *rev*. Achievement of Brulart

580 *obv*. Antoine de Lomenie

580 *rev*. Sun driving along the zodiac

581 *obv*. Jean de Saulx, Vicomte de Tavanes et de Lugny

581 *rev*. Rampant lion on a chain

UNIDENTIFIED FRENCH MEDALLISTS

583 *obv*. Emperor Charles V

583 *rev*. Coats of arms around double-headed eagle

585 *obv*. Melchior Pfinzing

584 Kunz von der Rosen, Councillor of Maximilian I

586 Self-portrait of Bruchsal

585 *rev*. Inscription in wreath

587 *obv*. Ambrosius Jung, physician

587 *rev*. Coat of arms

ALBRECHT DÜRER (583) · HANS SCHWARZ (584–585) · ALEXANDER VON BRUCHSAL (586)
CHRISTOPH WEIDITZ (587)

588 *obv*. Francisco Covo, Chancellor of Charles V

588 *rev*. Man riding towards a cliff, carrying scroll

588b Augustin Lösch, Chancellor of Bavaria

588a *obv*. Caspar Winntzrer

588a *rev*. Inscription

590a Margaret von Firmian, wife of Caspar von Frundsberg

590 Giovanni Alessandro Balbiani of Chiavenna

591 Unknown man

CHRISTOPH WEIDITZ (588) · FRIEDRICH HAGENAUER (588a, 588b, 590, 590a, 591)

589 *obv*. Sebastian Liegsalz

589 *rev*. Ursula Liegsalz

FRIEDRICH HAGENAUER

592 *obv*. Johannes Mulicum

592 *rev*. Inscription

593 *obv*. Philipp Melanchthon

593 *rev*. Inscription

594 *obv*. Philipp Melanchthon

594 *rev*. Inscription

595 *obv*. Kaspar von Mühlheim

595 *rev*. Shield with house-mark

596 *obv*. Hans Hauschel

596 *rev*. Inscription

596a *obv*. Barbara Reihingin, wife of Georg Hermann

596a *rev*. Coat of Arms

596b *obv*. Christoph Kress von Kressenstein

596b *rev*. A blazon of arms

596c *obv*. Frederick, Archduke of Brandenburg-Ansbach

596c *rev*. A blazon of arms

FRIEDRICH HAGENAUER (592–596) · HANS KELS THE YOUNGER (596a)
MATHES GEBEL (596b, 596c)

597 *obv*. Philipp, Count Palatine

597 *rev*. Shield with casques and crests

597a *obv*. Hieronymus Holzschuher

597a *rev*. Shield of arms, crest and mantling

597b *obv*. Georg Hermann

597b *rev*. Shields and helm

599 *obv*. Charles V

599 *rev*. Inscription in wreath

599a *obv*. Raimond Fugger, scholar

599a *rev*. Allegory of Liberality

599b *obv*. Lorenz Truchses von Pomersfelden

599b *rev*. Hour-glass on inscribed tablet

599c *obv*. Johann Friedrich, Elector of Saxony

599c *rev*. Blazon of arms

599d *obv*. Lorenz Staiber

599d *rev*. Frau Staiber

600 *obv*. Ludwig X, Duke of Bavaria-Landshut

600 *rev*. Shield with casques and crests

601 *obv*. Wilhelm Löffelholz von Kolberg

601 *rev*. Shield, cuirass, casque, and crest

MATHES GEBEL

598 Marx Rechlinger

603 *obv*. Wenzeslaus Beyer, physician

603 *rev*. Book, skull and bones, rider in landscape

604 *obv*. Charles V

604 *rev*. Double-headed crowned eagle on pillars of Hercules

604a *obv*. Francis I, King of France

604a *rev*. Salamander in flames

602 Emilia, Margravine of Brandenburg

605 *obv*. Johann Friedrich, Elector of Saxony

605 *rev*. Shield with helms and crests

606 *obv*. Charles V

606 *rev*. Double-headed eagle, charged with shield

MATHES GEBEL (598) · MASTER OF THE PISTORIUS MEDAL (602) · M. P. (603)
LUDWIG NEUFAHRER (604, 604a) · HANS REINHART THE ELDER (605–606)

607 *obv*. Johann Fichard

607 *rev*. Elisabeth Fichard

609 *obv*. Margarethe Balbus, née Ganzhorn

609 *rev*. Two shields

608 *obv*. Hieronymus Paumgartner of Nuremberg

608 *rev*. Arms of Paumgartner

610 *obv*. Anna Hofmann

610 *rev*. Venus and cupids

611 Jakob Muffel of Nuremberg

612 *obv*. Matthäus Schyrer

612 *rev*. Fortune with veil

613 Jakob Fugger the Elder

614 *obv*. Hans Schel

615a *obv*. Luna

615a *rev*. Diana

614 *rev*. Arms and inscriptions

615 Julius Geuder, Nuremberg patrician

HANS BOLSTERER (607) · JOACHIM DESCHLER (608–609) · JAKOB HOFMANN (610)
VALENTIN MALER (611–613) · MATTHÄUS CARL (614) · JOHANN PHILIPP VON DER PÜTT (615)
CONCZ WELCZ (615a)

616 *obv.*
Maximilian I as Archduke

617 *obv.*
John Huss Centenary

618 *obv.*
Friedrich the Wise of Saxony

620 *obv.*
Ludwig II of Hungary

616 *rev.* Maria of Burgundy

617 *rev.* Huss at the stake

618 *rev.* Cross within a circle

620 *rev.* Maria, wife of Ludwig II

621 *obv.* Ferdinand I,
Archduke of Austria

619 *obv.* Ferdinand I, Archduke of Austria

623 Willibald Pirkheimer
and Albrecht Dürer

621 *rev.* Eagle displayed,
charged with shield

619 *rev.* Anna, wife of Ferdinand I

624 Emperor Frederick III

MEDALS OF THE XVI CENTURY BY GERMAN OR AUSTRIAN MASTERS (616–621)
GEORG HOLDERMANN (623) · GEORG SCHWEIGGER (624)

626 Sigmund Gabriel Holtzschuher

627 *obv*. Christoph Fürer von Haimendorf, Nuremberg patrician

627 *rev*. Shields of Fürer and his two wives

625 Maximilian I

629 Pope Adrian VI

629a Desiderius Erasmus

GEORG SCHWEIGGER (625) · JOHANN BARTHOLOMÄUS BRAUN (626–627)
UNIDENTIFIED MEDALLIST OF THE LOW COUNTRIES (629) · QUENTIN MASSYS (629a)

630 *obv*. Frédéric Perrenot, Sieur de Champagney

630 *rev*. Ship, and putto holding scales

632 Viglius van Zuichem

633 *obv*. Viglius van Zuichem

631 Antoine Perrenot, Cardinal Granvelle

633 *rev*. Candle, hour-glass and book on table

635 *obv*. Antoine Perrenot, Cardinal Granvelle

634 *obv*. Viglius van Zuichem

634 *rev*. Table

636 *obv*. Sigismund Augustus, King of Poland

635 *rev*. Ship at sea

637 Antonis Mor, the painter

636 *rev*. The King on horseback

JACOB ZAGAR (630) · JACOB JONGHELINCK (631–634) · GIOVANNI V. MELON (635) STEVEN VAN HERWIJCK (636–637)

638 *obv*. William I of Orange

638 *rev*. Charlotte de Bourbon

639 *obv*.
Fernando Alvarez de Toledo,
Duke of Alba

639 *rev*.
Pallas in car
drawn by two owls

640 *obv*. Sir Richard Shelley,
Prior of the Knights of Malta

640 *rev*. Griffin, ducally gorged,
in a landscape

COINS

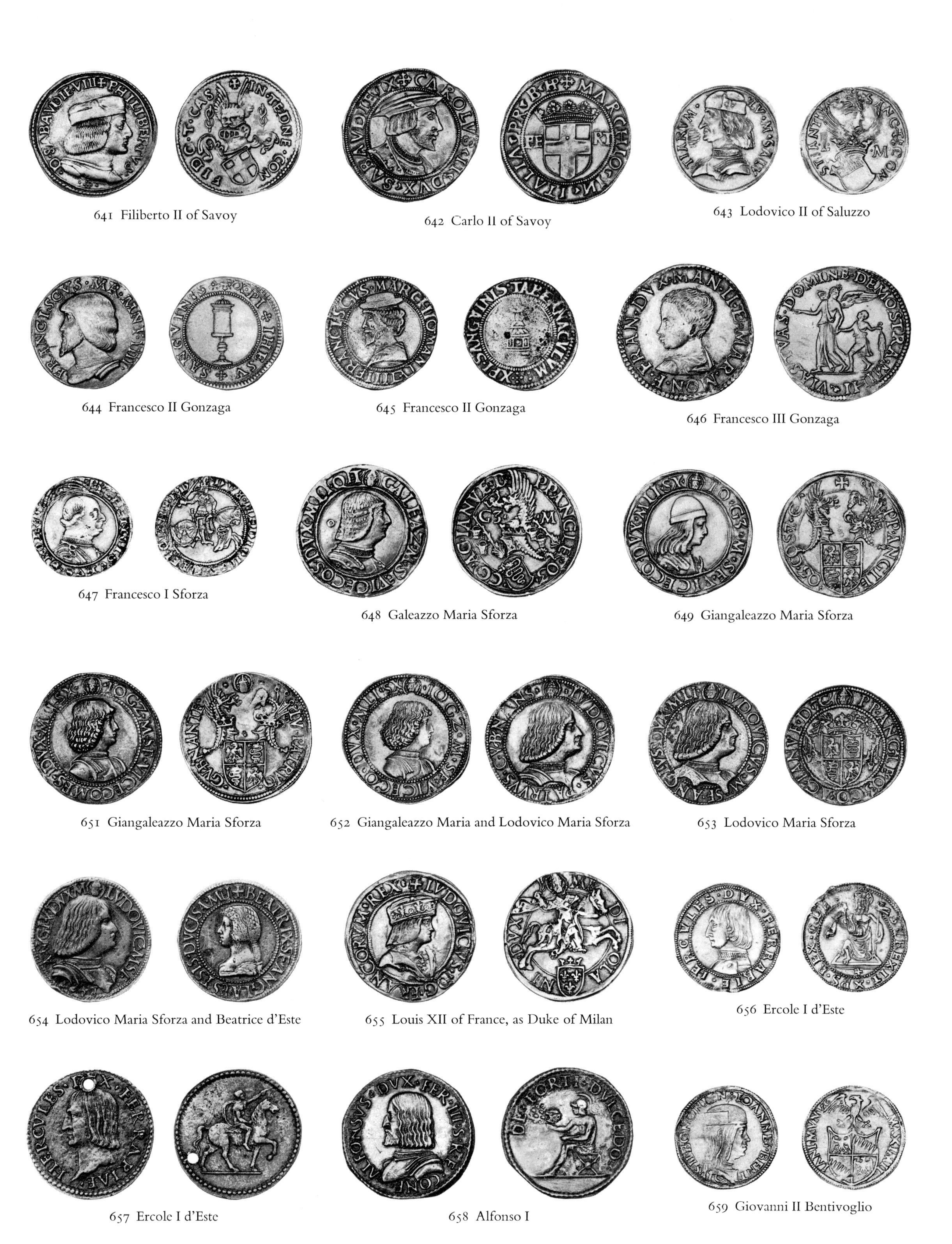

641 Filiberto II of Savoy

642 Carlo II of Savoy

643 Lodovico II of Saluzzo

644 Francesco II Gonzaga

645 Francesco II Gonzaga

646 Francesco III Gonzaga

647 Francesco I Sforza

648 Galeazzo Maria Sforza

649 Giangaleazzo Maria Sforza

651 Giangaleazzo Maria Sforza

652 Giangaleazzo Maria and Lodovico Maria Sforza

653 Lodovico Maria Sforza

654 Lodovico Maria Sforza and Beatrice d'Este

655 Louis XII of France, as Duke of Milan

656 Ercole I d'Este

657 Ercole I d'Este

658 Alfonso I

659 Giovanni II Bentivoglio

COINS OF THE MINTS OF SAVOY (641–642) · CARMAGNOLA (643) · MANTUA (644–646)
MILAN (647–655) · FERRARA (656–658) · BOLOGNA (659)

660 Pope Julius II

661 Pope Leo X

662 Giovanni Sforza

663 Alessandro I de' Medici

664 Pope Sixtus IV

665 Ferdinando I

666 Duke Antoine

667 Ferdinand and Isabella

COINS OF THE MINTS OF BOLOGNA (660–661) · PESARO (662) · FLORENCE (663) · ROME (664)
NAPLES (665) · LORRAINE (666) · SPAIN (667)

APPENDIX

21 *obv*. Pisanello: King Alfonso V of Aragon. Late cast

21 *rev*. Pisanello: An angel in a car drawn by horses. Late cast.

41 *obv*. Este Medal: Alfonso I d'Este. Late cast

41 *rev*. Este Medal: Alfonso as infant Hercules. Late cast

77 *obv*. Giancristoforo Romano: Isabella of Aragon. Late cast

77 *rev*. Giancristoforo Romano: Figure before a palm-tree. Late cast

81 *obv*. In the neighbourhood of Giancristoforo Romano: Maddalena Rossi. Late cast

81 *rev*. Captive Love. Late cast

122 *obv*. Sperandio: Parupus. Late cast

122 *rev*. Sperandio: Unicorn-pegasus. Late cast

121 *obv*. Sperandio: Pellegrino Prisciano of Ferrara. Late cast

121 *rev*. Sperandio: Man standing on an eagle. Late cast

129 *obv*. Sperandio: Guido Pepoli. Late cast

129 *rev*. Sperandio: King Evilmerodach playing chess. Late cast

130 *obv*. Sperandio: Camilla Sforza. Late cast

130 *rev*. Sperandio: Female figure and serpent. Late cast

132 *obv*. Sperandio: Agostino Barbadigo, Doge of Venice. Late cast

132 *rev*. Sperandio: Doge Barbadigo kneeling before the winged lion. Late cast

133 *obv*. Sperandio: Lodovico Brognolo. Late cast

133 *rev*. Sperandio: Two forearms joined in prayer. Late cast

APPENDIX

134 *obv*. Sperandio: Antonio Vinciguerra. Late cast

134 *rev*. Sperandio: Apollo on a car drawn by swans. Late cast

137 *obv*.
Antonello della Moneta:
Cristoforo Moro,
Doge of Venice. Late cast

137 *rev*.
Antonello della Moneta:
Venetia. Late cast

200 Savoy, early XVI century:
Filippo, Count of Genevois. Late cast

205 *bis obv*.
Medallist of the Roman Emperors:
Marcus Croto. Reworked

257 Niccolò Fiorentino: Lorenzo dei Medici, il Magnifico.
Late casting

274 *obv*.
In the manner of Niccolò Fiorentino:
Giovanni Paolo Orsini. Recent cast

274 *rev*.
In the manner of Niccolò Fiorentino:
Orsini on horseback. Recent cast

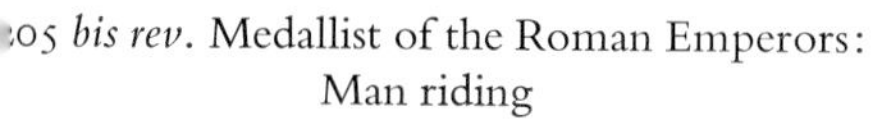

205 *bis rev*. Medallist of the Roman Emperors:
Man riding

275 *obv*. In the manner of Niccolò Fiorentino: Giuliano Particini. Late cast

293 In the manner of Niccolò Fiorentino: Francesco Lancilotti. Late, rough cast

283 *obv*. In the manner of Niccolò Fiorentino: Caterina Sforza-Riario. Late cast

275 *rev*. In the manner of Niccolò Fiorentino: Hope gazing at the sun. Late cast

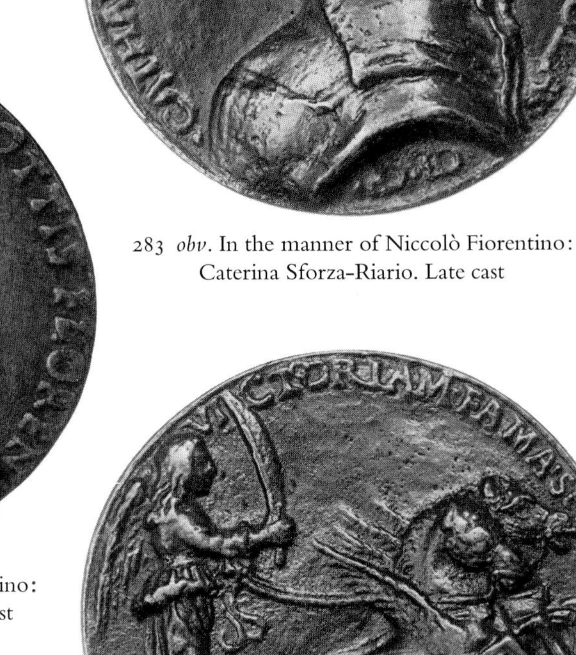

283 *rev*. In the manner of Niccolò Fiorentino: Victory in a car drawn by horses. Late cast

338 *obv*. Giampaolo Poggini: King Philip II. Electrotype

297 *obv*. In the manner of Niccolò Fiorentino: Lodovica Tornabuoni. Late cast

338 *rev*. Giampaolo Poggini: Hercules bearing the globe. Electrotype

297 *rev*. In the manner of Niccolò Fiorentino: Unicorn before a tree. Late cast

385a Valerio Belli: Self-portrait. Lead reproduction

433 *obv*. Attributed to Leone Leoni: Ippolita di Ferdinando Gonzaga. Late cast

433 *rev*. Attributed to Leone Leoni: Ippolita looking at a crown of stars. Late cast

522 *obv*. Unattributed Italian: Euclid

522 *rev*. Unattributed Italian: Inscription

523 Unattributed Italian: Niccolò Gander

503 *obv*. Unattributed Italian: Marguerite de France. Late cast

543 Jacopo Primavera: Mary Stuart, Queen of Scots. Lead reproduction

582 Jean-Baptiste Nini: Albertine de Nivenheim, 1768

628 W. Sommer (Pseudo-Dürer, working 1880–1900): Sebald Schreier

APPENDIX

CONCORDANCES

INDEX OF INSCRIPTIONS

GENERAL INDEX

INDEX OF PERSONS

INDEX OF ARTISTS

CONCORDANCE WITH ARMAND

Vol. I page	Vol. I no.	Kress no.
2	I	22
3	4	6
3	8	10, 11
4	10	9
4	11	2
5	12	17
5	13	16
5	14	13, 14
5	15	12
6	16	15
6	17	19
7	19	21 (Appendix)
7	20	1
7	21	4
8	22	5
8	23	3
8	24	18
9	25	32
9	26	30
10	30	29
10	32	247
11	33	251
16	2	28
17	1	56
18	2	55
18	3	57
20	9	61
20	13	67
20	15	58
21	17	66
21	19	63
21	20	59
22	23	64
22	24	65
25	—	136
26	2	23
28	1	31
31	1	210
31	2	211
33	—	35
33	1	36
34	86	138
35	4	135
36	1	142
36	2	141
37	4	143
37	5	139
37	6	140
41	3	27
41	4	24, 25
42	6	26
43	1	94
44	6	92
44	7	93
45	9	97
45	10	95
45	11	96
46	2	137 (Appendix)
47	—	100
47	3	172
49	5	207
49	7	208
50	10	209
50	11	214
51	12	276
53	1	38
59	1	252
59	2	253
60	5	258
61	1	201
62	1	71 *bis*
62	5	72
64	3	119
64	4	125
65	6	128
65	10	133 (Appendix)
66	13	114
67	16	115*a*
67	17	126
68	19	117
68	21	116
69	23	131
71	31	122 (Appendix)
71	32	112
72	34	129 (Appendix)
72	35	121 (Appendix)
73	40	127
74	41	113
74	42	115
74	43	130 (Appendix)
75	46	132 (Appendix)
76	1	248
76	47	134 (Appendix)
78	—	144
79	2	102
80	2	68
80	4	69
81	1	71
81	2	73
82	—	475
83	3	75
84	1	256
85	4	257 (Appendix)
85	5	265
85	6	271
86	8	261
86	9	277
86	11	279
87	13	280
87	15	283 (Appendix)
87	16	284
88	18	297 (Appendix)
88	19	296
88	20	288
89	22	262
90	25	263
94	6	266
95	9	275 (Appendix)
95	11	285
95	13	289
97	4	269
97	5	272
98	6	286
99	3	294
99	4	290
100	1	202
100	3	204
101	—	520
101	1	104
101	2	105
104	1	184
106	2	250
107	1	193
108	2	194
108	4	195
108	5	190
109	8	191
110	11	192
114	1	147
115	2	146
115	3	148
115	4	150
116	7	236
116	9	145
117	13	150*a*
118	1	80
118	2	81 (Appendix)
120	1	385
121	4	419
122	—	156
122	—	235
124	2	159
125	1	178
125	3	158
126	4	176
127	5	179
127	6	181
127	7	175
127	8	182
128	11	177
129	13	180
134	23	170
135	1	385*a* (Appendix)
136	4	386
137	1	484*c*
138	4	365
140	3	412
142	1	471
142	4	472

Vol. I page	Vol. I no.	Kress no.
144	2	315
146	1	484*b*
149	17	424
150	19	316
151	4	317
154	1	414
155	4	413
155	6	416
156	9	415
157	2	314
159	10	239
160	4	421
162	1	426
163	4	428
163	6	429
163	7	432
164	8	430
164	9	431
166	18	434
170	37	631
170	38	441*a*
172	5	366
173	13	367
174	1	318
175	3	444
176	1	445
179	4	390
180	10	389
180	12	391
181	14	392
182	20	393
182	22	394
183	25	395
184	30	396
184	31	397
184	33	398
185	—	417, 473
187	—	347
189	6	319
190	14	320
191	17	321
192	24	322
193	30	324
195	40	325
199	64	326
204	94	328

Vol. I page	Vol. I no.	Kress no.
205	102	329
206	108	330
206	109	331
206	113	332
209	128	333
209	129	327
209	130	334
210	133	335
211	144	337
213	1	451
213	2	452
213	3	453
214	1	454
214	2	455
215	4	459
216	2	447
216	3	448
216	4	449
216	5	450
222	4	374
222	6	375
226	33	373
228	3	348
229	8	358
230	13	351
231	17	353
231	20	352
232	25	354
232	26	355
232	27	356
233	28	357
233	31	349
235	38	360
235	39	359
238	1	338 (Appendix)
241	1	438
241	2	437
242	7	439
242	8	440
243	9	441
244	5	370
247	26	371
250	5	446
253	1	442
254	2	339, 443

Vol. I page	Vol. I no.	Kress no.
256	13	341
258	27	344
259	28	345
259	30	346
260	36	340
262	4	376
263	5	377
265	13	635
268	4	464
268	5	464
269	7	465
271	21	466
272	25	467
273	33	469
282	27	378
287	4	474

Vol. II page	Vol. II no.	Kress no.
7	4	244
8	5	524
8	6	525
9	9	39
9	10	227
11	1	299
12	4	301
12	8	300
14	14	91
14	19	188
21	2	40
23	1	247
23	2	246
23	3	245
28	11	221
28	13	220
29	1	20
30	10	106
31	2	206
33	19	215
37	2	212
39	1	249
40	1	223
40	2	224
40	4	213
43	2	42

Vol. II page	Vol. II no.	Kress no.
44	3	267
46	17	282
49	5	291
49	6	264
49	8	268
50	10	293 (Appendix)
50	11	273
50	12	281
51	15	295
51	19	44
62	1	219
64	15	260
64	16	196
65	19	274 (Appendix)
65	21	185
66	23	34
67	32	33
68	33	287
68	35	123
68	37	99
70	1	151
70	4	155
70	5	168
71	6	254
72	14	157
72	15	160
76	15	259
77	17	217
77	19	278
80	1	225
81	7	492
82	9	297*a*
82	10	83
85	5	70
85	7	228
85	9	222
86	10	226
86	13	229
87	15	237
89	1	41 (Appendix)
89	2	79
90	3	78
93	19	218

Vol. II page	Vol. II no.	Kress no.
94	note	240
94	2	154
95	8	418
96	11	534
96	12	534
97	16	533
98	21	309
98	22	89
99	3	84
99	4	85
100	8	88
100	9	86
100	10	305
100	11	73*a*
101	12	82
101	14	87
101	15	74
102	4	197
103	5	199
104	12	161
104	16	310
105	19	187
106	1	103
107	7	485
108	11	111
108	12	110
108	13	109
109	2	230
110	4	238
118	54	107
122	11	200 (Appendix)
124	1	152
124	4	164
125	6	169
125	8	165
126	12	173
126	13	174
128	2	242
128	5	234
129	7	205
129	7	205 *bis* (Appendix)
130	16	51
138	15	521
139	1	306

Vol. II page	Vol. II no.	Kress no.
139	3	529
140	7	307
142	17	231
143	19	540
151	3	493
153	11	484*a*
154	16	101
155	2	90
160	10	509
160	11	425
161	15	303
162	21	436*a*
163	1	388
163	2	484
164	10	495 *bis*
166	4	380
166	6	381
170	32	469*a*
170	33	507
174	3	153
175	11	166
175	12	167
176	14	507 *bis*
178	6	615*a*
179	9	423
185	2	420
187	1	232
187	5	183
188	6	308
188	11	535
189	14	538
190	20	553
196	17	499
196	18	417*a*
196	20	417*b*
199	20	342
202	4	347*a*
203	2	347*b*
206	14	506
206	15	510
207	23	457
208	24	456
212	46	495
213	3	443 (Appendix)
215	8	369*a*

Vol. II page	Vol. II no.	Kress no.
216	15	370*a*
217	18	272
218	24	496
219	28	486
224	1	504
225	3	498
226	9	498
229	22	358
230	6	519
232	14	350
233	22	468
238	13	436
248	2	545
249	7	547
250	10	551
251	15	549
259	10	361
260	12	362
265	12	338*a*
288	—	129 (Appendix)
293	—	236
293	2	79
293	3	78
295	35 *bis*	323
297	—	352
298	4	421
299	24	508
300	1 *bis*	163
302	13 *bis*	360*a*

Vol. III page	Vol. III no.	Kress no.
2	*a*	20
5	B	135
7	*a*	26
16	A	123
17	*a*	133 (Appendix)
18	*a*	144
20	D	257 (Appendix)
32	E	186
32	F	187
48	*a*	80

Vol. III page	Vol. III no.	Kress no.
49	A	76
49	*a*	419
49	B	77 (Appendix)
55	B	470
58	*b*	315
59	*e*	316
64	*a*	426
66	*g*	428
66	*i*	429
66	*j*	432
68	K	436
68	*k*	430
68	*l*	431
70	*v*	434
72	Q	484*a*
74	*nn*	441*a*
77	*a*	445
77	*b*	367
78	A	388
81	—	473
95	*a*	451
95	*b*	452
95	*c*	453
98	*a*	455
98	*b*	459
100	*a*	447
105	I	372
113	*f*	359
115	C	441*a*
123	F	343
139	E	475
140	A	639
144	M	379
147	D	476
151	L	108
152	N	233
153	C	312
154	G	303
156	*b*	188
158	H	518
163	*e*	215
167	*b*	223
169	*a*	42
169	G	292
173	*c*	291

Vol. III page	no.	Kress no.	Vol. III page	no.	Kress no.	Vol. III page	no.	Kress no.	Vol. III page	no.	Kress no.
175	C	302	192	F	533	246	E	420*a*	265	MMM	497
178	C	234	195	*c*	73*a*	249	*c*	342	268	*k*	486
179	H	217	215	*d*	162	250	*a*	347*a*	271	*f*	508
180	*d*	260	223	D	423	251	D	350	276	Y	461
182	D	278	231	*e*	469*a*	255	*c*	510	285	D	542
187	*a*	492	235	F	171	257	*a*	433	288	X	552
190	*b*	78	242	B	537			(Appendix)	290	*a*	549

TABLE OF THE CHANGES BETWEEN DREYFUS AND KRESS

Dreyfus no.	Kress no.	Dreyfus no.	Kress no.	Dreyfus no.	Kress no.	Dreyfus no.	Kress no.
21 moved to		200 moved to		384	370*a*	501	420*a*
Appendix		Appendix		418	419*a*	502	417*b*
41	do	205 *bis*	do	422	484*b*	503 moved to	
77	do	255	297*a*	427	484*a*	Appendix	
81	do	257	do	433 moved to		505	360*a*
121	do	274	do	Appendix		517	416*a*
122	do	275	do	435	441*a*	522	do
129	do	283	do	487	347*a*	523	do
130	do	293	do	488	347*b*	536	604*a*
132	do	297	do	489	436*a*	543	do
133	do	313	omitted	490	338*a*	582	do
134	do	338	do	491	469*a*	622	615*a*
137	do	364	484*c*	494	omitted	628	do
149	150*a*	383	369*a*	500	417*a*		

TABLE OF THE MEDALS WHICH WERE NOT CATALOGUED BY HILL FOR HIS CATALOGUE OF THE DREYFUS COLLECTION

Kress no.	National Gallery of Art no.	Kress no.	National Gallery of Art no.	Kress no.	National Gallery of Art no.	Kress no.	National Gallery of Art no.
73*a*	A1465–725A	588*a*	A1450–710A	596*c*	A1455–715A	599*c*	A1435–695A
115*a*	A1417–677A	588*b*	A1457–717A	597*a*	A1434–694A	599*d*	A1439–699A
385*a* (in		590*a*	A1445–705A	597*b*	A1440–700A	629*a*	A1408–668A
Appendix)	A1456–716A	596*a*	A1461–721A	599*a*	A1437–697A		
575*a*	A1672–	596*b*	A1447–707A	599*b*	A1438–698A		

Two medals published in Hill's Dreyfus catalogue were not received by the National Gallery of Art. They are nos. 313 and 494.

INDEX OF INSCRIPTIONS

The numbers are those of the medals.

GREEK INSCRIPTIONS

Ανεθηκε τοις αχαιοις 405
Αντινοος ηρως 516
Απολιπις 525
Αριστοτελης 298
Διδω βασιλισσα 368
Δοξα εν νψιστις χω το θω οτι διερριξε . . . 525
Εκ παλαι μοι μηνιζομενη 182
Ελενη βασιλισσα 387
Ελλαδος σωθεισης δωρον 425
Εργον του πισανου ζωγραφου 1
Ευραινει 366
Ηραχλειος εν χω τω θω πιστος βασι . . . 525
Θεος απο μηχανης 545
Ιλιον 369
Ιππων 516
Ιωανης μπωλντου ζωγραφου βεναιτια 142
Ιωανης μπωλντυ ζωγραφου 141
Ιωαννης βασιλευς και αυτοκρατωρ ρωμαιων ο παλαιολογος 1
Καδχαδονιοις 516
Καρχηδων 368
Λεων αρητινος 432
Ομηρος 399
Ομονοια ελληνων 387
Ονειρον 436*a*
Οστιλιος μαρκελλος ο ιερευς του αντινοου 405
Πριαμος βασιλευς 369
Συρακοσιων 400
Την κρειττω τα συγγραμματα δειξει 629*a*
Τροια 369
Φερνη ζηνος 366
Φιλελλην 425

HEBREW INSCRIPTION

יוחנו בולדו מונ יצייא צייר 141

LATIN AND OTHER INSCRIPTIONS

Ab dupre f 1624 572
Ab haimendorf in wolcrersdorf reip norib duumvir aet 67 1645 627
A caecinus vicent mene vit exerc imperat 478
Acceda 94
Achilles tibertus cesenas arm 287
Ad aethera 483
Ad civitat ditionisq tutel munim extructum 375
Ad mdxx ber fran fundavit hanc domum 309
Adolescentiae augustae 69
Adriaci regina maris 416
Adrianus aug co s iii ppp s c 203
Adversa coronant 570
Aequitas principis 152
Aesculapius uranie 119
Aet 39 360*a*
Aeternitas mant 390
Aeternos praebet lutetia fontes 577
Aet s li h 588*a*
A f 33, 367
Africa capta 388
A g 479
Agitis in fatum 253
Agrippina mf germanici caesaris 401
A iove et sorore genita 417*b*
Albertine nee baronne de nivenheim 1768 582 (Appendix)
Alessandro di gino vechietti 290
Alexand bassianus et iohan cavineus patavini 389
Alexand caymus p pauli f mediol i u d et bon art amator mdlvi 347*b*
Alexander farnesius p p princ an xiii nat 338*a*
Alexander med dux florentiae i 317
Alexander med florentiae dux p 316
Alexander m r p floren dux 663
Alexander tartagnus iure consultissimus ac veritatis interpres 124
Alexandro sfortiae divi sfortiae filio imperatori invictiss 96
Alf dav l mar gu cap g car v imp 318
Alfon avol mar guas cap gen car v imp 388
Alfonsus borgia gloria ispanie 208
Alfonsus dux fer iii s r e conf 658
Alfonsus estensis 256
Alfonsus marchio estensis 41 (Appendix)
Alfonsus rex aragonum 23
Alfonsus rex regibus imperans et bellorum victor 210
Alfos rex 20
Alf ruspagiarii regien idem a r 448
Alles in ehren kann niemand wehren 605
Alma Roma 378

Aloy diedo primice s mar ve an iii ae xxvii 1566 498
Aloysius anoalis iureconsultus 171
Alphon esten ferrar princeps 340
Alter adest cesar scipio roman et alter seu pacem populis seu fera bella dedit 100
Altobellus averoldus brixien polen eps ven leg t s apost 161
Altobelus averoldus epis polen bonon etc ter gubern 470
Alvira consalvi agidari magni fil 521
Amade mediolan arfex fect 28
Ambrosius iung artium et medicinae doctor an aetatis lvii 587
Amor 610
A n 136
An 1603 574
An ab 464, 466, 467, 469
And carafa s severine comes 110
Andreae grito procur d marci io f 156
Andreas barbatia mesanius eques aragonu q regis consiliarius iuris utriusq splendidissimu iubar 125
Andreas car de valle ar anno iubilei 507
Andreas carrafa sante severine comes 111
Andreas carrafa s severinae comes 109
Andreas crispus patavinus aereum d ant candelabrum f 385
Andreas doria p p 430, 431
Andreas griti dux venetiar etc 153
Andreas griti dux venetiar mdxxiii 413
Andreas guacialotus 207
Andreas mattheus iii de aquaviva 103
And spineli f 1540 415
And spinelli f 416
And spin f 414
Angeli politiani 279
An ideo tibi bellus quia fausto nomine vocaris 265
Animi conscientia et fiducia fati 315
Ann 27 425
Anna augus galliae et navarae regina 565
Anna austriaca franc et navar regina 575
Anna i hoefmenne 610
Anna maurella isea aet ann xv 456
Anna maurella oldofredi d ise aet xv 457, 458
Annas mommorancius militiae gallicae praef 553
Anni 26 290
Annibal 445
Annib ml 445
Ann nat chr mdcx 559
Anno 65 doctor ioa balbus vicecan eliche hausfrau ires alters xxv 609
Anno a christ nato 1415 io hus 617
Anno mccccclxxv 68
Annona augusti ceres 403
An sp f 413
Ant casoni 477
Ant de lomenie consellier et secretaire destat mdcxxx 580
Ant grimanus dux venetiar 164
Anthon d g lotho et ba dux 666
Anthonius b de burgundia 224
Anthonius de toledo medicine doctor 1518 532
Anthonius d g lothor et ba dux 539
Anti 71 *bis*, 72
Anticus 73
Antidotum vitae 371
Ant mula dux cretae x vir iii cons iiii 414
Antonia augusta 402
Antonii pizamani 278
Antoninus aug pius p p tr p xvi 406
Antoninus pius augustus 143
Antonio casoni f 476
Antonio marescoto da ferara f 31
Antonius calmone aet an 34 348
Antonius de royzellis monarcha sapientie 91 172
Antonius flo dantis f de castilionio 266
Antonius gratiadei cesareus orator 250
Antonius mor tra pictor 637
Antonius sarzanella de manfredis sapientiae pater 113
Ant s r e p b r card granvelanus 631, 635
Ant vinciguerra rei p venet a secretis integerimus 134 (Appendix)
A r 447, 449, 450
Arciorganum archicembalum 508
Argentina rangona pa dicavit 472
Argutamque chelum docte parupe dedit 122 (Appendix)
Arideat usque 294
Arioni 139
Armandus ioannes cardinalis de richelieu 575*a*
Armanus ioan card de richelieu 576
A ruzem deffiat et d loniumeau surt des finances 569
Ascanius padula nobilis italus mdlxxvii 441
Asia euro africa 119
A s o 180
Assiduus 272
Augu i ep la melis est orare cu silentio cordis qua solum verbum sine intuitu mentis mdxxxx 592
Augustinus barbadicus venetorum dux 132 (Appendix)
Augustinus barbadic venetor dux 155
Augustus vates 160
A v 421

Bacius ban sculp flo 428
Balduinus de monte comes 394
Balthasar castilion cr f 305
Bapt fulgos ianue ligur q dux petr du fil 201

Bapt spaniolus 87
Barbara gonz borr com novell ann xvii 347*a*
Barbara reihingin uxor aetatis an xxxxvii 596*a*
Barthol caput leonis ma c ve se 138
Bartholomaeus pendalia insigne liberalitatis et munificentiae exemplu 112
Bartholomeus panciatic civis flore ti 533
B d 40
Beati qui in domino moriuntur 614
Beatrice de sena 319
Beatrix rangona rovorella 499
Beatrix sf angla estsis ducisa mli 654
Beatus laurentius iustinianus primus patriarcha venetiarum 163
Benedicite in excelsis deo domino de fontibus israel ibi beniamim adolescentulus in mentis excessu 244
Benedictus card lomellinus 474
Benedit qui venit i no d 238
Bene facere et letari 261
Bene hanc capias et captan teneto 73*a*
Bene merentium ergo 76
Ber gamb innocentii viii c s an xxx 1485 260
Bernardinus carvaial card s 235
Bernardinus francisconus senesis 309
Bern rantwic f 640
Ber ru co b eps tar le bo vic gu et prae 187
Blanca pansana carcania 349
Bom 454, 459, 460
Bona fortuna 295
Bononia mater studiorum 661
Borsius dux mutine et regi 40
Borsius dux mutine et regii marchio estensis rodigiiq comes etc 35
Borsius dux mutine & regii marchio estensis rodigiiq comes 36
Braccius 4
Bramantes asdruvaldinus 193
Burghesius senen eques iuris utr consultis p p 101
B varchi 346

Caesariana liberalitas 112
Caesar imperator pont p p p et semper augustus vir 211
Calidonia vicecomes virago 509
Calistus papa tertius 208
Camilla albitia flos virg aetat suae 347
Camillae rugeriae 447
Camilla pallavicina 463
Camilla peretta 344
Camilla peretta syxti v p m soror 344
Camilla sfor de aragonia matronar pudicissima pisauri domina 130 (Appendix)
Camillus de castiliono bal f 321
Candidior pura carbo poeta nive 114
Cap pet plantanida aet an xxxvi 423
Captis subac fusisq reg navar daciae et olim persa turc duce 444
Capue princeps 104
Car maria mommorantia princip condaei uxor 560
Carolus ii dux sabaudie ix 642
Carolus hespery rex et moderator iberi in 604
Carolus v dei gratia roman imperator semper augustus rex his anno sal mdxxxvii aetatis suae xxxvii 606
Carolus vicecomes 510
Carolus v imp bonon coronatus mdxxx 484*c*
Carolus v ro imper 583
Caspar van mullem synes alders im xxxvii iaer 595
Cassandra marin lup march so 356
Cassianum sol et impensa restauratum 162
Caste et suppliciter 439
Castellum sismondum ariminense mccccxlvi 60
Castellum sismundum ariminense mccccxlvi 62
Castitas pulchritudo amor 288
Castitati virtutiq invictae 77 (Appendix)
Castr ant lucen 312
Caterina capalla 519
Caterina regina franciae 547
Caterina sandella 421
Catharina sf de riario forlivii imolae q c 283 (Appendix)
Catherina riva 467
Cautius 69
C c 388
C c n s mdxxii 618
Cedatur a morte inique lacessentes lingue viperibus similes v 1555 417
Celitum benivolentia 172
Celo musa beat 134 (Appendix)
Centum revolutis annis deo respondebitis et mihi 617
Cessi dea militat istat p m 80, 81 (Appendix)
Chandor illesis 428
Charle ix d g francor rex 1561 549
Charles de lor duc de guise 550
Charlotte de bourbon pr daurenge a 1577 638
Christia a f(ran)cia ducissa sab reg cy 571
Christianae reip propugnatori 537
Christof furer 627
Christophor madrucius car ac prin tridenti brixinq eps 353
Christophorus hierimia 210
Christophorus hierimiae f 211
Cicilia virgo filia iohannis francisci primi marchionis mantue 17
Clara de gonz comiti mont penserii et delphina alvie 70
Clara tol taberna ux sup cancell 359

Clemens de ruvere eps mimaten 230
Clemens vii pontifex max 380
Clementia et armis parta 190
Clem vii pont max 365
Coen bloc f 638
Coepit facere et postea docere 31
Colit hanc regide moderatur et istam 573
Concordia augg 211
Concordia augusta 27
Concordia fratrum 1538 414
Concordia parvae res crescunt 416
Condemnatur 617
Confundantur superbi quia iniuste iniquitatem fecerunt in me 599*b*
Consalvus iii dictator magni ducis cognomento et gloria clarus 445
Consecracio 507
Constantia 209, 214, 276
Constantia bentivola de la miran concor comit 276
Constantia bocchia virgo achillis f mdlx 451
Constantinus in xpo deo fidelis imperator et moderator romanorum et semper augustus 524
Constantius f 102
Constantius sf de arago pisau d 99
Constantius sfortia de aragonia di alexan sfor fil pisaurens princeps aetatis an xxvii 95, 97
Constantius sfortia de aragonia filius benemerito parenti d d mcccclxxv 96
Constatia 280
Conteret contraria virtus 110, 111
Contubernalis b f 207
Coradus gonzaga aloisii fil 91
Cor alit 510, 519
Corman f a 1636 482
Cormano f 481
Cornelia siciliana 322
Cornelius mussus epus bitunt 495
Cos iii 406, 408
Cosi quaggiu si gode 346
Cosmus med floren et senar dux ii 341
Cosmus med florentiae dux ii 316
Cosmus medices decreto publico p p 246, 247
Cosmus med ii reip flor dux 315
Cosmus scaptius 398
Costantia de buti 320
Costantia oricellaria h e et fr fillia 281
C p 241
Credo unam esse ecclesiam sanctam catolicam 617
Cristoff kres vom kresenstain md xxvi 596*b*
Cristof kres xxxxii iar alt 596*b*
Cristoforus mauro dux 137 (Appendix)
Cristophorus madr car ep s prin q tridentinus 352
C v 172
Cum pudore laeta foecunditas 342
. . . cus crot 205 *bis* (Appendix)
C w 615*a*
Cxxii equites creat kalendi ianuari mccccixix 249

Da mihi virtutem contra hostes tuos 636
Danthes florentinus 299
De car 304
De forti dulcedo 658
Dei gratia invicta virtus friderich ann nat lxx superst 596*c*
Deo et opt princ 440
Deo favente et imperatoris virtute 308
Deo optimo fav 391
Deus op ma 1568 633
Dextera tua dom percussit inimicum 1571 373
D franciscus gon d fred iii m mantuae f spes pub salusq p redivi 69
D g dux mant iiii et mont f ii etc 363
D iacobus de vitri 1518 531
Diana dux valentinorum clarissima ae 26 551
Difficultas initii ferenda 348
D io francisi d rangonibus p v v 218
D iohannes de talaru 1518 530
Dionysius de rata utr sig ref et s inquisit praelatus cons 476
Discite iustitiam moniti 426
Discutit hac flama fracisc robore metis o nia p vi cit reru i mersabilis u d 604*a*
Discutit ut coelo phoebus pax nubila terris 550
D isottae ariminen mccccxlvi 65
D isottae ariminensi 63, 64
Diva antonia bautia de gonz mar 72
Diva augusta divae faustina 204
Diva beatrix hungariae regina 83
Divae genevrae sfortiae bentivollae 34
Divae philippinae 436
Diva faustina dius antoninus 204
Divai iulia primum felix 73
Diva iulia astallia 75
Diva iustina 150
Diva laura . . . rixiensis 303
Divi francisci mdxxxiiii 413
Divi heroes francis liliis cruceq illustris incedunt iugiter parantes ad superos iter 24, 25
Divi m pii f p m tr p iiii cos ii p p 410
Divinum dare humanum accip liberalitas 84
(D) iulius iii pont ot max an v 369*a*
Divo petro martyri templum erexit et sepulchrum sibi construxit sedente clemente viii pont max a d mdxcii 476

Divorum maximil et caroli eius nepot rom impp tributus milit caspar vvinntzrer auratus md xxvi h 588*a*
Divus alphonsus aragoniae utriusque siciliae valenciae hie hun maio sar cor rex co ba du at et neo ac co ro et c 21 (Appendix)
Divus alphonsus rex triumphator et pacificus mccccxlviiii 19
Divus lodovicus rex francorum 27
Divus petrus aretinus 484*a*
D n acharius atest ferrariolae p i 39
Docebo iniquos v t et impii ad te conver 429
Doctori doctor nob philippo de casolis 520
Dominicus cardinalis grimanus 236
Dominus borsius marchio estensis 28
Dom pog f 339
Don inigo de davalos 22
Dottus patavus militie prefetus propter res bene gestas 214
D p 344, 345, 346
D p i 520
D sigismudus ii rex polonie a o regni n ri iii aetatis xiii anno d mdxxxii 412
Dubia fortua 73
Duce virtute 254
Duce virtute comite fortuna mdxiii 154
Dum spiritus hos reget artus 423
Dupre 1611 560
Durate 635
Dux equitum praestans malatesta novellus cesenae dominus 15
Dux hadrie teramique 103
Dux karolus burgundus 223
Dux mediolani ac ianue d 647

Ecclesia restituta 212
Eciam si occiderit me in ipso sperabo mdxxviii 597
Effig ferdin princip et infant hispan arch austr & ro imp vicar ano etat sue xxi 619
Effigies augustini lesch de hilkers i v doc baio ducum cancella mdxxvi 588*b*
Effigies ser anne hu ga regine arch austr duciss burgu & com tyro ano aeta sue xx 619
Ego sum joseph frater vester 365
Elegiae 64, 65
Eleonora florentiae ducissa 342
Elisabet fichardin ge grunbergerin ae 29 a o 1547 607
Elisabet gonzaga feltria ducis urbini 107
Elisabettae quirinae 419
Emanuel philibertus iii d sabaudiae x 367
Enricus de ambanelis ann 58 d 518
Er rot 629*a*
Et in carne mea videbo deum salvatorem meum 251
Et paci et bello mdxxvii 176
Euclides 522 (Appendix)
Exalto 212
Exemplum unicum for et pud 75
Exinanitus repleo 319
Expecto 272
Expugnata alexandria deleto exercitu ludovicum . . . capit 192
Extensio alarum dei 471

F a 358
Fama super aethera notus 125
Fata viam invenient 588
Fatum 122 (Appendix)
Faustina aug antonini aug pii fil 407
Faustina ro o p 469*a*
Faveat for votis 71
Fave for 148
F b et longius vivat servata fide 180
F co 376
F diedus literar et iustitie cultor 254
Fed coc 377
Federicus ii marchio mantuae v 181
Federicus ii mar v mantuae 90
Fed parm 374
Felice ludovico regnate duodecimo cesare altero gaudet omnis nacio 527
Felix fortuna diu exploratum actulit 1493 526
Ferdinand fran davalos de aquin mar p 442
Ferdinandus alfonsi duc calab f ferd reg n divi alfon pron aragoneus 104
Ferdinandus alvarez a toleto dux alvae 639
Ferdinandus d g rom hung boem dalma croa rex 1541 621
Ferdinandus ii de aragonia rex siciliae ungariae hierusalem 105
Fernandus et elisabet d g rex et r 667
Ferrands arago rex si hie 665
Fert 528, 642
Fertilitas in pace et quiete 359
F h 590, 593
Fide et pietate egrediar 499
Fidelitas labor 193
Fides 181, 265
Fides et sancta societas 472
Fides publica 507
Fido et sapienti principi fides et pallas assistunt 68
Fingitur fortuna moribus 612
F io valleta m m hosp hier 376
Firmae et perpetuae caritati mdxxiii 158
Firmavi 289
Florentia 245, 246, 247

Floresco calore partenii 217
F nibii novar cura ob eius patriam domumq servat 183
F noel brulart de silleri chevalier de l'ordre de s jean de hierusal 1632 578
Foelicitas virtus fama 278
Folgore di guerra 419*a*
Formae pudicitiae q s 356
Fortitudo mea et laus mea dominus et factus est michi in salutem 21 (Appendix)
Fort red 261
Fortuna non mutat genus 347
For victrici 71 *bis*
F p 373
Fr alidoxius car papien bon romandiolae q c legat 186
Fran bonattus mant iur cos eq ac mar aud 86
Franc esten march massae 324
Franciscus lancilottis florentinus 293 (Appendix)
Franciscus sfortia vic 647
Francisco covo magno comed legionis caes caroli v a secret cons a mdxxxi 588
Franciscus foscari dux 136
Franciscus gonzaga mantuae marchio ac veneti exerc imp 131
Franciscus i christianisimus rex francor 179
Franciscus i francorum rex 537
Franciscus i francorum rex co 43 604*a*
Franciscus ii franc delphi brita dux i 538
Franciscus laurana fecit 24, 25, 27
Franciscus marchio mantuae iiii 71
Franciscus marchio mantue iiii 645
Franciscus maripetro andreae f an xxx 158
Franciscus mar mant iiii 644
Franciscus mar mantue iiii 84, 85
Franciscus petrarca florentinus 301
Franciscus primus f r invictissimus 535
Franciscus sfortia vicecomes dux mediolani quartus 115
Franciscus sfortia vicecomes dux mli quartus 190
Franciscus sfortia vicecomes marchio et comes ac cremone d 5
Francis data munera coeli xvii octob 1610 n b 555
Francis r x francor p mus domitor elvetior 308
Franc maria s r e cardinalis brancatius 482
Francois duc de valois comte dangolesme au x an d s ea 232
Franc quirinus 396
Franc sangallius facieb 314
Francus lercarius r cons 351
Franc visdominus ferrarien 335
Fran dux man ii et mar mon f 646
Fran iiii d g dux mantu mont fer iii an i aet xxvi 561
Fran mauroc ven regni cretae proconsul 481
Fra taberna co landr magn canc sta medio an lxvi 360
Frater ioannes mulicum de novimagio et infirmarius campensis 592
Fr cesarius fer ordinis ser b m v divin lit excellen doc ac divi ver famosis predicator 115*a*
Fr d dux saxon s ro imp elect 618
Fredericus perrenot n f 630
Fredericus tercius romanorum imperator semper augustus 249
Fr fr regi victori max ac vindici opt 183
Fridericus iii ro imperator etc . . . 1493 aet 78 624
Fr sfortia vicecomes mli dux iiii belli pater et pacis autor mcccclvi 92, 93
F s k i p f t 30, 32
Fui sum et ero 360*a*
Fundatori quietis mdxxx 599
Fundator quietis mdxxxiiii 317

Gabriel lipp 452
Gades herculis 38
Galeaz maria sfortia vicecomes fr sfortiae mli ducis iiii primogents mcccclviii 93
Galeaz m sf vicecos dux mli qit 648
Ganozo di bernardo di marcho di mesere forese salviati 294
Gasparis a borgia epi segobricen 420
Gasp molo f 363
G destoutevilla epis osti car rotho s r e cam 213
G d p 1613 562
G dupre 566
G dupre 1623 565
G dupre f 1603 556
G dupre f 1607 557
G dupre f 1610 559
G dupre f 1612 561
G dupre f 1613 563
G dupre f 1618 564
G dupre f 1620 565
G dupre f 1624 567, 568
G dupre f 1635 571
G e 478
Genio benevolentiae dulcis 389, 392, 395
Genio melsi 393
Gentilis belinus venetus eques comesq 147
Gentilis bellinus venetus eques auratus comesq palatinus f 144
Gentili tribuit quod potuit viro natura hoc potuit victor et addidit 147
Gerocomio 1579 377
G g 606
Ginevera trotti a a xxiii 333
Giorgius herman aetatis suae an xxxviii 597*b*

Giovanni dandrea da stia 285
Giovanni de medici 419*a*
Giuliano particini mccccIxxxxii 275 (Appendix)
Gladius domini sup teram cito et velociter 282
Gloria et honore coronasti eu de 239
Gloria in altissimis deo et in terra pax hominibus burgus 528
Got vormagk alle dingk 1540 602
Gretie trapesunty asie 248
Guarinus veronensis 55
Guido pepulus bononiensis comes 129 (Appendix)
Guidus rangonus bello paceq insignis 471
Guil dupre f 1634 570
Guilel d g pr auraicae co nassauiae 1577 aet 44 638
Guilielmus batonatti etat sue ano 37 259
Guliermus m de poitiers 237

H 590*a*
Haec dignior 457
Haec sola dominatur 198
Hanc cappella fundavit ano dni mdxvii 533
Hanc tibi calliope servat lodovice coronam 114
Hannibalis fi r p bonon princeps 185
Hanricus iiii d g francorom et navar rex 558
Hans hauschel siens alters 24 iar 596
Hans schel aeta lxxiiii verschidt den xxix september a o mdxcii 614
Has aedes condidit anno christi mcccclv 206
Has aedes condidit anno christi mcccclxv 216
H b (and a bird) 411
H bilibaldi birkeym alber durer 623
H borbon condaeus prim regiae franc domus princeps 1611 560
Hec damus in terris aeterna dabuntur olimpo 219
Henricus ii dei g franco rex 541
Henricus ii francor rex invictiss p p 542
Henricus ii francorum rex 545
Henr iiii r christ maria augusta 556
Henr ursin 496
Hercules dux fera mu et 267
Hercules dux ferarie mutine et regii mcccclxxii 38
Hercules dux ferrariae 657
Hercules dux ferrarie 656
Hercules dux ferrarie mutine et regii rodigiiq comes 1505 42
Hercules estensis ii ferr dux iiii 446
Hercules ii ferrariae dux iiii 323
Herculi galliae pacatori 538
Herczog in obern und nidern bairn zc ann dom mdxxxv 600
Her dux 116
Her fere dux 1472 37
Hic belli fulmen populos prostravit et urbes 102
Hic vir optimus pauperu pate diebus suis . . . ad supe volavit 127
Hier arsagus eps nicien iulii ii alumnus 242
Hier cardanus aetatis an xlviiii 436*a*
Hier cornelius 391
Hieronima farnesia d s vitali 332
Hieronima sacrata 1560 331
Hieronima sacrata mdlv 330
Hieronimus figinus mdlxii 350
Hieronimus pisaurus b f proc 174
Hieronimus priol vene dux an o p viii ae lxxx 1566 498
Hieronymus hoitzschuer senior aetatis suae lx 597*a*
Hieronymus panicus pat pompeius lodovisius bon 395
Hieronymus paumgartner anno aetatis 56 1553 608
Hieronymus pisaurus paduae praefectus benedicti procuratoris f mdxv 173
Hieronymus savo fer vir doctiss ordinis predichatorum 282
Hippolita gonzaga ferdinandi fil aet an xv 433 (Appendix)
Hippolyta gonzaga ferdinandi fil an xvi 432
Hippolyta gonzaga ferdinandi fil an xvii 438
Hippolytus estensis 292
Hippolytus esten s r e presb card ferrar 374
His avibus curruq cito duceris ad astra 186
Hoc fugienti fortunae dicatis 107
Hortensiai picolomineai m p d 89
H r 606
H s 584
Huius aura mdlxxii 338*a*
Huius benignitate nobilis et clarus 343
Hunc regunt omniaq domant 351
Hyero zane senat opt 415

Iac ant sorra 1561 468
Iacoba corrigia forme ac morum domina 80
Iacob fuggr der elter 613
Iacob muffel v ekenhaid aeta lix anno mdlxix 611
Iacques boiceau s r de la barrauderie 572
Iac tr 441
Iac tr 1578 440
Iac trez 438, 439
Iac trezzo f 1555 437
Iac urb 473
Ia med march meleg et caes cap gnalis zc 355
Iam illustrabit omnia 437
Iam portum inveni spes et fortuna valete 603
Ianellus turrian cremon horolog architect 441*a*
Ia primave 543 (Appendix)
I a v f 417
I b keller 1654 561

Ich anym got zu hilff md xxxv 599*d*
Ich habs gestalt in gots gewalt m d xxxxiiii 596
Iean de saulx commandent en bourgongne normandie mareschal p fi de camp 581
Ie lai emprins bien en aviengne 223
Iesus christus deus dei filius humani generis salvator 57
I f parm 375
Ihs xpc salvator mundi 243
I l a lavaleta d espern p et tot gal pedit praef 557
Illumina vultum tuum deu 525
Illustrissimus sigismundus estensis 117
Imago ad viva effigie expressa 1519 629*a*
Imor l tas 416*a*
Impavidum ferient ruinae 552
Imp caes carolus v aug 426
Imp caes carolus v p f august an aet xxx 599
Imp caes maximil ii aug 464
Inclite iohanne alme urbis veneziar ducise 135
Inclusus mundo seclusit gaudia mundi 578
In constantia et fide felicitas 360
In domino confido anno md xxxviii 596*a*
Inexpugnabile castellum constantium pisaurense saluti pubilicae mccccl xxv 97
Infans hispanien archidux austrie dux burgundie 621
(In)genio mortali ingenium praeb . . . t immortali dea orta 101
Ingenium mores formam tibi pulcher apollo 122 (Appendix)
Innocentii ianuensis viii pont max 258
I n r i 31
Inspice mortale genus mors omnia delte 115*a*
Instaurator 507 *bis*
Intactus utrinque 557
In te cana fides prudentia summa refulget 113
In te dne confido t cas 641
Inter onnes veritas 322
In umbra alarum tuarum sperabo donec transeat iniquitas 608
In umbra manus sue protexit me dns 229
Inventrix oleae et altrix ingenior 362
Invictus federicus c ubini anno d mcccclxviii 100
Ioach a castroveteri com confluentis 579
Ioa hus 617
(Io) alvisius confaloner 358
Ioanes maria pomed f 181
Ioan herrera phil ii reg hispp architec 440
Ioanna austriaca mag dux etruriae 483
Ioann alexander balbianus comes clavene anno salutis mdxxix 590
Ioannes aemo venet veronae praetor 176
Ioannes aloisius tusca auditor cam 220
Ioannes bellinus venet pictor op 146
Ioannes bentivolus ii bononien 659
Ioannes bentivolus ii bononiensis 184
Ioannes de nores comes tripolis 495 *bis*
Ioannes faseolus v 165
Ioannes fichardus u i d zc aetatis suae xxxvi a o mdxlvii 607
Ioannes galeacius 188
Ioannes iovianus pontanus 106
Ioannes kevenhuller baro 466
Ioannes mannellus florentinus ci xxi 170
Ioannes maria pomedellus veronesi f 180
Ioannes maria pomedelus veronensis f mdxix 175
Ioannes medices dux fortiss mdxxii 314
Ioannes melsius iur c 393
Ioannes picus mirandulensis 277
Ioannes secundus bentivolus 185
Ioannes viretus 554
Ioanns fridericus elector dux saxonie fieri fecit etatis suae 32 605
Ioanns sfortia pisauri p 662
Io ant rub mediol 370
Io an vin dulcius iur con can patavin aeta lvii 1539 392
I o b 376
Io ba cas car v caes fer ro reg et boe re exergit dux 444
Io bent ii hanib filius eques ac comes patriae princeps ac libertatis columen 128
Io car lothoringiae 424
Io cornelius monacor casin columen 168
Io dumas chevalier s r delisle et de bannegon chambellan du roy 263
Io f 156
Io franciscus marchio pallavicinus co 302
Io franc martinio mediolan medicus 425
Io fran tri mar vig co muso ac val ren et stosa d 360*a*
Io fr enzolae parmensis opus 92
Io fr i io i ro imp elect primog d sax 599*c*
Io fr parmen 95, 97
Io fr ruberto opus 71
Io g3 m sf viceco dux mli sx 649
Io gonzaga marchio ar 88
Io gz m sf viceco dux mli sx 652
Io gz m sf vicecomes dux mli sx 650, 651
Iohanes dux calaber et lothoringus siculi regis primogenitus 26
Iohanes franciscus de gonzaga capit maxi armigerorum primus marchio mantue 2
Iohannes aloisius tuscanus advocatus 221
Iohannes carondeletus praes burgund 1479 226
Iohannes franciscus gonz 71 *bis*
Iohannes maria patavinus f 412

Iohannis candida 222
Ioh es bocatius flore 300
Io iacobus trivuls mar vig fra marescalus 192
Io ia tri mar vig fran mares 199
Io maria pomedellus veronensis f 176
Io maria pomedelus veronen f mdxxvii 177
Io melon f 635
Io pa lup ii mar so fil aetatis annorum vi 357
Io paulus lomatius pic 443
Io paulus ursinus atripalde comes 274 (Appendix)
Io pet man bonavi medicus pater 390
Io picus mirandule dom phil acutis s 475
Io son fine mccccIxvi 143
I paul pog f 338 (Appendix)
Isabella aragonia dux mli 77 (Appendix)
Isabella capua princ malfict ferdin gonz uxor 439
Isabella esten march ma 76
Isabella filia henrici ii rex uxor philippi hispa rex 1559 548
Isabella manfro de pepoli 1571 328
Isabella mariana carcass 455
Isabella sessa michael veneta 182
Isote ariminensi forma et virtute italia decori 59
Ispero in deo an xxii 275 (Appendix)
Iulian g f 639
Iulianus ep ostien car s p ad vincula 230
Iulianus medices 252
Iulianus medices l f p r 240
Iulia pratoner 453
Iulia ursina 497
Iulia ursina rangona camilli filia ann atat sue xvii 473
Iulius caesar pont ii 238
Iulius geuder v heroltzberg ae 60 615
Iulius ii pontifex maximus 660
Iulius iii pont o t max an v 369*a*
Iulius ligur papa secundus mcccccvi 194, 195
Iulius nobilius p flor 343
Iuppiter ex alto nobis adamanta remisit 42
Iusta tuenda 665
Iusticia ambulabit ante te ut ponat in via gressus tuos 126
Iusticia nostra christus mdxxviii 587
Iustitia et pax osculate sunt 164
Iustitia pax copia 258
Iustizia augusta et benignitas publica 138
Iustus es domine et rectum iudium tuum miserere nostri do miserere nostri 215
Iustus sicut leo 412
I warin 576
I warin 1630 575*a*
I zagar f 1574 630

Karolus octavus francorum ierusalen et cicilie rex 262
Karolus rex catolicus 178
Krolus secundus de manfredis faven 123

Labor actus in orbem 563
Labor omnia 361
Laeta deum partu 567
L aquilegiensium patriarca ecclesiam restituit 212
Laura gonz trivl 506
Lauren stauberus eq aur ac angl et franc regis orator 599*d*
Laurentius medices 252, 253, 493
Laurentius tornabonus io fi 296
Laurent truchses a bomersfelden decanus eclie magunt mdxxx 599*b*
Lavinia fontana zappia pictrix 1611 477
Legiferae cereri 397
Le mareschal de toyras 570
Leo 429, 434
Leo baptista albertus 56
Leo imperat sol et apollo 420*a*
Leonar lauredanus dux venetiar etc 152
Leonellus marchio estensis 6, 7
Leonellus marchio estensis d ferrarie regii & mutine 9
Leonellus marchio estensis d ferrarie regii et mutine ge r ar 10, 11
Leonora ducissa mantuae 326
Leonorae camb uxoris 454
Leo x p max 239
Leo x pontifex max 379
Leo x pontifex maximus 661
Liberalitas 84, 599*a*
Liberalitas augusta 19
Liberalitas pontificia 379
Liberatori urbium 105
Lionora de altoviti 264
L m 643
L n 604*a*
Lodovicus brognolo patricius mantuanus 133 (Appendix)
Lodovicus rex francorum mccccc 529
Lorfelin f 575
L parm 378
L septimius severus pertinax aug imp vii 410
Lucas d zuharis prepositus ponponeschi 74
Lucas salvionus pat iur con 397
Lucdovica de tornabonis io fi 297 (Appendix)
Lucia bertana 486
Lucretia esten borgia ducissa 78
Lucretia estn de borgia duc 79
Lucretia med esten ferr princeps 340
Lucretia med ferr princ a a xiii 325
Luctus publicus 252
Lud neifa 604

Ludovica felicina rubea 329
Ludovic m sf anglu dux m 654
(Lu)dovic unga ec rex contra turca pugnando occubuit 1526 etatis sue 30 320
Ludovicus ariostus 339
Ludovicus de gonzaga capitaneus armigerorum marchio mantue et cet 16
Ludovicus d g francorum rex 655
Ludovicus d g rex francorum 306
Ludovicus ii marchio mantuae quam preciosus xpi sanguis illustrat 68
Ludovicus ma sf vi co dux bari duc guber 191
Ludovicus m sf anglus dux mli 653
Ludovicus patruus gubnans 652
Ludovicus ugonius 310
Ludovicus xiii d g francorum et nav rex christianissimus 555
Ludovic xiii d g francor et navarae rex 565, 566
Ludovic xiii d g rex chr gall et navar henr magni fil p f aug 559
Ludvig von gotsgnaden pfalczgraf bei rhein seins alters im xxxviii iar 600
Lud xii 307
Lugdun republica gaudete bis anna regnante benigne sic fui conflata 1499 527
Lu m salutiarum 643
Luna 1543 615*a*
Lu ne 604
Lu patruo gubnante 650, 651
L verus aug arm parth max tr p viiii 408
Lx 533

Madalene mantuane pm 82
M adriaen van god ghekoren paus va romen tutrecht geboren 629
Magdalena mantuana die xx no mcccccfiii 73*a*
Magdalena rubea morib et forma incomparabil 81 (App.)
Magis vici sed tibi 394
Mag iulianus medices 241
Magni soultani f mohameti imperatoris 144
Magnus cosmus medices p p p 245
Magnus iulianus medices 154
Magnus laurentius medices 257 (Appendix), 271
Mai piu 72
Manifestavi nomem tuum hominibus inri 31
Mansuetudo 474
Marcellus de capodeferro 234
Marcellus ii pont max 370
Marcet sine adversario virtus 228
March brand du steti pome casub vand burgr nuren prin rug mdxxviii 596*c*

Marchio in italia pr b hp 642
Marchio rodericus de bivar 233
Marcus 205
Marcus antonius trivixano dei gratia dux venetiarum et c vixitano i in principatu obit mdliiii 504
Marcus ant trivisano dux v 504
Marcus barbadico dux veneciar 151
Marcus croto 205
Margareta doctor willelm ganczhorns lleibliche docht 609
Margarita a firmian d casparis a fruntsperg uxor anno etatis sue xx 590*a*
Margarita de chasse 226
Margarita de frantia d sabaudiae 503 (Appendix)
Margarita fra c reg f d sabaudiae 367
Maria aug gall et navar regin 567
Maria augusta galliae et navarae regina 568
Maria de muciny 272
Maria imper mdlxxv 464
Maria karoli f dux burgundiae austriae brab c flan 225
Maria karoli filia heres burgund brab coniuges etatis 20 616
Maria politiana 279, 280
Maria regina ec quos deus coniunxit homo no se 620
Maria stouuar regi scoti angli 543 (Appendix)
Mar magdalenae arch austr mag d etr 562
Mars 233
Mars ferus et sumhum tangens cytherea tonantem dant tibi regna pares et tua fata movent 100
Marsilius ficinus florentinus 268
Mars viptor 203
Marte ferox recti cultor gallusq regalis mccccIxiiii 26
Marti fautori 297*a*
Marx rechlinger gestalt do ich wurt xx iar alt 598
M a s f 480
Mathematicus et omnis humanitatis pater 18
Mathias rex hungariae 492
Mathias rex hungariae bohemiae dalmat 297*a*
Mathias ugo eps phamaug 310
Matthaei pastii veronensis opus 56, 57
Matthaeus schyrer aetat 34 1584 612
Mattheus de pastis f 55
Matura celeritas 470
Maumhet asie ac trapesunzis magneque gretie imperat 248
Maximiliani imperatoris munus mccccIxxxxiiii 184
Maximiliani munus 659
Maximilian magnanim archidux austrie burgund etatis 19 1479 616
Maximilianus fr caes f dux austr burgund 225
Mccccciii 231
Mcccccxix aet xxxvii 585
Mccclviii 141, 142
Mccclvii opus ioanis boldu pictoris 139, 140

Mccccl xvi 143
Mcccclxxv 254
Mcccclxxvii 41 (Appendix)
Mcccclxxxi 209
Mcccclxxxxiii 289
Mccccxlvi 61, 63
Mccccxlviiii 19
M commodus antoninus aug pius brit 409
Md 13 306
Mdxix 175
Mdxxiii 158, 159
Mdxxix fungendo consumor 597*b*
Mdxxvii 177
Mediolani dux 655
Meliolus dicavit 69
Meliolus sacravit 68
Memoriae agrippinae 401
Mens sidera volvit 1631 576
Mercurialium hospes virorum 234
Michaelangelus bonarrotus flor aet s ann 88 429
Michelangelus d ni g de tanagli 295
Mihi absit gloriari nisi in cruce domini nostri ihu xpi 524
Minc 506
Minerva 267
Mitis esto 272
M m 225
Moneta nanceii cusa 1523 666
Moriens revivisco 177
Mortalibus ab inmortalibus antipandora 1554 473
Mortalium cura 250
M osp fran cancel 552
Munificentia amicos patientia inimicos vince mdxxix 597*a*

N 583
N a 291
Natus humi post opus astra peto 572
Nec cedit umbra soli 199
Nec tempus nec aetas 433 (Appendix)
Nero aug 202
Nero claud caesar aug ger p m tr p imp p p 403
Nero claud imp caes aug cos vii p p 202
Ne transeas servum tuum 374
N g i f 1601 573
Ni brulartus a sillery franc et navar cancel 563
Ni ça ni la 630
Nico de bailleul propraet urb et praef aedil curante 1623 577
Nicolai marchio estensis fer 29
Nicolas vincentinus 508
Nicolaus corigiens brixili ac corigiae comes armorum ductor etc 126
Nicolaus langaeus lugd aet 78 574
Nicolaus malegrassi eps uceciensis 229
Nicolaus palmerius siculus eps ortan 207
Nicolaus picininus vicecomes marchio capitaneus max ac mars alter 4
Nicolaus sanutus eques do co senatorq bonon itegerimus 127
Nicolaus schlifer germanus vir modestus alterq orpehev 140
Nicolaus tempe tar 157
Nicolo gander 523 (Appendix)
Nicolosa bacci de vasari 334
Nicol todin anc arcis s ang prefectus 345
Nic urs pet et nol comes sante rom eccle armor cap 196
Nic urs petiliani et nolae comes reip flor cap 196
Nihil hoc fortius 314
Nil abest 109
N m 29
Nobilis thomas de guadagnis civis florentinus 534
Non ab re 441
Non confundas me ab expectacione mea 531
Non est mortale quod opto 575
Non ignara mali miseris succurrere disco 85
Non impar oneri fortitudo 369*a*
Non nisi laedentem laedimus 496
Non sana 82
Non semper 468
Non toledi tabula est ista sed est speculum 532
Non ulli obnoxia vento 347*a*
Notrisco al buono stingo el reo mcccccilii 232
N picininus 4
Nubifugo 439
Nudus egresus sic redibo 207
Nuia 542
Nulli largius 486
Nul ne si frote 224
Nunquam siccabitur estu 354
Nutrisco extingo 179

Ob cives servatos 253
Ob restitutam italiae libertatem 131
Obstante genio 385
Ob virtutes in flaminiam restitutas 187
Octavianus sf de riario forlivii imolae q c 284
Octavius ri 284
O hymlichscher vater dyn genaed und barmhertzichkeit sonst ist alles verloeren arbeyt mdxliii 595
Oldofredi d ise aet xv 457
O m d p v mccccxlvi 58
Omnis in hoc sum 350
Omn italiae gymnas lectori 520

Omnium victorem vici 551
Optanda navigatio 347*b*
Opt de patria merito grat civ 156
Optimo conscilio sine armis restituta 191
Opus bertoldi florentin scultoris 248
Opus clementis ubinatis 100
Opus coradini m 38
Opus iacobus lixignolo mccccclx 35
Opus ioanis boldu pictoris 139, 140
Opus ioanis boldu pictoris veneti 141
Opus ioanis boldu pictoris venetus xografi 142
Opus io fr parmensis 94
Opus mathei de pastis v mccccxlvi 59
Opus m guidizani 138
Opus nicolai floretini mccccclxxxxii 256
Opus pauli de ragusio 23
Opus petricini de floretia mcccclx 36
Opus pisani pictoris 1, 2, 3, 5, 6, 7, 12, 15, 16, 21 (Appendix), 22
Opus pisani pictoris mccccxliiii 10, 11
Opus pisani pictoris mccccxlv 13, 14
Opus pisani pictoris mccccxlvii 17
Opu speradei 124
Opus speradei 127
Opus sperandei 112, 113, 114, 115, 115*a*, 116, 117, 119, 125, 126, 128, 129 (Appendix), 130 (Appendix), 131, 132 (Appendix), 133 (Appendix), 134 (Appendix)
Op victoris camelio ve 145
Oriens augusti tutrice minerva 559

P 319, 325, 328, 330, 331
P 1555 334
P 1556 332
P 1557 336
P 1561 326
Paduae praefectus mdxv 174
Pantagaton 473
Parcere subiectis et debellare superbos iustus sicut leo 412
Parcere subiectis et debellare superbos sixte potes 209
Parnasus 124
Parthenius amicus 217
Par ubiq potestas 432
Pasqualis maripetrus venetum d dux 135
Patriarum excubitor opum 640
Paula carlina 479
Paulus dedus venetus mccccevii 169
Paulus iii pont max 381
Paulus iii pont max an iiii mdxxxviii 434
Paulus iii pont max an xi 366
Paulus ii venetus pont max 216
Paupertatis patavinae tutor mdxxxx 391
Pax 211
Pax augusti mcccclxiii 24, 25
Pax libertasque publica 245, 246, 247
P decreto 191
Peculiares audacia et victus 201
Perfectae musicae divisionisq inventor 508
Periculum in falsis fratribus michi hodie cras tibi 599*b*
Perpetua soboles 396
Per te stato gioioso mi mantene 477
Perusia 4
Per vui se fa 22
Petri bembi 386
Petri bembi car 484*b*
Petrus barbus venetus cardinalis s marci 206
Petrus bonus avogarius ferrariensis medicus insignis astrologus insignior 119
Petrus de machiaveliis za fi 269
Petrus ieannin reg christ a secr cons et sac aera praef 564
Petrus paulus rom 353
Petrus victorius aet suae an lxxx 362
Philibertus d sabaudie viii 641
Philibertus dux sabaudie viii margua maxi cae aug fi d sa 528
Philippo maserano veneto musis dilecto 139
Philippus co pa rhe dux baio zc na an xxv 597
Philippus d g et car v aug pat benignit hisp rex 1557 338 (Appendix)
Philippus maria anglus dux mediolani etcetera papie anglerie que comes ac genue dominus 3
Philippus melanthon anno aetatis suae xlvii 593
Philippus melanthon a o aetatis suae xlvii 594
Philippus rex princ hisp aet s an xxviii 437
Philippus stroza 286
Ph us de sabaudia comes gebenaru 200 (Appendix)
Phylippus de medicis archiepischopus pisanus 251
Pie aeq pub 573
Pierius valerianus bellunensis 507 *bis*
Pietas evangelica 168
Pisani pictoris opus 9, 18, 19
Pisani p opus 4
Pisanus pictor 30, 32
Pisanus pictor fecit 8
Pius iiii pon max o p 372
Pius iiii pont opt max an i 370*a*
Pius v pont opt max anno vi 373
Platone 268
P loysius f parm et plac dux i 375
P lucet alma virtus ramis virens semper c v 47 417
Plus de fermete que declat 571
Plus oultre 606

Plus ultr 583
Plus ultra 604
Pm 80
P m tr p x imp vi cos iii p p 398, 409
Pompeius 446
Pomponius de believre franciae cancel aet 71 573
Porta aure fides publica 507
Porta pia roma 372
Post iulii ii cineres mdxiii 242
Pp angle q3 co ac ianue d 648
Pp angleq3 co ac ianue d 7c 653
Pp angleq3 cos 7 c 649
P p r 348, 349, 351, 354, 355, 356, 357, 359, 360
P p r 1552 352
Praecl arimini templum an gratiae v f mccccl 66
Presit decus 263
Prevenit aetatem ingenium precox 221
Pr hen et fr reges franc 546
Priscianus ferrariensis equestri decoratus auro ducibus suis ac mercurio gratissimus super grat et imis 121 (Appendix)
Prius mori qua turpari 290
Pro bono malum 339
Propago imperi 1603 556
Prosper sanctacrucius s r e card 377
Protec noster aspice 363
Providentia ducis fortiss ac foeliciss 553
Psal 36 subditus esto deo et ora eum anno mdxliii 594
Psal 36 subditus esto deo et ora eum anno mdxxxxiii 593
Publicae commoditati 341, 662
Publicae felicitatis spes 104
Publicae utilitati 664
Pudeat amici diem per didisse 599*a*
Pulcrae opes et arma sd amor puicrior 89
Pulcritudo ammor voluptas 277
P victorius aet suae an lxxix 361

Quamvis custodita dracone 442
Quidquid est iussum leve est 1629 569
Quid tum 56
Quies securitas copia martis honos & salus patriae mccccLxxv 95
Quietum nemo me impune lacesset 92
Qui me dilvcidant vitam eternam habeb 235
Quo me fata vocant 355
Quorum opus adest aetatis ano xxvi 233

Raimundus fugger august vind aetatis xxxx 599*a*
Raimundus lavagnolus comes et commissar saxonie 227
Raynaldus de ursinis archiepiscopus floren 261
Reconciliatis civibus magnificentia e pietate 240
Regalis constantia mdxxiii 159
Religionem et obedientiam redintegravit mdlxviii 639
Renata de borboia lothor et ba ducissa 539
Rhemis 555
Ricardus scelleius prior angliae 640
R l 227
Rob briconet parlamenti inquestar presid 228
Robertus macingius 1495 270
Roma 241
R p lugdunen anna regnante conflavit 526
Ruberto di bernardo nasi 273
Rudolphus ii rom imp aug 465

S 451, 452, 453, 541
Sabina augusta hadriani aug pi 404
Sacrif 148
Sacrum publicum apostolicum concistorium paulus venetu p p ii 215
Salus 398, 409
Salus publica 252
Saluti et memoriae condidit 99
Saluti publicae 465
Salvionus iur con 397
Sanct constantius 643
Sans varier 540
Santa lucia an d mdlxxxx 344
Satiabor cu apparuerit 260
S c 162, 202, 203, 204, 205, 205 *bis* (Appendix), 211, 402, 403, 404, 407, 434
Scaramutia trivul car comih io firmi primi f 198
S cosmus s damianus 663
Sebaldus schreier 1512 628 (Appendix)
Sebastians ligsalcz gestalt war im xxxxiiii iar alt mdxxvii 589
Sebastianus monteniac p v 162
Sebastian zäh anno aet xxxxv 1572 469
Securitas populi romani 378
Securitas p p 218
Semper 581
Semper illaesa 506
Sempiternitas 416*a*
Senatus venetus 416
Servavi bello patriam . . . 151
Se ve 254
Sic docui regnare tyrannum 129 (Appendix)
Sic fama virescit 1552 e 541
Sic itur ad astra 130 (Appendix), 424
Sic te rex magne sequebar 580
Sic virus a sacris 495
Sigismondus pandulfus de malatestis s ro eclesie c generalis 60

Sigismondus p d malatestis s r ecl c generalis 58
Sigismund augustus d g rex poloniae 636
Sigismundo scotto magno militi anno theogoniae mccv 108
Sigismundus de malatestis arimini &c et romane ecllesie capitaneus generalis 13, 14
Sigismundus pandulfus de malatestis arimini fani d 12
Sigismundus pandulfus de malatestis s ro eclesie c generalis 61
Sigismundus pandulfus malatesta pan f 62, 66
Sigismundus pandulfus malatesta pan f poliorcites et imp semper invict 67
Sigm gabriel holzschuher ae 67 626
Si iovi quid homini 469*a*
Sil vient a point 231
Simon costiere an et ae 97 1566 544
Simon de tabernis de m l o 197
Simon michael prothonotarius 166
Sixtus iiii pon max sacricult 209
Sixtus iiii pontifex maximus urbe restaurata 145
Sixtus iiii pont max sacri cult 219
Sixtus iiii pont max urbe rest 664
Sixtus v pont opt max 378
S m 218
Sola virtus hominem felicitat 94
Soli deo gloria 614
Sol per che troppo glie 169
S p bononia docet 660
Sperandeus mantuanus dedit anno legis gratiae mcccclxxiii in perfecto 121 (Appendix)
Spes 285
Spes mea in deo est 133 (Appendix), 599*c*
Spes mea in deo est anno nostri salvatoris mdxxxv 605
S p q r memoriae agrippinae 401
Ste h f 636
Stephanus magnus domini andreae filius 175
Sub umbra alarum tuarum proteg 667
Sultanus mohameth othomanus turcorum imperator 102
Superanda omnis fortuna 446
Super aspidem et baziliscum ambulavit et conculcavit 525
Superest m spes 72
Super tenebas nostras militabor in gentibus 525
Surexit xps rex gle 656
Susanna schlechtin sein hausfraw irs alters im xxxi iar 1572 469

Tadeus manfredus comes faventie imoleq d ac incliti guidatii unicus genitus 94
Taire ou bien dire 540
Tandem victa sequor 575*a*
Te copia lauro et fama bearunt 542
Templi petri instauracio vaticanus m 194, 195
Templum belli pac 521
Tempore conradi imper ann cristi mxlviii 227
Tenebrarum et lucis 305
Ter max 87
Te sequar 357
Te sequor an xxxv 274 (Appendix)
Te sine non possum ad te 349
Theod trivultius s r i mesochii et val mes prin etc 480
Theologia philosophia 236
Thomas bohier general de normandie 231
Thomas marinus dux terraenovae 354
Thomas maurus venetus veronae praefectus 177
Thomas mocenico 167
Thomas philologus ravennas 417*a*, 417*b*
Thomas rangonus raven 420*a*
Ti claudius caesar aug p m tr p imp 402
Tornabonus fr fi ioannes 289
T r 474, 475
Tu es christus filius dei vivi qui in hunc mundum venisti 243
Tulit aurifero romula sceptra tago anno 1542 604

Valerius bellus vicentinus 385*a* (Appendix)
Vas electionis paulus apostolus 244
Vaticanus m 194, 195
V camelio 150, 150*a*
Vellus aureum 223
Vene 155
Vener et mars victor 74
Venet 153
Venetia magna a n 136, 137 (Appendix)
Venus 233
Verbum domini manet in aeternum 618
Veritas odium parit 484*a*
Veritati d 161
Veritatis interpres 86
Veterum volvit monumenta virorum 574
V f 92, 93, 94
Vias tuas domine demostra mihi 646
Viconte de tavanes ligni marquis de mirebet 1614 581
Victa iam nursia fatis agitur 220
Victis gallis ad cannas et lirim pacata italia ianum clausit 445
Victor camelius faciebat 146
Victor camelius sui ipsius effigiator mdviii 148
Victorem regni mars et bellona coronant 210
Victoria columnia davala 485
Victoriae aguste 205, 205 bis (Appendix)
Victoriam fama sequetur 283 (Appendix)
Victorinus feltrensis summus 18
Vigilantia 270
Vigilantia florui 124

Viglius praep s bav praes secr con r ma et canc ord au vel aet lxii 633
Viglius zuichemus praeses 634
Viglius zuichemus praeses sec con caes z reg ma aet xlix 632
Viii id ian 493
Vinc bovius bononien prothonot apost 371
Vincentius gonzaga 363
Vincentius maripetro and f an aet xlvii 159
Violantis pignae ann 459
Virginitas amoris frenum 273, 281
Virtus nunq deficit 441*a*
Virtute duce et comite fortuna 167
Virtute parta deo et labore 417*a*
Virtute supera 251
Virtuti omnia parent 139
Virtuti regis invictissimi 535
Virtutis et ingenii 146
Virtutis formaeq praevia 438
Visus et animus idem 509
Vita mortalium vigilia 633, 634
Vitoria 178
Vix an lxv obiit ad mcccclxvii 207
V m 611
Una ti diro altra ti fero 51
Unversucht unerfarn anno mdxxxxi 601
Unus x millia 376
Volentem ducunt nolentem trahunt 250
Vox domini in virtute 335
Urania 106, 160
Ursula sebasti ligsalcz hausfrau was im xxviii iar alt mdxxvii 589
Ut gentes tollatque premat que 1623 566
Ut quiescat atlas 338 (Appendix)
Utriusque 443
Uxor laurentii de tornabonis ioanna albiza 288

Wences beyer maedi natioe boemus aetatis sue 38 603
Wilhelm lofflholcz zu kolberg etatis xxxx 601

Xix deo vindicata et ipse retribuet an md 585
Xpi ihesu sanguinis 644
Xpi sanguinis tabernaculum 645

Y h s 31
Yssab trot negrisoli a e xxxiii 327

1423 enricus de ambanelis ann 58 d 518
1479 226
1499 expugnata alexandria deleto exercitu . . . 192
1539 416
1541 416*a*
1551 327
1554 p 324
1556 r c 347
1557 p 329
1558 325
1561 341
1561 p 321
1564 p 335
1570 343
1586 p 333

GENERAL INDEX

The numbers are those of the medals. The few page references are indicated by p.

Abraham and three angels 374
Abundance, Fame, Victory 542
Abundance, Peace, Justice 258
Adige, landscape of 352
Aesculapius and Urania 119
Africa mourning 388
Altar, flaming tripod on 150*a*
Altar, on a mountain 181
Alviano group of medals 165
Amerbach collection 629*a*
Ammanati, relief ascribed to 385 (Appendix)
Amor, Castitas, Pulchritudo 288
Amor, Voluptas, Pulchritudo 277
Andromeda and Perseus 545
Angel driving car 21 (Appendix)
Annona and Ceres 403
Antinous on a griffin 516
Apollo 574
Apollo, blazing tripod and raven on a cauldron 441
Apollo with lyre and scroll 140
Apollo crowning lion 420*a*
Apollo driving Sun's car 563
Apollo in car drawn by swans 134 (Appendix)
Apollo and Daphne 347
Apollo and Marsyas, intaglio of 140
Apollo *see also* Sun God
Architecture, seated 440
Ares, Ludovisi 150
Arethusa, head of 400
Aretino, letters concerning medals 419*a*, 421
Arion riding dolphin 139
Armourer's marks 4, 16
Arms, coats of
- Acquaviva (quarterly 2 and 3) 103
- Adrian VI, Pope 629
- Alidosi 660
- Antoine, Duke of Lorraine 666
- Austria-Burgundy 583
- Avalos 22
- Balbus 609
- Barbò 206
- Bentivoglio 128, 185, 659
- Bohier 231

Arms, coats of (*continued*)
- Borgia 208
- Brulart 578
- Caraffa 110, 111
- Córdoba, Gonsalvo de 445
- Du Mas de l'Isle 263
- Este 29, 40
- Estouteville 213
- Ferdinand I, Archduke of Austria 621
- Ferdinand and Isabella of Castile 667
- France, modern 655
- Francesconi 309
- Frederick of Brandenburg-Ansbach 596*c*
- Fürer 627
- Ganzhorn 609
- Gruder 627
- Guadagni 534
- Hadrian VI, Pope 629
- Hermann 597*b*
- Holzschuher 597*a*
- Johann Friedrich, Elector of Saxony 599*c*, 605
- Jung 587
- Kress 596*b*
- Lodovico II, Marquess of Saluzzo 643
- Löffelholz 601
- Ludwig X, Count Palatine 600
- Machiavelli 269
- Malatesta 12, 13
- Manfredi 113
- Margaret of Austria and Philibert II, Duke of Savoy 528
- Maugras 229
- Medici 239, 240, 661
- Musso 495
- Panciatichi 533
- Paumgartner 608
- Pepoli 129 (Appendix)
- Philibert II, Duke of Savoy, and Margaret of Austria 528
- Philipp, Count Palatine 597
- Poemer 627
- Reihingin 596*a*

Arms, coats of (*continued*)
- della Rovere 238, 664
- Savoy 641, 642
- Schel 614
- Sforza 192, 283 (Appendix), 648–651, 653
- Strozzi 286
- Talaru 530
- Trivulzio 192
- Utrecht, city 629
- Vecchietti 290
- Vitry 531

Astrology and serpent 76
Athenion, cameo by 256
Atlas 369*a*
Atlas and Hercules bearing Globe 569
Aurora 305, 438

Bacchus, statuette of 398, 409
Badile, Giovanni 32
Bal . . ., Antonio (relief by) 184
Barbacane 224
Bartolommeo, Fra, paintings by 282
Battle of Lepanto 373
Battle scene 71, 73
Battle scene before city 445
Battle scene, between Hungarians and Turks 297*a*
Beauty *see* Pulchritude
Bees, chasing Cupid 610
Bees, flying round hive 496
Bees, swarm of, issuing from dead lion 482
Beham, Hans Sebald, engraving by 411
Bellini, Gentile 163
Bellona and Mars crowning king 210
Bembo, Pietro, letters of 386
Bembo, Pietro, reclining under trees 386
Benavides, Marco Mantova 390, 397
Benedetto da Maiano 286
Bergamo, siege of 156
Berry, duc de, collections 524
Blind man led by dog 429
Boat, Fortune in prow and armed woman at tiller 347*b*

Boethius, vision of 235
Bologna, Giovanni 355
Bologna, coronation of Charles V 484*c*
Bologna, S. Giacomo Maggiore, portrait relief of Giovanni II Bentivoglio 184
Bologna, San Petronio, bust in 125
Bonsignori, drawing by 108
Book, closed 64, 65
Book, from which the figure of Truth escapes 86
Book, skull, bones 603
Bossetti, Camillo, sculptor 417
Botticelli, paintings by 252
Botticelli school, painting of 245
Bourg-en-Bresse, medal for entry into 528
Bramante, design for St Peter's, Rome 193–195
Brantôme 469*a*
Brescia, monument to Marc Antonio Martinengo at 142, 204
Brescia, siege of 156
Bridle 92, 107, 182, 470
Bronzino, portrait by, after medal 245
Building with four cupolas 115
Bull, ridden by woman 471
Burgkmair, Hans, woodcut by 194, 243
Butterflies and caterpillars 572

Calliope, giving wreath to poet 114
Cameo, by Athenion, of Jupiter 256
Cameo, by Domenico de' Cammei 189
Cameo, of Andrea Caraffa 111
Cameo, of Christ and St Paul 243
Cameo, of Cosimo de' Medici 247
Cameo, of Lodovico Maria Sforza 189
Cameo, *see also* Gem
Canale, Joseph, engraving by 419
Cap of Liberty, two daggers 493
Capricorn 360
Capricorn, device of Cosimo I de' Medici 315
Capricorn and eight stars 315
Car, drawn by dragon and eagle 187
  drawn by two eagles 186
  drawn by horses, led by Mars 248
  drawn by four horses, led by two men 21 (Appendix)
  drawn by two winged horses 283 (Appendix)
  drawn by lion 250
  drawn by two lions 359
  drawn by two owls 639
  drawn by Peace 262
  drawn by swans 134 (Appendix)
  driven by angel 21 (Appendix)
  driven by Apollo 563
  driven by Sun God 437
  driven by Emperor, 525
Car, Fame, Abundance, Victory 542
Car, with France, Fortune and Fame 575*a*
Car, with Sun, Mercury 580
Car, the Sun's, driven by Apollo 563
Car, funeral, drawn by mules 401
Car *see also* Chariot, Triumphal car
Caraffa, Andrea, cameo of 111
Caro, Annibal, *imprese* from 338*a*
Caro, Annibal, letters of 346
Carro of Carrara 304
Carthage, view of 368
Cassacco, castle of 162
Castitas, Pulchritudo, Amor 288
Castle of Cassacco 162
Castle of Pesaro 97, 99
Castle of Rimini 60, 62
Caterpillars and butterflies 572
Ceres holding book and cornucopiae 397
Ceres, holding corn and torch 404
Ceres and Annona 403
Cerignola, battle of 445
Chariot, four-horse 400
Chariot, *see also* car
Cherico, Antonio del, MS illumination by 245
Cherub between swan and eagle 87
Chess-players 129 (Appendix)
Christ, crucifixion 631
Christ, dead, supported by winged putto 57
Christ, resurrection scene 656
Christ and St Paul, cameo of 243
Church, the, seated reading, holding rudder 370
Church, the, and Constantine the Great 211
Church, the, and Mercury 237
Church, the, and Paganism 524
Claudius in toga 402
Clemens collection 527
Coats of arms, *see* Arms
Concord seated, holding cornucopiae 387
Concord seated, holding lily-sceptre and olive branch 27
Constancy 209, 214, 276, 280
Constantine the Great and the Church 211
Coral, branch of 510, 519
Coronation at Bologna, Charles V 484*c*
Coronation at Rheims, Louis XIII 555
Coronation of Pope Sixtus IV 219
Courage, Fortune, Prudence 553
Crocodile and trochilus 201
Cross, voided 618
Crown in clouds 575
Crowns, three 144
Cupid *see* Love
Cybele, in car drawn by lions 359
Cymbalum 508

Dante, before the mountain of Purgatory 299
Daphne and Apollo 347
David and Goliath 376
Deianira, Rape of 254
Diamond, mounted on pin 571
Diamond rings, shower of 42
Diana 432, 615*a*
Diana, *see* Poitiers, Diane de
Diomede and the Palladium 183
Doge, kneeling to winged lion 132 (Appendix)
Doge and Senators before Christ 416
Dolphin, carrying Arion 139
Dolphin, carrying Fortune 290, 294, 360*a*
Dolphin, carrying Neptune 175, 353
Domenico de' Cammei, cameo by 189
Domenico di Michelino, painting by 299
Door-knocker 28
Doria, Andrea, as Neptune, flanked by Liberty and Peace 430
Doria, Giannettino 430
Dragon, winged 157

Dragon and St George 363
Dragon and St Michael 665
Drawings related to medals 1, 3, 4, 6, 8, 15, 17, 19, 22, 28, 31, 57, 108, 385*a* (Appendix), 448
Dream landscape 436*a*
Dürer, Albrecht, monogram of 628 (Appendix)

Eagle on armillary sphere 272
Eagle bearing five eaglets 483
Eagle bringing Hercules to Juno 417*b*
Eagle, crowned 159
Eagle displayed 269, 286, 621
Eagle, double-headed 583
Eagle, double-headed, the pillars of Hercules 604, 606
Eagle, emblem of liberality 19
Eagle, flying 465
Eagle, on fulmen 100
Eagle, standing 509
Eagle and Ganymede 366
Eagle, with swan and cherub 87
Electrotypes 338 (Appendix)
Elephant in meadow 59, 63
Emilia, school of *see* Ruspagiari (artist, p. 85)
Empress and five women sacrificing 407
Equestrian figure 1, 2, 3, 13, 14, 16, 95, 102, 128, 263, 274 (Appendix), 284, 293 (Appendix), 306, 524, 588, 603, 636, 647, 655, 657
Equestrian figure, before city wall 156
Equestrian figure and a friar 126
Equestrian figure bearing standard 205, 205 *bis* (Appendix)
Equestrian figure and two halberdiers 196
Equestrian figure with soldiers near a city 190
Equestrian figures and foot soldiers 131
Equestrian figures in combat 394
Equestrian figures and the Doge of Genoa 191
Equestrian figures, Pope, Cardinals, Emperor 249
Equity, with scales and cornucopiae 341
Equity, with scales and sceptre 152
Ermine, with a scroll 290
Escorial, view of 440
Este devices 9, 28, 36, 38, 42
Este *impresa* of mast and sail 10, 11
Eternity standing holding globe 416*a*
Evilmerodach, King, and Philosopher 129 (Appendix)
Excavated medals 4, 60, 66
Eye, winged 56

Faith, 265, 423, 507
Faith and Pallas 68
Faith and Penitence 141
Fame, seated, blowing two trumpets 416*a*
Fame, six-winged 125
Fame, Abundance, Victory 542
Fame, France, Fortune 575*a*
Fame, Virtue, Felicity 278
Fano, medal for the recovery of 12
Farnese, *imprese* 338*a*
Felicity seated 104
Felicity, Fame, Virtue 278
Ferrara, Council of 1
Festina Lente, *impresa* of 7, 8
Ficino, legend from 277
Fleece, Golden, between two briquets 223
Florence, reclining under tree 240
Florence, seated, holding orb and olive 245, 246, 247
Florence, Duomo, choir of 252
Florence, Duomo, painting by Domenico de Michelino 299
Florence, Palazzo Riccardi, medallion of Diomede and the Palladium 183
Florence, Palazzo Strozzi, foundation medal 286
Florence, Uffizi, view of 341
Florence, Uffizi, Botticellesque portrait of man with a medal 245
Font, baptismal 36
Fornovo, Battle of 131, 132 (Appendix)
Fortitude 61
Fortress *see* Castle
Fortune 612
Fortune, seated holding rudder and cornucopiae 261
Fortune in a boat 347*b*
Fortune on dolphin 290, 294, 360*a*
Fortune receiving Lomazzo, presented by Mercury 443
Fortune (chained), France, Fame 575*a*
Fortune, Mars, Minerva 71 *bis*
Fortune, Prudence, Courage 553
Fortune, Virtue 154
Fortune, *see also* Occasion
Foulc collection (former), terracotta bust of Lucretia 290
Foundation medals
  Florence, Strozzi Palace 286
  Lyon, Church of the Jacobins 533
  Pesaro, Castle 99
  Rimini, S. Francesco 66
  Rome, Palazzo di Venezia 206, 216
  Rome, St Peter's 194, 195
  Siena, Palazzo Francesconi 309
Foundations medals, practice of using 206
Fountain 55
Fountain of Life 524
Fountain of the Sciences 441*a*
Fountain *see* Hippocrene
Fox, Lion, Fury 557
France in chariot, Fortune, Fame 575*a*
France pursued by Mars pursuing another 306
France, queen of, as Mother of the Gods 567
Frederick III, visit to Rome 211, 249
Fury with two torches, Lion, Fox 557

Galley 88, 431
Ganymede, watering Farnese lilies, Eagle 366
Garigliano, battle of 445
Gazzuolo, Giulia of 75
Gem, intaglio of Apollo and Marsyas 140
Gem, intaglio of Diomede 183
Gem, intaglio of Savonarola 282
Gem, *see also* Cameo
Genius sacrificing, holding dolphin 389, 392, 395
Genius sacrificing, holding patera and cornucopiae 393
Genius, winged, writing on shield 178
Genoa, Doge of, seated on platform 191

Gentleness, standing on serpent, holding dove 474
Gericomio, view of 377
Giovanni delle Corniole, gem by 282
Giovio, Paolo, *impresa* from 342
Giovio, Paolo, writings of 188, 312, 342, 445
Giulia of Gazzuolo 75
Globe, turned by a genius 576
God the Father in clouds 260
Gods, assembly of 484
Golden Fleece between two briquets 223
Goldsmith's ornaments 70
Goliath and David 376
Gonzaga devices 68, 71 *bis,* 181
Gonzaga, Francesco II, giving alms 84, 85
Graces, three 277, 288, 419, 486
Great Captain, legend of 445, 521
Greyhound, seated 92, 190
Griffin 4, 640
Griffin bearing Antinous 516
Griffin and serpent fighting 381
Grottamare, S. Lucia, facade of 344
Gussenbrot, U 55

Hand, holding *ampulla* 555
Hand, holding dagger, threatening Italy 282
Hand, holding flaming sword 335
Hand with shears, cutting serpent's tongue 339
Hands, praying 133 (Appendix)
Harbour 353
Head, janiform 105
Head, triple-faced 6
Health 69
Hercules, infant, Jupiter and Juno 417*b*
Hercules, infant, strangling snakes 41 (Appendix)
Hercules, plucking the apples of the Hesperides 442
Hercules with Globe 338 (Appendix)
Hercules, fighting Hydra 538
Hercules, with the shirt of Nessus 411
Hercules, standing 38
Hercules and Atlas bearing Globe 569
Hercules, Minerva, Vice 466
Hercules, Nessus, Deianira 254

Hippocrene, Fountain started by Pegasus 484*b*
Hope 72, 275 (Appendix), 285, 289
Horse, head of 5
Horseman, *see* Equestrian figure
Hound, the Gonzaga 68
Hound in landscape, gazing at Capricorn 360
Huss, John, at the stake 617

Innocence and Unicorn 17
Intaglio *see* Gem
Island in stormy sea 349
Italy, map of 282
Italy, mourning French invasion 306

Janiform head 105
Joseph and his brethren 365
Juno, Jupiter, and infant Hercules 417*b*
Judgement of Paris 89, 457
Jupiter, cameo of 256
Jupiter, in car drawn by two eagles 186
Jupiter, Juno, infant Hercules 417*b*
Justice, seated, with sword and scales 566
Justice and Peace 164
Justice and Peace embracing 498
Justice, Peace, Abundance 258
Justice and Piety 573

King crowned by Bellona and Mars 210
King crowned by Victory and Mars 535
King and Philosopher 129 (Appendix)

Landscape, butterflies and caterpillars 572
Last Judgement 251
Laurel tree, broken and withered 385
Lead casts of medals, early 55
Leda and Swan 469*a*
Leonardo da Vinci, drawing by 304
Leonardo da Vinci, equestrian figure of Francesco Sforza 657
Leoni, L, letters of 441*a*
Lepanto, Battle of 373
Liberality 379, 599*a*, *see also* Eagle
Lilies, creation of 417*b*
Lilies (Farnese) 366, 378

Lille, Wicar collection 282
Lily, growing 217
Lion 412
Lion, crowned by Apollo 420*a*
Lion, dead, swarm of bees 482
Lion, rampant 581, 661
Lion, singing 10, 11
Lion, Fox, Fury 557
Lomazzo, presented by Mercury to Fortune 443
Louis XIII, instructed by Minerva 559
Love, captive 80, 81 (Appendix), 273, 281
Love, chucking chin of woman 479
Love, standing, holding palm branch and balance 117
Love, standing on globe, kneeling male figure 180
Love, teaching lion to sing 10
Love, tied to tree by Virginity 273, 281
Lucretia, bust of 521
Lucretia, terracotta bust of attributed to Andrea della Robbia 290
Ludovisi Ares 150
Luna 615*a*
Lynx, blindfolded 8
Lyon, Church of the Jacobins, chapel foundation medal 533
Lyon, medal for entry into 526, 527

Machiavelli, writings by 312
Man: standing
- armed 12
- armed, addressed by child 357
- armed, seated woman with cornucopiae, seated man, Victory 399
- armed, woman, Turk, bearded man 444
- in armour 253
- nude, holding Victory and branch 165
- holding hour-glass and staff 207
- shooting arrow at target 468
- on eagle 121 (Appendix)
- on wolf 218
- giving alms 84, 85

Man: seated 172
- giving alms 391
- nude, holding globe and sphere 112
- nude, with plummet 138

with genius of Death 142, 143
meditating on skull 115*a*
under sapling 150
on car drawn by swans 134 (Appendix)
receiving man with a bridle 470
crowned by Mars and Bellona 210
between Faith and Penitence 141
Man: kneeling
before crucifix 15
carrying fruits, Love 180
Man: ploughing 550
Man: reclining
on griffin 516
before a rock 9
by a laurel tree 346
under trees 386
Man: walking
carrying stag 150*a*
armed, before a town 520
blind, led by dog 429
Men, two, standing 7, 414
Mantegna, portrait by 212
Mars, resting on spear, shield 410
Mars and Bellona, crowning king 210
Mars, Minerva, Fortune 71 *bis*
Mars, mounted, pursuing France 306
Mars and Pallas 176
Mars, Pallas, infant 556
Mars and Venus, confronted 233
Mars and Venus, running 74
Mars and Victory, crowning king 535
Martinengo, Marc Antonio, monument to 142, 204
Marzari, G, Histories by *see* Mariani (artist, p. 91)
Medici, Cosimo de', cameo of 247
Médicis, Marie de, as Mother of the Gods 567
Men, two, standing 7, 414
Mercury, holding caduceus, resting on broken obelisk 507 *bis*
Mercury, sword bearing 296
Mercury, and the Church 237
Mercury seated on dragon 124
Mercury presenting Lomazzo to Fortune 443
Mercury and the nine Muses 250
Mercury taming Pegasus 405, 405 *bis*
Mercury, accompanying the Sun 580
Mercury, Giovanni Bologna's statue of 355
Milky Way, creation of 417*b*
Minerva 101, 267, 350, 362
Minerva, instructing Louis XIII 559
Minerva, Hercules, Vice 466
Minerva, Mars, Fortune 71 *bis*
Mino del Reame 213
Model for medal, in stone 628 (Appendix)
in wax *see* Wax model
in wood 589, 591, 594, 596, 599*a*
in wood, *see* Schwarz (artist, p. 110)
Monegro (sculptor) 441*a*
Montolmo, battle of 15
Mountain with altar of Faith 181
Mühlberg, battle of 426
Muses, nine, with Mercury 250

Naples, San Domenico Maggiore, monument in 111
Neptune in sea-car 220
Neptune on dolphin 175, 353
Nessus, Deianira, Hercules 254
Neuss, siege of 223
Nibbia, Francesco, medal for 183

Obelisk, broken 507 *bis*
Occasion, seated, holding bridle and nails 182
Occasion in pursuit of time 73*a*
Olive branch 361
Olivieri, Maffeo, monument by 142, 204
Olympus and altar 181
Organ 508
Orpheus 451
Otranto, expulsion of Turks from 209
Owl 146
Owls, two, drawing Pallas in car 639
Ox 234
Ox, crowned by female figure 417*a*
Ox and Religion 371

Paduans (imitations of ancient coins) see note to Cavino (artist, p. 73)
Paganism and the Church 524
Pallas in car drawn by two owls 639
Pallas and Faith 68
Pallas and Mars 176
Pallas, Mars, infant 556
Pallas *see also* Minerva
Pandora 69
Pandora's vase 473
Papal audience 145
Papal consistory 215
Paris, Judgement of 89, 457
Paris, Palais de Luxembourg, painting by Rubens 556
Parma, view of 375
Parnassus, and Mercury 124
Patience 446
Pavia, Certosa, marble medallion at 142
Pazzi conspiracy 252
Peace, *impresa* of 7
Peace, seated, firing a pile of arms 317
Peace, with olive-branch and helmet 24, 25
Peace and Justice 164
Peace and Justice embracing 498
Peace, Justice, Abundance 258
Pea-Hen with six chicks 342
Pegasus, flying 347*a*
Pegasus, and the fountain Hippocrene 484*b*
Pegasus tamed by Mercury 405, 405 *bis*
Pegasus *see also* Unicorn-Pegasus
Pelican in her piety 18, 158, 168
Perseus and Andromeda 545
Perugia, salt tax 381
Pesaro, castle 97, 99
Pesaro, castle, foundation medal 99
Philosopher and King 129 (Appendix)
Philosophy, holding MSS and sceptre 235
Philosophy and Theology 236
Phoenix on pyre 75, 177
Piety and Justice 573
Pilgrim, carrying staff and scroll 295
Pillars of Hercules 38, 604, 606
Pindus, two summits of 347*a*
Plummet, symbol of Justice 138
Poet and Calliope 114
Poetry 301
Poggio Imperiale, battle of 101
Poitiers, Diane de, trampling Love 551
Pope in audience 145
Pope in consistory 215
Praying hands, rosary 133 (Appendix)

Prudence, seated 109
Prudence, double-headed, seated on two greyhounds 113
Prudence, triple-headed figure 6
Prudence, with mirror and compasses 198, 424
Prudence, Courage, Fortune 553
Pulchritudo, Amor, Castitas 288
Pulchritudo, Amor, Voluptas 277
Putti receiving shower of diamond rings 42
Putto with flame, skull 142, 143
Putto with scales 630
Putto holding shield of arms 530, 531
Pyxis of the Blood of Christ, 68, 644, 645

Ram between two briquets 223
Raphael, medal attributed to 305
Raphael, portrait of Belli 385*a* (Appendix)
Ravenna, disturbances at 187
Ready, R. C. and A. P. (electrotypists) 338 (Appendix)
Religion holding cross, Ox 371
Rembrandt, etching of the Three Crosses 2
Restrikes of papal medals 365, 379
Rheims, coronation at 555
Rheims, view of 555
Rimini, castle of 60, 62
Rimini, S. Francesco, by Alberti, foundation medal 66
River God reclining 506
River Gods, two, reclining 399
Robbia, Andrea della, terracotta of Lucretia by 290
Robbia, Paolo and Marco della 282
Roma, seated 241
Roma, seated, Wolf and Twins, seated Tiber 434
Roma, seated, Emperor, Victory 406, 408
Rome, Castel Sant'Angelo 345
Rome, Ponte Sant'Angelo 249
Rome, Palazzo Venezia, foundation medals 206, 216
Rome, Porta Pia 372
Rome, St Peter's, golden door of 507
Rome, St Peter's, design by Bramante 193–195
Rome, St Peter's, foundation medals 194, 195
Rome, St Peter Martyr church 476
Romolo da Settignano, monument by 111
Rubens and Guillaume Dupré 556

Sacrifice 148, 389, 392, 393, 395, 407, 439
St Ambrose on horseback 655
St Anthony *see* St Francis and St Anthony
St Catherine 90
St Cosmas and St. Damian 663
St Francis and St Anthony, crowning pope 219
St George and the dragon 363
St Jerome, in landscape 415
St Michael and the dragon 665
San Petronio 660
Salamander in flames 232, 308, 604*a*
Salamander on tazza, in flames 179
Salus, feeding serpent 398, 409
Savonarola, gem of 282
Savonarola, majolica roundel of 282
Sciences, Fountain of 441*a*
Scopetta, device 100
Sea and Earth, both reclining 248
Seascape, sunlit 354
Security, seated 378
Seine, Nymph of 577
Serpent and Griffin, fighting 381
Seven Virtues 30,32
Sforza, Lodovico Maria, cameo of 189
Sforza devices 92, 93, 190, 192, 283 (Appendix), 648, 653
Shepherd and flock 168
Ship 635
Ship in storm 499
Ship, sailing through strait 630
Shrub, flowering amongst thorns 348
Siege Perilous 248
Siena, Palazzo Francesconi, foundation medal 309
Sphere of the earth, sea, sky 22
Statecraft, *impresa* of 8
Strozzi, Filippo, iron portrait plaque of 286
Sun God in car 437
Sun God in car, Mercury 580
Sun God *see also* Apollo
Sun, radiant over landscape 570
Swan, wounded 82
Swan, with cherub and eagle 87

Table, bearing candle, hour-glass, book 632, 633, 634
Tau-cross 259
Temple, circular 356
Temple, circular, Time with scythe 521
Temple of St Michael 26
Terminus 629*a*
Theology and Philosophy 236
Three Graces 277, 288, 419, 486
Thunderbolt 419*a*
Thunderbolt, winged 314
Time with scythe 521
Time persued by Occasion 73*a*
Tintoretto, painting by 417*b*
Tobias and angel 646
Tower on rock, in seascape, struck by lightning 552
Tree, broken and withered 385
Triumphal car 256
Triumphal procession 212
Triumphal procession *see also* Car
Trochilus and crocodile 201
Troy, view of 369
Truth, escaping from book 86
Truth, seated, unveiling herself 322
Truth, unveiled by two men 161
Truth, seated, Victory, satyr 484*a*

Unicorn 273, 281
Unicorn, dipping horn into stream 35, 495, 537
Unicorn, recumbent 297 (Appendix)
Unicorn, springing 259
Unicorn-Pegasus 122 (Appendix)
Unicorn and Hound 130 (Appendix)
Unicorn and Innocence 17
Urania 106, 160
Urania and Aesculapius 119

Vasari, drawing the property of 385*a* (Appendix)
Vasari's 'Patience' 446
Vase, two-handled, in landscape 473
Venetia, seated, holding scales and cornucopiae 153
Venetia, seated on lion, holding scales and cornucopiae 416

Venetia, seated, holding sword 155
Venetia, seated, holding sword and shield, two Furies at feet 136, 137 (Appendix)
Venice, church of S. Francesco della Vigna 413
Venice, church of San Giuliano 417*a*, 420*a*
Venice, Ducal Palace, relief of Venetia 136
Venus, toilet of 167
Venus kneeling, three cupids 610
Venus and Mars, confronted 233
Venus and Mars, running 74
Verona, S. Maria della Scala, frescoes 32
Vice, Hercules, Minerva 466
Victory, seated on globe 541
Victory, in car drawn by two winged horses 283 (Appendix)
Victory, Fame, Abundance 542
Victory and Mars, crowning king 535
Vigilance, holding shield and peacock 270
Virginity tying Love to tree 273, 281
Virtue and Fortune 154
Virtue, Fame, Felicity 278
Virtues, seven 30, 32
Voluptas, Amor, Pulchritudo 277

Warrior, *see* Man, armed
Wax model 423, 426, 429, 464, 547, 548
Wax model, Strozzi 286
Wax models by Mola and Mazzafirri *see* Mola (artist, p. 68)
Wheatsheaf 319
Wicar collection 282
Winged eye 56
Winged genius writing on shield 178
Wisdom, gazing at serpent 300
Wolf and Twins 396
Woman: standing
  chained to rock 446
  crowning ox 417*a*
  holding book, looking at stars 433 (Appendix)
  holding purse and sceptre 23
  holding scales, swan 343
  in car drawn by dragon and eagle 187
Woman: seated
  with arrow and serpent 130 (Appendix)
  with palm-branch and wand 77 (Appendix)
  painting at easel 477
  with sword and wheel; putto with caduceus 94
  by river, crowned by Fame 472
  with caduceus, in car drawn by two lions 359
  on saddle, basket of fruits on head 532
  threatened by dragon-headed serpent 130 (Appendix)
Woman: reclining against rock and holding bridle 107
Woman: riding bull 471
Woman: walking, carrying cornucopiae 351
Wooden models *see* Model for medal in wood

Y h s in flaming circle 31

INDEX OF PERSONS

The numbers are those of the medals.

Acciaiuoli, Niccolò or Nerio 291
Acquaviva, Andrea Matteo III d' 103
Adrian VI, Pope 629
Agrippina Senior 401
Alba, Fernando Alvarez, Duke of 639
Alberti, Leone Battista 56
Albizzi, Camilla 347
Albizzi, Giovanna 288
Alfonso V of Aragon, King of Naples 19, 20, 21 (Appendix), 23, 210
Alidosi, Francesco degli 186
Altoviti, Lionora 264
Ambanelli, Enrico 518
Anjou, Jean d' 26
Anjou, Jeanne d' 24, 25
Anjou, René d' 24, 25
Anne d'Autriche, Queen of France 565, 575
Anne de Bretagne 526, 527
Anne of Hungary 619
Antelminelli, Castruccio degli 312
Antinous 405, 405 *bis*, 516
Antoine, Bastard of Burgundy 224
Antoine, duc de Lorraine 539, 666
Antonia 402
Antoninus Pius 204, 406
Aragon-Naples, Kings of, *see* under personal names, Alfonso, Ferdinand
Aragon, Beatrice of 83
Aragon, Eleonora of 116
Aragon, Isabella of 77 (Appendix)
Aragon, Maria of 484
Aretino, Pietro 484*a*
Ariosto, Lodovico 339
Aristotle 298
Arsago, Girolamo 242
Astallia, Giulia 75
Atti, Isotta degli 59, 63–65
Augusto da Udine 160
Augustus 150
Austria, Anna Archduchess of 619
Austria, Anne of 565, 575
Austria, Eleonora of 326
Austria, Ferdinand I Archduke of 619, 621
Austria, Giovanna of 483
Austria, Margaret of 528
Austria, Maria Magdalena Archduchess of 562
Austria, Maximilian of 225, 616, 625
Avalos, Alfonso II d' 318, 388
Avalos, Don Iñigo d' 22
Avalos, Fernando Francesco II d' 442
Avalos, Maria d' 484
Avalos, Vittoria d' 485
Averoldo, Altobello 161, 470
Avogario, Pietro Bono 119

Bacci, Caterina 421
Bacci, Pietro 484*a*
Bacci de' Vasari, Nicolosa 334
Bailleul, Nicolas de 577
Balbiani, Giov. Alessandro 590
Balbus, Margarethe 609
Balzo, Antonia del 72
Bandinelli, Baccio 428
Barbadigo, Agostino 132 (Appendix), 155
Barbadigo, Marco 151
Barbazza, Andrea 125
Barbò, Pier, *see* Paul II
Bassiano, Alessandro 389
Batonatti, Guglielmo 259
Bavaria, dukes of, *see* under personal names, Ludwig, Philipp
Beatrice, Queen of Hungary 83
Beatrice da Siena 319
Belli, Alberto 265
Belli, Valerio 385*a* (Appendix)
Bellièvre, Pomponne de 573
Bellini, Gentile 147
Bellini, Giovanni 146
Bembo, Pietro 386, 484*b*
Benavides, Giampietro Mantova 390
Benavides, Marco Mantova 397
Bentivoglio, Costanza 276
Bentivoglio, Ginevra Sforza 34
Bentivoglio, Giovanni II 128, 184, 185, 659
Bentivoglio, Livia 548
Bernardino, Saint 31
Bertani, Lucia 486
Beyer, Wenzeslaus 603
Bivar y Mendoza, Rodrigo de 233
Boccaccio, Giovanni 300
Bocchi, Costanza 451
Bohier, Thomas 231
Boiceau, Jacques 572
Boldù, Giovanni 141, 142
Bolzanio, Pierio Valeriano 507 *bis*
Bolzanio, Urbano, 507 *bis*
Bonatti, Francesco 86
Borghesi, Borghese 101
Borgia, Gaspare 420
Borgia, Lucrezia 78, 79
Borromeo, Barbara 347*a*
Bourbon, Charlotte de 638
Bourbon, Charlotte-Marie de 560
Bourbon, Chiara de 70
Bourbon, Henri de, *see* Condé
Bourbon, Renée de, *see* Lorraine
Bovio, Vincenzo 371
Bramante, Donato 193
Brancacci, Francesco Maria 482
Brandenburg, Emilia, Margravine of 602
Brandenburg-Ansbach, Frederick, Archduke of 596*c*
Briçonnet, Anne 540
Briçonnet, Pierre 540
Briçonnet, Robert 228
Briosco, Andrea 385
Brittany, Anne of 526, 527
Brittany, Francis, Duke of 538
Brognolo, Lodovico 133 (Appendix)
Bruchsal, Alexander von 586
Brulart de Sillery, Nicolas 563
Brulart de Sillery, Noël 578
Buonarroti, Michelangelo 429
Buonfrancesco, Agostino 120
Burgundy, Antoine, Bastard of 224

Burgundy, Charles the Bold, Duke of 223
Burgundy, Maria of 225, 616
Buti, Costanza 320

Caecina, Aulus 478
Caimo, Alessandro 347*b*
Calixtus III 208
Calmone, Antonio 348
Cambi, Leonora 454
Camelio 148, 150
Campofregoso, Battista II di 201
Candida, Giovanni 222
Capalla, Caterina 519
Capodiferro, Marcello 234
Capua, Isabella 439, 519
Caracalla 143
Caraffa, Andrea 109–111
Carbone, Lodovico 114
Carcania, Bianca Pansana 349
Carcass . . ., Isabella 455
Cardano, Girolamo 436*a*
Carlina, Paula 479
Carondelet, Jean 226
Carondelet, Marguerite 226
Carrara, one of the 304
Carvajal, Bernardino 235
Casali, G. B. 470
Casoli, Filippo 520
Castaldi, Giambattista 444
Castiglione, Antonio di Dante 266
Castiglione, Baldassare 305
Castiglione, Camillo 321
Castile, *see* Ferdinand, Isabella
Castracane, Castruccio 312
Catherine, Queen of France, *see* Médicis
Cavanago, Calidonia 509
Cavino, Giovanni dal 389
Caylar de Saint-Bonnet, Jean de 570
Charles III, de Lorraine 550
Charles V, Emperor 178, 426, 484*c*, 583, 599, 604, 606
Charles VIII of France 262, 526, 529
Charles IX of France 549
Chassey, Marguerite de 226
Châteauvieux, Joachim de 579
Christ, Jesus 57, 243
Christine de France, *see* Savoy
Clement VII 365, 380
Colleone, Bartolommeo 138
Colonna, Vittoria 485
Commodus 409
Compaing, Anne 540
Condé, Henri de Bourbon, Prince de 560
Confolens, Comte 579
Constantine the Great 211, 524
Contughi, Cesario 115*a*
Córdoba, Elvira de 521
Córdoba, Gonsalvo de 445
Cornaro, Giovanni 168
Cornaro, Girolamo 391
Cornelia Siciliana 322
Correggia, Jacoba 80
Correggio, Niccolò da 126
Corvinus, Mathias 297*a*, 492
Costière, Simon 544
Covo, Francisco 588
Croto, Marcus 205, 205 *bis* (Appendix)

Dandolo, Giovanna 135
Dante 299
Deianira, Rape of 254
Deloscopos, Francisco 588
Dido 368
Diedo, Alvise 498
Diedo, Lodovico 498
Diedo, Paolo 169
Dolce, Giov. Ant. Vincenzo 392
Doria, Andrea 430, 431
Dotti, Paolo 214
Du Mas de l'Isle, Jean 263
Duplessis, Armand-Jean, Cardinal de Richelieu 575*a*, 576
Dürer, Albrecht 623

Effiat, Antoine Ruzé, Marquis d' 569
Elisabeth, *see* Isabelle de Valois
Emilia, Margravine of Brandenburg 602
Emo, Giovanni 176
Épernon, Duc d' 557
Erasmus 629*a*
Este, Acarino d' 39
Este, Alfonso I d' 41 (Appendix), 256, 658
Este, Alfonso II d' 340
Este, Beatrice d' 654
Este, Borso d' 28, 35, 36, 40, 45
Este, Eleonora of Aragon- 116
Este, Ercole I d' 37, 38, 42, 43, 116, 267, 656, 657
Este, Ercole II d' 323, 446
Este, Francesco d' 324
Este, Ippolito I d' 292
Este, Ippolito II d' 374
Este, Isabella d' 76
Este, Leonello d' 6–11
Este, Lucrezia Borgia d' 78, 79
Este, Lucrezia de' Medici d' 325, 340
Este, Niccolò III d' 29
Este, Sigismondo d' 117, 118
Estouteville, Guillaume d' 213
Euclid 522 (Appendix)

Farnese, Alessandro 338*a*
Farnese, Girolama 332
Farnese, Pierluigi 375
Fasiol, Giovanni 165
Faustina I 204
Faustina II 407
Faustina Romana 469*a*
Felicina Rossi, Lodovica 329
Feltre, Vittorino Rambaldoni da 18
Ferdinand the Catholic, King of Castile 667
Ferdinand I, King of Naples 665
Ferdinand II, King of Naples 104, 105
Ferdinand I, Archduke of Austria 619, 621
Fiamma family, lady of the 460
Fichard, Elisabeth 607
Fichard, Johann 607
Ficino, Marsilio 268
Figino, Girolamo 350
Firmian, Margaret von 590*a*
Fontana, Lavinia 477
Foscari, Francesco 136
France, Christine de, Duchess of Savoy 571
France, Kings of, *see* under names of Kings Charles, Francis, Henry, Louis. Consorts: Anne d'autriche, Catherine de Médicis, Marie de Médicis.
France, Marguerite de, Duchess of Savoy 367, 503 (Appendix)
Francesconi, Bernardino 309
Francis I of France 179, 183, 232, 308, 535, 537, 546, 604*a*
Francis II of France 546, 549

Francis, Dauphin 538
Frederick, Archduke of Brandenburg-Ansbach 596*c*
Frederick the Wise of Saxony 618
Frederick III, Emperor 249, 624
Frundsberg, Margaret von 590*a*
Fugger, Jakob, the Elder 613
Fugger, Raimond 599*a*
Fürer von Haimendorf, Christoph 627

Gambello, Vettor 148, 150
Gamberia, Bernardino 260
Gander, Nicolò 523 (Appendix)
Ganzhorn, Margarethe 609
Geuder, Julius 615
Giustinian, Beato Lorenzo 163
Gonfalonieri, Elisabetta 358
Gonfalonieri, Giov. Alvise 358
Gonzaga, Barbara 347*a*
Gonzaga, Cecilia 17
Gonzaga, Chiara 70
Gonzaga, Corrado 91
Gonzaga, Eleonora 326
Gonzaga, Elisabetta 107
Gonzaga, Federigo II 90, 181
Gonzaga, Francesco II 69, 71, 84, 85, 131, 644, 645
Gonzaga, Francesco III 646
Gonzaga, Francesco IV 561
Gonzaga, Gianfrancesco, di Ròdigo 71 *bis*
Gonzaga, Gianfrancesco I 2
Gonzaga, Giovanni, Marquess of Ariano 88
Gonzaga, Ippolita 432, 433 (Appendix), 438
Gonzaga, Isabella Capua 439, 519
Gonzaga, Isabella d'Este 76
Gonzaga, Laura 506
Gonzaga, Lodovico III 16, 68
Gonzaga, Vincenzo 363
Gonzalo de Toledo, Antonio 532
Granvelle, Cardinal, *see* Perrenot, Antoine
Gratiadei, Antonio 250
Graziani, Publio Augusto 160
Grimani, Antonio 164
Grimani, Domenico 236
Gritti, Andrea 153, 156, 413
Grünenberger, Elizabeth 607
Guadagni, Tommaso 534
Guarino da Verona 55
Guise, Charles III de Lorraine, duc de 550

Hadrian, Emperor 203
Hadrian VI, Pope 629
Hauschel, Hans 596
Helen of Troy 387
Henry II of France 541, 542, 545, 546
Henry IV of France 556, 558
Heraclius I 525
Hercules 411
Hercules, Nessus, and Deianira 254
Hermann, Barbara 596*a*
Hermann, Georg 597*b*
Herrera, Juan de 440
Hofmann, Anna 610
Holtzschuher, Sigmund Gabriel 626
Holzschuher, Hieronymus 597*a*
Homer 399
Hôpital, Michel de l' 552
Hungary, Anne, Queen of 619
Hungary, Beatrice Queen of 83
Hungary, Ludwig II, King of 620
Hungary, Maria, Queen of 620
Hungary, Mathias Corvinus, King of 297*a*, 492
Huss, John 617

Innocent VIII 258
Isabella of Castile 667
Isabelle de Valois, wife of Philip II 548

Jean de Lorraine, Cardinal 424
Jeannin, Pierre 564
Jesus Christ 57, 243
Johann Friedrich of Saxony 599*c*, 605
John VIII Palaeologus 1
Julia, Diva 73
Julius II 194, 195, 230, 238, 660
Julius III 369*a*
Jung, Ambrosius 587

Khevenhüller, Johann von 466
Kress von Kressenstein, Christoph 596*b*

Lancilotti, Francesco 293 (Appendix)
Lando, Pietro 416
Langes, Nicolas de 574
Laura of Brescia 303
Laura, Petrarch's 303
Lauro, Pietro 417
Lavagnoli, Raimondo 227
Laval, Jeanne de 24, 25
Lavalette, Jean-Louis de Nogaret de 557
Lavallette, Jean Parisot de 376
Leo X 239, 379, 661
Leoni, Leone 430
Lercari, Franco 351
Liegsalz, Sebastian 589
Liegsalz, Ursula 589
Lippi, Gabriele 452
Lodovico II, Marquess of Saluzzo 643
Löffelholz von Kolberg, Wilhelm 601
Lomazzo, Giov. Paolo 443
Lomellini, Benedetto 474
Lomenie, Antoine de 580
Loredano, Leonardo 152
Lorraine, Antoine, duc de 539, 666
Lorraine, Charles III de, duc de Guise 550
Lorraine, Jean de, Cardinal 424
Lorraine, Renée de Bourbon, Duchess of 539
Lösch, Augustin 588*b*
Louis XI of France 27
Louis XII of France 306, 307, 527, 529, 655
Louis XIII of France 555, 559, 565, 566
Ludovisi, Pompeo 395
Ludwig II of Hungary 620
Ludwig X, Duke of Bavaria-Landshut, Count Palatine 600
Luna 615*a*

Machiavelli, Pietro 269
Macinghi, Roberto de' 270
Maddalena of Mantua 73*a*, 82
Madruzzo, Cristoforo 352, 353
Magno, Stefano 175
Malatesta, Domenico Novello 15
Malatesta, Sigismondo Pandolfo 12–14, 58, 60–62, 66, 67
Malipieri, Francesco 158
Malipieri, Pasquale 135
Malipieri, Vincenzo 159
Malvezzi, Costanza 451
Manfredi, Antonio Sarzanella de' 113
Manfredi, Carlo 123
Manfredi, Taddeo 94

Manfro de' Pepoli, Isabella 328
Mannelli, Giovanni 170
Marcellus II 370
Maresio, Florio 507 *bis*
Margaret of Austria, Duchess of Savoy 528
Marguerite de France, Duchess of Savoy 367, 503 (Appendix)
Maria, Empress 464
Maria, Queen of Hungary 620
Maria, Duchess of Burgundy 225, 616
Mariani, Isabella 455
Marie Queen of France, *see* Médicis
Marini, Tommaso 354
Marinoni Melilupi, Cassandra 356
Martinioni, Gianfrancesco 425
Maserano, Filippo 139
Massolo, Elisabetta 419
Mathias Corvinus 297*a*, 492
Maugras, Nicolas 229
Maurella, Anna 456–458
Maximilian I; as Archduke 225, 616
Emperor 625
Maximilian II 464
Medici, Alessandro de' 316, 317, 663
Medici, Cosimo de', Pater Patriae 245–247
Medici, Cosimo I de' 315, 316, 341
Medici, Eleonora de' 342
Medici, Filippo de' 251
Medici, Giovanna d'Austria de' 483
Medici, Giovanni de', delle Bande Nere 314, 419*a*
Medici, Giuliano I de' 252
Medici, Giuliano II de' 154, 240, 241, 291
Medici, Jacopo de' 355
Medici, Lorenzino de' 493
Medici, Lorenzo de', il Magnifico 252, 253, 257 (Appendix), 271
Medici, Lucrezia, d'Este, de' 325, 340
Medici, Maria Magdalena de' 562
Médicis, Catherine de 547
Médicis, Marie de 556, 567, 568
Melanchthon, Philipp 593, 594
Melilupi, Cassandra 356
Melilupi, Giampaolo 357
Mels, Giovanni 393
Michelangelo Buonarroti 429
Michiel, Isabella 182
Michiel, Simone 166
Mocenigo, Tommaso 167
Mohammad II 102, 144, 248
Montagnacco, Sebastiano 162
Monte, Balduino del 394
Montefeltro, Federigo da 100
Montmorency, Anne de 553
Montmorency, Charlotte-Marie de 560
Montpensier, Claire, Comtesse de 70
Mor, Antonis 637
Moro, Cristoforo 137 (Appendix)
Moro, Tommaso 177
Morosini, Francesco 481
Mucini, Maria de' 272
Muffel, Jakob 611
Mühlheim, Kaspar von 595
Mula, Antonio 414
Mulicum, Johannes 592
Musso, Cornelio 495

Naples, Kings of, *see* under personal names, Alfonso, Ferdinand
Nasi, Ruberto 273
Negrisoli, Isabella 327
Nero 202, 403
Nessus, Deianira, Hercules 254
Nibbia, Francesco 183
Nicola Vicentino, Don 508
Nivenheim, Albertine de 582 (Appendix)
Noale, Alvise da 171
Nobili, Giulio 343
Nogaret de Lavalette, Jean Louis de 557
Nores, Giovanni de 495 *bis*
Noves, Laura de 303

Oldofredi, Anna 456–458
Orange, Charlotte de Bourbon, Princess of 638
Orange, William I of 638
Orsini, Enrico 496
Orsini, Giovanni Paolo 274 (Appendix)
Orsini, Giulia 473, 497
Orsini, Niccolò 196
Orsini, Rinaldo 261

Padula, Ascanio 441
Palaeologus, John VIII 1
Palatinate, *see* under personal names, Ludwig, Philipp
Pallavicini, Argentina 472
Pallavicini, Camilla 463
Pallavicini, Gianfrancesco 302
Palmieri, Niccolò 207
Panciatichi, Bartolommeo 533
Panico, Girolamo 395
Pansana Carcania, Bianca 349
Parisot de la Vallette, Jean 376
Parthenio, Bartolommeo 217
Particini, Giuliano 275 (Appendix)
Parupus 122 (Appendix)
Paul, St. 244
Paul II 206, 215, 216
Paul III 366, 381, 382, 434
Paula Carlina 479
Paumgartner, Hieronymus 608
Pendalia, Bartolommeo 112
Pepoli, Guido 129 (Appendix)
Pepoli, Isabella Manfro de' 328
Peretti, Camilla 344
Perrenot, Antoine, Card. Granvelle 631, 635
Perrenot, Frédéric 630
Perrenst, Nicolas 260
Pesaro, Girolamo 173, 174
Petrarca, Francesco 301, 303
Pfinzing, Melchior 585
Philip II of Spain 338 (Appendix), 437
Philipp Count Palatine, Duke of Bavaria 597
Piantanida, Pietro 423
Piccinino, Niccolò 4
Piccolomini, Ortensia 89
Pico della Mirandola, Costanza 276
Pico della Mirandola, Giovanni 277, 475
Pigna, Violante 459
Pirkheimer, Willibald 623
Pisano, Antonio, called Pisanello 30, 32
Pius IV 370*a*, 372
Pius V 373
Pizzamani, Antonio 278
Poitiers, Diane de 551
Poitiers, Guillaume de 237
Poland, Sigismund Augustus, King of 412, 636
Poliziana, Maria 279, 280
Poliziano, Angelo 44, 279

Pontano, Giovanni Gioviano 106
Popes, *see* under personal names Calixtus, Clement, Hadrian, Innocent, Julius, Leo, Marcellus, Paul, Pius, Sixtus
Pratonieri, Giulia 453
Priam 369
Prisciano, Pellegrino 121 (Appendix)
Priuli, Girolamo 498

Quirini, Elisabetta 419
Quirini, Francesco 396

Ragogna, Francesco da 498
Rambaldoni, Vittorino 18
Rangone, Tommaso 417*a*, 417*b*, 420*a*
Rangoni, Argentina 472
Rangoni, Beatrice 499
Rangoni, Giov. Francesco de' 218
Rangoni, Giulia 473, 497
Rangoni, Guido 471
Ratta, Dionisio 476
Rechlinger, Marx 598
Reihingin, Barbara 596*a*
René d'Anjou 24, 25
Riccio 385
Richelieu, Armand-Jean Duplessis, Cardinal de 575*a*, 576
Riva, Caterina 467
Romana, Faustina 469*a*
Roselli, Antonio 172
Rosen, Kunz von der 584
Rossi, Bernardo de' 187
Rossi, Lodovica Felicina 329
Rossi, Maddalena 81 (Appendix)
Rovere, Clemente della 230
Rovere, Giuliano della, *see* Julius II
Roverella, Beatrice 499
Rucellai, Costanza 281
Rudolph II 465
Ruggieri, Camilla 447
Ruspagiari, Alfonso 448
Ruzé, Antoine, Marquis d'Effiat 569

Sabina 404
Sacrata, Girolama 330, 331
St. Paul 244
Saluzzo; Lodovico II, Marquess of 643
Salviati, Gianozzo 294
Salvioni, Luca 397
Sandella, Caterina 421
Santacroce, Prospero Publicola 377
Sanuti, Niccolò 127
San Vitale, Girolama Farnese di 332
Sarzanella de' Manfredi, Antonio 113
Saulx, Jean de 581
Savonarola, Girolamo 282
Savoy, Carlo II, Duke of 642
Savoy, Christine de France, Duchess of 571
Savoy, Emanuele Filiberto, Duke of 367
Savoy, Filiberto II, Duke of 528, 641
Savoy, Filippo of 200 (Appendix)
Savoy, Margaret of Austria, Duchess of 528
Savoy, Marguerite de France, Duchess of 367, 503 (Appendix)
Savoy, Philibert le Beau, Duke of 528, 641
Saxony, Friedrich the Wise 618
Saxony, Johann Friedrich, Elector 599*c*, 605
Scapti, Cosimo 398
Scarampi, Lodovico 212
Schel, Hans 614
Schlecht, Susanna 469
Schlifer, Nicolaus 140
Schreier, Sebald 628 (Appendix)
Schyrer, Matthäus 612
Scotland: Mary Stuart, Queen of Scots 543 (Appendix)
Scotti, Elisabetta 358
Scotto, Sigismondo 108
Senffel, Ursula 589
Sesso, Isabella 182
Severus, Septimius 410
Sforza, Alessandro 96
Sforza, Beatrice 654
Sforza, Camilla (Covella) 130 (Appendix)
Sforza, Costanzo 95–97, 99
Sforza, Francesco I 5, 92, 93, 98, 115, 190, 647
Sforza, Francesco di Giangaleazzo 304 *note*
Sforza, Galeazzo Maria 93, 648
Sforza, Giangaleazzo Maria 50, 649–652
Sforza, Ginevra 34
Sforza, Giovanni 662
Sforza, Isabella 77 (Appendix)
Sforza, Lodovico Maria 189, 191, 650–654
Sforza-Riario, Caterina 283 (Appendix)
Sforza-Riario, Ottaviano 284
Shelley, Sir Richard 640
Siciliana, Cornelia 322
Siena, Beatrice da 319
Sigismund Augustus, King of Poland 412, 636
Sixtus IV 145, 209, 219, 664
Sixtus V 378
Soliman 515
Sorra, Jacopo Antonio 468
Spagnoli, Battista 87
Spain, King of, *see* under personal name Philip
Staiber, Lorenz 599*d*
Stia, Giovanni di Andrea da 285
Strozzi, Filippo 286
Stuart, Mary, Queen of Scots 543 (Appendix)

Talaru, Jean de 530
Tanaglia, Michelangelo 295
Tartagni, Alessandro 124
Tavanes, Vicomte de 581
Taverna, Chiara 359
Taverna, Francesco 360
Taverna, Simone 197
Tempestà, Niccolò 157
Tiberti, Achille 287
Todini, Niccolò 345
Toledo, Antonio Gonzalo de 532
Toledo, Eleonora de 342
Tornabuoni, Giovanna 288
Tornabuoni, Giovanni 289
Tornabuoni, Lodovica 297 (Appendix)
Tornabuoni, Lorenzo 296
Torre, Gianello della 441*a*
Toscani, Giov. Alvise 220, 221
Toyras, Marquis de 570
Trevisan, Marcantonio 504
Trivulzio, Ercole Teodoro 480
Trivulzio, Gianfrancesco 360*a*
Trivulzio, Giangiacomo 192, 199
Trivulzio, Laura Gonzaga 506
Trivulzio, Scaramuccia 198
Trotti, Ginevra 333
Trotti Negrisoli, Isabella 327

Truchses von Pomersfelden, Lorenz *599b*
Turk 515
Turriano, Juanelo 441*a*
Tuscany, *see* Medici

Udine, Augusto da 160
Ugoni, Ludovico 310
Ugoni, Mattia 310
Urbino, Elisabetta of 107
Urbino, Federigo of 100

Valeriano, Pierio 507 *bis*
Valle, Andrea della 507
Vallette, Jean Parisot de la 376
Valois, François de, *see* Francis I
Valois, Isabelle de 548
Varano, Giulio Cesare 33
Varchi, Benedetto 346
Vasari, Nicolosa 334
Vecchietti, Alessandro 290
Verus, Lucius 408
Vettori, Pietro 361, 362
Vicentino, Nicola 508
Vinciguerra, Antonio 134 (Appendix)
Viret, Jean 554
Visconti, Calidonia 509
Visconti, Carlo 510
Visconti, Filippo Maria 3
Visconti, Giangaleazzo 188
Visdomini, Francesco 335
Vitry, Jacques de 531

Welser, Philippina 436
William I of Orange 638
Winntzrer, Caspar 588*a*

Zäh, Sebastian 469
Zäh, Susanna 469
Zane, Girolamo 415
Zappi, Lavinia 477
Zuhari, Luca de' 74
Zuichem, Viglius van 632–634

INDEX OF ARTISTS CONCERNED WITH MEDALS

The numbers are those of the medals. The few page references are indicated by p.

Abondio, Antonio 423, 425, 464–469*a*, 508
Adriano Fiorentino 104–108
A G monogrammist 479
Alexander von Bruchsal 586
Alviano group of medals 165–167
Amadio da Milano 28, 29, 40
Annibal 444, 445
Antico, l' 71 *bis*–75
Antonello della Moneta 137 (Appendix)
Antonio da Brescia, Fra 157
Antonio Vicentino 470–472
Ardenti, Agostino see Ruspagiari, Alfonso, p. 86

Baffo, Battista 484*a*
Bagno, Cesare da 318
Battista Elia da Genova 201
Bellano, Bartolommeo 172
Belli, Valerio 381, 385*a* (Appendix), 386, 387, 400
Bellini, Gentile 144
Bernardi, Giovanni 365, 484*c*
Bertoldo di Giovanni 248–254, 297*a*
Bloc, Conrad 638
Boldù, Giovanni 139–143
Bolsterer, Hans 607
Bombarda 454–460
Bonacolsi, Pier Jacopo 71 *bis*–75
Bonzagni, Gian Federigo 372–375
Bonzagni, G. G. 381
Borgognone, Annibale 506
Braun, Joh. Bartholomäus 626, 627
Brescia, Fra Antonio da 157
Briosco, Andrea, follower of 385
Briot, Nicolas 555
Bruchsal, Alexander von 586

Cambi, Andrea 454–460
Camelio 145–155, 170, 236
Candida, Giovanni 222–232, 250
Caradosso Foppa, Cristoforo 190–196
Carl, Matthäus 614
Casellesi, Raffaello 347
Casoni, Felice Antonio 476, 477
Cattaneo, Danese 419, 419*a*, 484*b*
Cavallerino, Nicolò 470–472
Cavalli, Gian Marco 84, 85
Cavino, Giovanni dal 388–410, 493
Cellini, Benvenuto 316, 484*b*, 663
Cesare da Bagno 318
Cesati, Alessandro 366–369, 378, 381, 400, 545
Clemente da Urbino 100
Coc . . ., Federigo 376, 377
Coccapani, Regolo 347
Coradino, Lodovico 38
Cormano 481, 482
Costanzo da Ferrara 102
Cristoforo di Geremia 100, 210–214, 237, 305

Danet, Regnault 540
Darmand, Jean 575
Deschler, Joachim 608, 609
Domenico di Polo 315, 316, 342
Dupré, Abraham 572
Dupré, Guillaume 556–571
Dürer, Albrecht 583
Dürer, pseudo 628 (Appendix)

Elia, Battista 201
Enzola, Gianfrancesco 92–99
Este, Baldassare d' 37

Falier, Giovanni 156
Fano, Pietro da 135
Ferrara, Costanzo da 102
Fiorentino, Adriano 104–108
Fiorentino, Niccolò 246, 256, 257 (Appendix), 258–273, 274 (Appendix), 275 (Appendix), 276–282, 283 (Appendix), 284–292, 293 (Appendix), 294–296, 297 (Appendix), 523 (Appendix)
Florence, Nicolas de 526
Foligno, Giannantonio da 657
Fontana, Annibale 442, 443
Foppa, Cristoforo Caradosso, 190–196
Fragni, Lorenzo 378
Francesco dal Prato 316, 317, 380
Francesco di Giorgio Martini 101
Francia, Francesco 184, 185, 186, 187

Galeotti, Pier Paolo 347*a*–360*a*, 443, 495
Gambello da San Zaccaria, Antonio 136, 137 (Appendix)
Gambello, Vettor di Antonio 145–155, 170, 236
Gauvain, Jacques 533, 534
Gebel, Mathes 596*b*–601
Geremia, Cristoforo di 100, 210–214, 237
Giancristoforo Romano 76, 77 (Appendix), 78–80, 81 (Appendix), 82, 83
Giannantonio da Foligno, 657
Giannini, Giuliano 639
Giovanni, Bertoldo di 248–254, 297*a*
Guacialoti, Andrea 207–209, 214, 252
Guidizani, Marco 138

Hagenauer, Friedrich 588*a*–596, 599*a*
H B monogrammist 411
Henry, Jéronyme 530–532
Herwijck, Steven van 636, 637
Hofmann, Jakob 610
Holdermann, Georg 623

Iac Urb 473
I.A.V.F. 417

Jacquet, Nicolas Gabriel 573
Jonghelinck, Jacob 631–634

Keller, J. B. 561
Kels, Hans, the younger 596*a*
Kornmann, Johann Jakob 481, 482
Krafft, Hans, the Younger 618

Laliame, Philippe 574

Laune, Etienne de 541, 542
Laurana, Francesco 24–27
Leclerc, Nicolas 527
Leoni, Leone 426, 428–432, 433 (Appendix), 434, 436, 436*a*, 441*a*, 484, 484*a*, 508, 510
Leoni, Pompeo 446
Lepère, Jean 526, 527
Lepère, Louis 526
Lixignolo, Jacopo 35
L.N. 604*a*
Lombardi, Alfonso 380
Lorfelin, Jean Darmand called 575
Lysippus Junior 217–221

Maestri, Adriano de' 104–108
Magdeburger, Hieronymus 617
Maler, Valentin 611–613
Marende, Jean 528
Marescotti, Antonio 31–34
Mariani, Camillo 478
Mars, medallist of the sign of, *see* Domenico de' Vetri, p. 59
Martini, Francesco di Giorgio 101
M.A.S. 480
Massys, Quentin 629*a*
Master L 599*d*
Master of the Pistorius medal 602
Mea 86–88
Medallist of the Alviano group 165–167
Medallist of the Medici Restoration 239, 240
Medallist of the Roman Emperors 202–205, 205 *bis* (Appendix)
Medallist of the sign of Mars *see* Domenico de' Vetri, p. 59
Medallist of 1518 530–532
Melioli, Bartolommeo 68–70, 89, 305
Melon, Giovanni V 635
Mercandetti, Tommaso 305
Metsys, Quentin 629*a*
Milano, Amadio da 28, 29, 40
Mola or Molo, Gaspare 363
Moneta, Antonello della 137 (Appendix)
Mosca, Giovanni Maria 412
M.P. 603

Nassaro, Matteo dal 535
Neufahrer, Ludwig 604, 604*a*
Niccolò Fiorentino 246, 256, 257 (Appendix), 258–273, 274 (Appendix), 275 (Appendix), 276–282, 283 (Appendix), 284–292, 293 (Appendix), 294–296, 297 (Appendix), 523 (Appendix)
Nicholaus 30
Nicolas de Florence 526
Nini, Jean-Baptiste 582 (Appendix)
Nizolla, Jacopo 437–441*a*, 519

Olivieri, Maffeo 142, 158–162
Olriet, Florentin 539
Orfini, Emiliano 215

Paladino, Giovanni 379
Paolo da Ragusa 23
Pasti, Matteo de 55–67
Pastorino of Siena 319–337, 513, 514
Perréal, Jean 526, 527
Petrecino 36
Pietro da Fano 135
Pisanello, Antonio Pisano, called 1–20, 21 (Appendix), 22, 30, 32
Pistorius Master 602
P.M. 80, 82
Poggini, Domenico 316, 339–346, 347, 347*a*
Poggini, Giampaolo 338 (Appendix), 338*a*, 548
Polo, Domenico di 315, 316, 342
Pomedelli, Giovanni Maria 175–183
Pozzi, Giambattista *see* Paladino, Giovanni, p. 71
Prato, Francesco dal 316, 317, 380
Primavera, Jacopo 543 (Appendix)
Pütt, Johann Philip von der 615

Ragusa, Paolo da 23
Rantvic, Bernardo 640
Raphael 305
R.C. 347
Refatus, Timotheus *see* T.R.
Reinhart, Hans, the Elder 605, 606
Riccio, follower of 385
Romanelli, Gasparo 361, 362
Roman Emperors, Medallist of the 202–205, 205 *bis* (Appendix)
Romano, Giancristoforo 76, 77 (Appendix), 78–80, 81 (Appendix), 82, 83
Romano, Pier Paolo 347*a*–360*a*, 443, 495
Rossi, Giovanni Antonio de 369*a*–371
Ruberti, Gianfrancesco 71, 74
Ruspagiari, Alfonso 447–450

Saint-Priest, Jean de 527
Sangallo, Francesco da 314, 380
Sansovino 417*a*–417*b*
Santacroce, Girolamo 109
Saulmon, Michelet 524–525
Schwarz, Hans 584–585
Schweigger, Georg 624–625
Segala, Francesco 484*a*
Selvi, Anton Francesco 483
Signoretti, Gian Antonio 451–453
Sommer, W. 628 (Appendix)
Soranzo, M. Aurelio 480
Sperandio 42, 112–120, 121 (Appendix), 122 (Appendix), 123–128, 129 (Appendix), 130 (Appendix), 131, 132 (Appendix), 133 (Appendix), 134 (Appendix)
Spinelli, Andrea 413–416*a*
Spinelli, Niccolò di Forzore 246, 256, 257 (Appendix), 258–273, 274 (Appendix), 275 (Appendix), 276–282, 283 (Appendix), 284–292, 293 (Appendix), 294–296, 297 (Appendix), 523 (Appendix)
Steven van Herwijck 636, 637

Tatti, Jacopo 417*a*, 417*b*
Torre, Giulio della 170
Tortorino, Francesco 510
T.R. 474, 475
Trezzo, Jacopo Nizolla da 437–441*a*, 519

Urbino, Clemente da 100

Varin, Jean 575*a*, 576
'Venetian Medallist of 1550' 419, 419*a*
Vetri, Domenico de' 315, 316, 342
Vicentino, Antonio 470–472
Vittoria, Alessandro 420, 420*a*, 421, 508

Warin, Jean *see* Varin
Weiditz, Christoph 587, 588
Welcz, Concz 615*a*
Woeiriot de Bouzet, Pierre 544

Zagar, Jacob 630

SAMUEL H. KRESS FOUNDATION

FOUNDED BY SAMUEL H. KRESS IN 1929

Trustees